AQA Science

Exclusively endorsed and approved by AQA

Jim Breithaupt • Ann Fullick • Patrick Fullick

Series Editor: Lawrie Ryan

GCSE Additional Science

Nelson Thornes

a Wolters Kluwer business

Turn 2 page
32

Published in 2006 by:
Nelson Thornes Ltd
Delta Place
27 Bath Road
CHELTENHAM
GL53 7TH
United Kingdom

07 08 09 10 / 10 9 8 7 6 5

A catalogue record for this book is available from the British Library

ISBN 978 0 7487 9638 0

Cover photographs: embryo by Biophoto/Science Photo Library; chemical crystals by Photodisc 4 (NT); static electricity by Photodisc 29 (NT)

Cover bubble illustration by Andy Parker

Illustrations by Bede Illustration, Kevin Jones Associates and Roger Penwill
Page make-up by Wearset Ltd

Printed and bound in Slovenia by Korotan – Ljubljana Ltd

GCSE Additional Science

Contents

Welcome to AQA Science!

LEARNING OBJECTIVES

By the end of the lesson you should be able to answer the questions posed in the learning objectives; if you can't, review the content until it's clear.

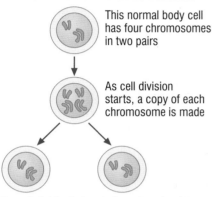

This normal body cell has four chromosomes in two pairs

As cell division starts, a copy of each chromosome is made

The cell divides in two to form two daughter cells. Each daughter cell has a nucleus containing four chromosomes identical to the ones in the original parent cell.

Figure 1 Key diagrams are as important as the text. Make sure you use them in your learning and revision.

Key words

Important scientific terms are shown like this:

observation or **anomalous**

You can look up the words shown like this – **bias** – in the glossary.

Avoid common mistakes and gain marks by sticking to this advice.

KEY POINTS

If you remember nothing else, remember these! Learning the key points in each lesson is a good start. They can be used in your revision and help you summarise your knowledge.

How to use this book

This textbook will help you throughout your GCSE course and to prepare for AQA's exams. It is packed full of features to help you to achieve the best result you can.

Some of the text is in a box marked HIGHER. You have to include these parts of the book if you are taking the Higher Tier exam. If you are taking the Foundation Tier exam, you can miss these parts out.

The same applies to any Learning Objectives, Key Points or Questions marked [Higher].

HIGHER

a) What are the yellow boxes?

To check you understand the science you are learning, questions are integrated into the main text. The answers are always on the same page, so you don't waste your time flicking through the entire book.

PRACTICAL

Become familiar with key practicals. A simple diagram and questions make this feature a short introduction, reminder or basis for practicals in the classroom.

E.g.

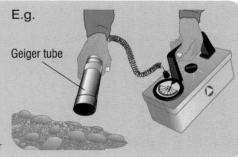

Geiger tube

Figure 2 Using a Geiger counter

DID YOU KNOW?

Curious examples of scientific points that are out of the ordinary, but true…

FOUL FACTS

Some science is just too gruesome to ignore. Delve into the horrible yet relevant world of Foul Facts.

At the start of each unit you will find a double-page introduction. This reminds you of ideas from previous work that you will need. The recap questions and activity will help find out if you need some revision before starting.

SCIENCE @ WORK

When will you ever use science in 'real life'? Check this feature to find out.

SUMMARY QUESTIONS

Did you understand everything? Get these questions right, and you can be sure you did. Get them wrong, and you might want to take another look.

You will find a useful reminder of How Science Works on pages 276–282.

B2 | Additional biology

What you already know

Here is a quick reminder of previous work that you will find useful in this unit:

- Both plant and animal cells have a cell membrane, cytoplasm and a nucleus. Plants cells also have cell walls and chloroplasts.

- Some cells, such as sperm, ova and root hair cells, are specially adapted to carry out particular functions in an organism.

- Enzymes play an important part in breaking down large molecules into smaller ones during digestion.

- Food is used as a fuel during respiration to keep your body activity levels up. You also need it as the raw material for growth and repair of your body cells.

- Plants and animals all carry out aerobic respiration.

- Aerobic respiration involves a reaction in our cells between oxygen and food. Glucose is broken down into carbon dioxide (CO_2) and water (H_2O).

- Plants need carbon dioxide, water and light for photosynthesis. They produce biomass, in the form of new plant material, and oxygen.

- Plants also need nitrogen and other elements to grow.

RECAP QUESTIONS

1 a) Make a list of the things all living things need or do.

 b) Write down three differences between animals and plants.

 c) What are the jobs of:
   i) the nucleus,
   ii) the cell membrane,
   iii) the cytoplasm,
   in a cell?

2 a) Why do we need food?

 b) What has to happen to the food you eat before it can be useful to your body?

 c) What is an enzyme?

 d) Why are enzymes so important in digestion?

3 a) Respiration takes place in all living cells. Why is it so important?

 b) Write a word equation for what happens during respiration in your cells.

4 a) What would happen if you put a plant in a dark cupboard and left it for several weeks?

 b) There is more carbon dioxide in the air people breathe out than in the air they breathe in. Some people claim that talking to house plants makes them grow better. What might be a scientific explanation for this claim?

 c) Sunlight and water are not enough for plants to grow well.
 What else do they need – and why?

Making connections

The plant production line!

Plants produce food for all the animals that live on Earth, including us. They do this through the process of photosynthesis. They use carbon dioxide, water, and energy from light, to make sugars and oxygen.

Feeding the world

Plants could provide enough material to feed everyone in the world. If everyone understood how pyramids of biomass work, perhaps we would all eat differently and no-one would starve!

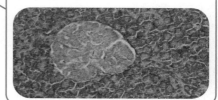

Enzymes

The food you eat is made up of big molecules. They can't get out of your gut and into your bloodstream. So they can't reach the cells where they are needed. Fortunately your body makes digestive enzymes. They work in your gut to break your food down into much smaller molecules, which your body can use.

Food – vital for life!

Specialised cells

The cells in your pancreas are very specialised. Some of them (stained pink in this photo) produce enzymes needed to break down your food. Others (stained purple) make the hormone insulin which controls your blood sugar levels.

Balancing blood sugar

After you have eaten and digested a meal, the levels of sugar in your blood shoot up. You need to be able to take this sugar into your cells so they can use it. You also need to store some of the sugar to use later. The hormone insulin is vital for you to balance your blood sugar.

Inheriting problems

Most babies are born with guts that work perfectly. But some inherit genes which mean they can't feed properly. With pyloric stenosis, the baby vomits all its food back. It needs surgery to correct the fault in its gut. In cystic fibrosis the glands that make many of the digestive enzymes get clogged up with thick sticky mucus. Then they don't work at all.

ACTIVITY

Lots of what you will learn in this unit is linked in some way to food. Every living thing needs food to survive. List, draw or find images of as many different types of food as you can.

Think about the food eaten by different types of animals and by different people around the world. There are some amazing sources of energy out there – see how many you can think of!

Chapters in this unit

 Cells   How plants produce food   Energy flows   Enzymes    Homeostasis   Inheritance

B2 1.1

Animal and plant cells

The Earth is covered with a great variety of living things. The one thing all these living organisms have in common is that they are all made up of cells. Most cells are very small. You can only see them using a microscope.

The **light microscopes** you will use in school may magnify things several hundred times. Scientists have found out even more about cells using **electron microscopes** which can magnify more than a hundred thousand times!

Animal cells – structure and function

All cells have some features in common. We can see these clearly in animal cells. The cells of your body have these features, just like the cells of every other living thing!

- A **nucleus,** which controls all the activities of the cell. It also contains the instructions for making new cells or new organisms.
- The **cytoplasm**, a liquid gel in which most of the chemical reactions needed for life take place. One of the most important of these is respiration.
- The **cell membrane**, which controls the passage of substances in and out of the cell.
- The **mitochondria**, structures in the cytoplasm where oxygen is used and most of the energy is released during respiration.
- **Ribosomes**, where protein synthesis takes place. All the proteins needed in the cell are made here.

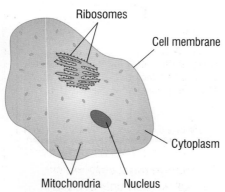

Ribosomes
Cell membrane
Cytoplasm
Mitochondria   Nucleus

Figure 1 A simple animal cell like this shows the features which are common to all living cells

a) What are the main features found in all living cells?

Plant cells – structure and function

Plants are very different from animals, as you may have noticed! They make their own food by photosynthesis and they do not move their whole bodies about. So while plant cells have all the features of a typical animal cell, they also contain structures which are needed for their very different way of life.

All plant cells have:

- a cell wall made of cellulose which strengthens the cell and gives it support.

Many (but not all) plant cells also have these other features:

- chloroplasts, found in all the green parts of the plant. They are green because they contain the green substance chlorophyll which gives the plant its colour. They absorb light energy to make food by photosynthesis.
- a permanent vacuole (a space in the cytoplasm filled with cell sap), which is important for keeping the cells rigid to support the plant.

b) How do plant cells differ from animal cells?

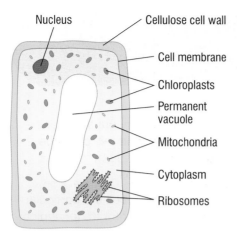

Nucleus — Cellulose cell wall

— Cell membrane

— Chloroplasts

Permanent vacuole

— Mitochondria

— Cytoplasm

— Ribosomes

Figure 2 A plant cell has many features in common with an animal cell, but others which are unique to plants

PRACTICAL

Looking at cells

Set up a microscope to look at plant cells, e.g. from onions and rhubarb. You should see the cell wall, the cytoplasm and sometimes a vacuole but you won't see chloroplasts.

- Why won't you see any chloroplasts?

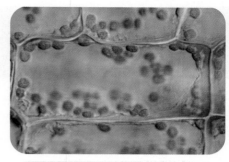

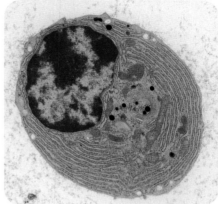

Figure 3 Diagrams of cells are much easier to understand than the real thing seen under a microscope. These pictures show a magnified plant cell and animal cell.

Chemical reactions in cells

Imagine 100 different reactions going on in a laboratory test tube. Chemical chaos and probably a few explosions would be the result! But this is the level of chemical activity going on all the time in your cells.

Cell chemistry works because each reaction is controlled by an enzyme. Each enzyme is a protein which controls the rate of a very specific reaction. It makes sure that the reaction takes place without becoming mixed up with any other reaction.

We find enzymes throughout the structure of a cell, but particularly in the mitochondria (and the chloroplasts in plants).

c) What are enzymes made of?

The enzymes involved in different chemical processes are usually found in different parts of the cell. So, for example, most of the enzymes controlling the reactions of:

- respiration are found in the mitochondria,
- photosynthesis are found in the chloroplasts,
- protein synthesis are found on the surface of the ribosomes.

These cell compartments help to keep your cell chemistry well under control.

DID YOU KNOW?

Although most cells are so small we can only see them under the microscope, the largest cells in the world weigh 1.35 kg and are easily visible with the naked eye. The largest single cell is . . . an ostrich egg!

SUMMARY QUESTIONS

1. a) List the main structures you would expect to find in an animal cell.
   b) You would find all of these things in a plant cell. There are three extra features which are found in plant cells. What are they?
   c) What are the main functions of these three extra structures?

2. Root cells in a plant do not have chloroplasts. Why?

3. A nucleus and mitochondria are important structures in almost all cells. Why are they so important?

4. Explain how enzymes control the chemistry of your cells.

KEY POINTS

1. Most animal cells contain a nucleus, cytoplasm, cell membrane, mitochondria and ribosomes.
2. Plant cells contain all the structures seen in animal cells as well as a cell wall and, in many cases, chloroplasts and a permanent vacuole filled with sap.
3. Enzymes control the chemical reactions inside cells.

B2 1.2   Specialised cells

1 What different types of cells are there?
2 How is the structure of a specialised cell related to its function?

The smallest living organisms are single cells. They can carry out all of the functions of life, from feeding and respiration to excretion and reproduction. Most organisms are bigger and are made up of lots of cells. Some of those cells become **specialised** in order to carry out particular jobs.

When a cell becomes specialised its structure is adapted to suit the particular job it does. As a result, specialised cells often look very different to our 'typical' plant or animal cell. Sometimes cells become so specialised that they only have one function within the body. Good examples of this include sperm, eggs, red blood cells and nerve cells.

PRACTICAL

Observing specialised cells

Try looking at different specialised cells under a microscope.

When you look at a specialised cell there are two useful questions you can ask yourself:

- How is this cell different in structure from a generalised cell?
- How does the difference in structure help it to carry out its function?

Fat cell

Nucleus
Fat store
Cytoplasm
Mitochondria

Fat cells are storage cells. If you eat more food than you need, your body makes fat and fills up the fat cells. They are important for helping animals, including us, to survive when food is in short supply. They have three main adaptations:

★ They have very little normal cytoplasm – this leaves plenty of room for large amounts of fat.
★ They have very few mitochondria as they use very little energy.
★ They can expand – a fat cell can end up 1000 times its original size as it fills up with fat.

Cone cell from human eye

Cone cells are in the light-sensitive layer of your eye (the retina). They make it possible for you to see in colour. They have three main adaptations:

Outer segment – containing visual pigment
Middle section – many mitochondria
Nucleus
Connections to nerve cells in optic nerve

★ The outer segment is filled with a special chemical known as a *visual pigment*. This changes chemically in coloured light. It then has to be changed back to its original form. This uses up energy.
★ The middle segment of the cell is packed full of mitochondria. They produce lots of energy. This means the visual pigment can reform and so the eye can see continually in colour.
★ The final part of the cell is a specialised nerve ending or synapse. This connects to the optic nerve which carries impulses to your brain. When coloured light makes your visual pigment change, an impulse is triggered which crosses the synapse. This is how the response of the cone cell to coloured light passes to your brain.

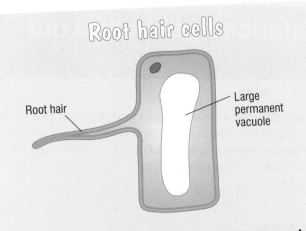

Root hair cells

Root hair
Large permanent vacuole

We find root hair cells close to the tips of growing roots. Their function is to enable plants to take in the water which they need. Root hair cells have three main adaptations:

★ The root hairs themselves, which increase the surface area for water to move into the cell.
★ A large permanent vacuole, which affects the movement of water from the soil across the root hair cell.
★ Root hair cells are always positioned close to the xylem tissue that carries water up into the rest of the plant.

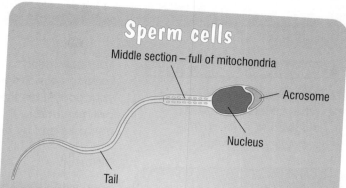

Sperm cells

Middle section – full of mitochondria
Acrosome
Nucleus
Tail

Sperm cells are usually released a long way from the egg they are going to fertilise. They contain the genetic information from the male parent to pass on to the offspring. They need to move through the female reproductive system to reach an egg. Then they have to break into the egg. They have several adaptations to make all this possible:

★ Long tails with muscle-like proteins so they can swim towards the egg.
★ The middle section is full of mitochondria, which provide the energy for the tail to work.
★ The acrosome, which stores digestive enzymes for breaking down the outer layers of the egg.
★ A large nucleus, which contains the genetic information to be passed on.

Organised cells

Specialised cells are often grouped together to form a **tissue**. Connective tissue joins bits of your body together. Nervous tissue carries information around your body and muscles move your body about.

Similarly in plants photosynthetic tissues make food by photosynthesis while storage tissues store any extra food made as starch.

In many bigger living organisms there is another level of organisation. Several different tissues work together to do particular jobs. They form an **organ** such as the heart, the kidneys or the leaf. In turn, different organs are combined in **organ systems** to carry out major functions in the body, such as transporting the blood or reproduction.

Cells → Tissues → Organs → Organ systems → Whole body

SUMMARY QUESTIONS

1 Explain how the structure of each cell on this spread is adapted to its functions.

2 Think back to two other types of specialised cells you have met in biology, e.g. motor neurones, photosynthetic cells in plants or white blood cells.
Draw the cells you have chosen. Label them fully to show how the structures you can see are related to the function of the cells.

KEY POINTS

1 Cells may be specialised to carry out a particular function.
2 Examples of specialised cells are fat cells, cone cells, root hair cells, sperm cells.

B2 1.3   How do substances get in and out of cells?

Figure 1 Everyone knows that bleeding in the sea when there are sharks around is a bad idea. Sharks are sensitive to just a few particles of blood in the water. Blood from an injury spreads quickly through the sea by diffusion – and brings the sharks to investigate!

Figure 2 The random movement of particles results in substances spreading out or diffusing from an area of higher concentration to an area of lower concentration

Your cells need to take in substances such as oxygen and glucose. They also need to get rid of waste products and chemicals that are needed elsewhere in your body. Dissolved substances move into and out of your cells across the cell membrane. They can do this in three different ways – by **diffusion**, by **osmosis** and by **active transport**.

Diffusion

Sharks can smell their prey from a long way away – the smell reaches them by **diffusion**. Diffusion happens when the particles of a gas, or any substance in solution, spread out.

It is the net movement of particles from an area of high concentration to an area of lower concentration. It takes place because of the random movement of the particles of a gas or of a substance in solution in water. All the particles are moving and bumping into each other and this moves them all around.

a) Why do sharks find an injured fish – or person – so easily?

Imagine a room containing a group of boys and a group of girls. If everyone closes their eyes and moves around briskly but randomly, people will bump into each other. They will scatter until the room contains a mixture of boys and girls. This gives you a good working model of diffusion.

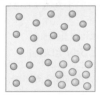
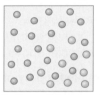
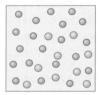

At the moment, when the blue particles are added to the red particles they are not mixed at all

As the particles move randomly, the blue ones begin to mix with the red ones

As the particles move and spread out, they bump into each other. This helps them to keep spreading randomly

Eventually, the particles are completely mixed and diffusion is complete

Rates of diffusion

If there is a big difference in concentration between two areas, diffusion will take place quickly. However when a substance is moving from a higher concentration to one which is just a bit lower, the movement toward the less concentrated area will appear to be quite slow. This is because although some particles move into the area of lower concentration by random movement, at the same time other identical particles are leaving that area by random movement.

The overall or **net** movement = particles moving in − particles moving out

In general the bigger the difference in concentration, the faster the rate of diffusion will be. This difference between two areas of concentration is called the **concentration gradient**. The bigger the difference, the steeper the gradient will be.

b) What is meant by the net movement of particles?

Both types of particles can pass through this membrane – it is freely permeable

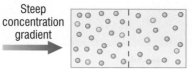

Beginning of experiment

Random movement means three blue particles have moved from left to right by diffusion

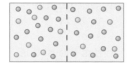

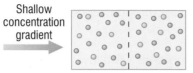

Beginning of experiment

Four blue particles have moved as a result of random movement from left to right – but two have moved from right to left. There is a *net* movement of *two* particles to the right by diffusion

Figure 3 This diagram shows us how the overall movement of particles in a particular direction is more effective if there is a big difference (a steep concentration gradient) between the two areas. This is why so many body systems are adapted to maintain steep concentration gradients.

Diffusion is **passive** – it takes place along a concentration gradient from high to low concentration and uses up no energy.

Concentration isn't the only thing that affects the rate of diffusion. An increase in temperature means the particles in a gas or a solution move more quickly. This in turn means diffusion will take place more rapidly as the random movement of the particles speeds up.

Diffusion in living organisms

Many important substances can move across your cell membranes by diffusion. Water is one. Simple sugars, such as glucose and amino acids from the breakdown of proteins in your gut, can also pass through cell membranes by diffusion. The oxygen you need for respiration passes from the air into your lungs and into your cells by diffusion.

Individual cells may be adapted to make diffusion easier and more rapid. The most common adaptation is to increase the surface area of the cell membrane over which diffusion occurs. Increasing the surface area means there is more room for diffusion to take place. By folding up the membrane of a cell, or the tissue lining an organ, the area over which diffusion can take place is greatly increased. So the amount of substance moved by diffusion is also greatly increased.

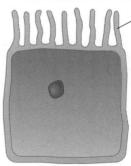

Infoldings of the cell membrane form microvilli, which increase the surface area of the cell

Figure 4 An increase in the surface area of a cell membrane means more diffusion can take place

SUMMARY QUESTIONS

Copy and complete using the words below:

Diffusion   gas   high   low   random   solute

1   ...... is the net movement of particles of a ...... or a ...... from an area of ...... concentration to an area of ...... concentration as a result of the ...... movement of the particles.

2   Explain why a cut in water looks much worse than a cut on land in terms of diffusion and the movement of particles.

3   a) Explain why diffusion takes place faster as the temperature increases.
    b) Explain in terms of diffusion why so many cells have folded membranes along at least one surface.

KEY POINTS

1   Dissolved substances move in and out of cells by diffusion, osmosis and active transport.
2   Diffusion is the net movement of particles from an area where they are at a high concentration to an area where they are at a lower concentration.

B2 1.4   Osmosis

Diffusion takes place where particles can spread freely from one place to another. However the solutions inside cells are separated from those outside by the cell membrane which does not let all types of particles through. Because it only lets some types of particles through, it is known as **partially permeable**.

Osmosis

Partially permeable cell membranes will allow water to move across them. It is important to remember that a dilute solution of, for example sugar, contains a *high* concentration of water (the **solvent**) and a *low* concentration of sugar (the **solute**). A concentrated sugar solution contains a relatively *low* concentration of water and a *high* concentration of sugar.

A cell is basically some chemicals dissolved in water inside a partially permeable bag of cell membrane. The cell contains a fairly concentrated solution of salts and sugars. Water will move from a high concentration of water particles (in a dilute solution) to a less concentrated solution of water particles (in a concentrated solution) across the membrane of the cell.

This special type of diffusion, where only water moves across a partially permeable membrane, is known as **osmosis**.

a) What is the difference between diffusion and osmosis?

PRACTICAL

Investigating osmosis

You can make model cells using bags made of partially permeable membrane. Figure 1 shows you some of these model cells. You can see what happens to them if the concentrations of the solutions inside or outside of the cell change.

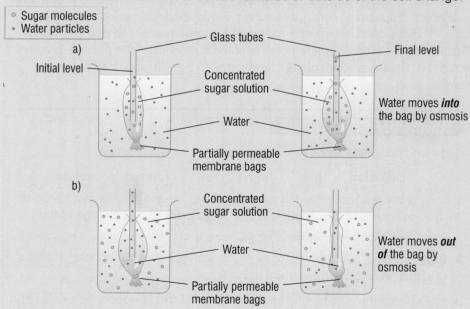

Figure 1 Using bags of partially permeable membrane to make model cells, we can clearly see the effect of osmosis as water moves across the membrane from a dilute to a concentrated solution

The internal concentration of your cells needs to stay the same all the time for the reactions of life to take place. Yet animal and plant cells are bathed in liquid which can be at very different concentrations to the inside of the cells. This can make water move into or out of the cells by osmosis.

Osmosis in animals

If a cell uses up water in its chemical reactions, the cytoplasm becomes more concentrated and more water will immediately move in by osmosis. Similarly if the cytoplasm becomes too dilute because water is produced during chemical reactions, water will leave the cell by osmosis, restoring the balance.

However osmosis can also cause some very serious problems in animal cells. (See Figure 2.) If the solution outside the cell is more dilute than the cell contents, then water will move into the cell by osmosis. The cell will swell and may burst.

On the other hand, if the solution outside the cell is more concentrated than the cell contents, then water will move out of the cell by osmosis. The cytoplasm will become too concentrated and the cell will shrivel up. Once you understand the effect osmosis can have on cells, the importance of homeostasis and maintaining constant internal conditions becomes very clear!

b) How does osmosis help maintain the body cells at the same concentration?

Osmosis in plants

Plants rely on well-regulated osmosis to support their stems and leaves. Water moves into plant cells by osmosis, making the cytoplasm swell and press against the plant cell walls. The pressure builds up until no more water can physically enter the cell. This makes the cell hard and rigid.

This swollen state keeps the leaves and stems of the plant rigid and firm. So for plants it is important that the fluid surrounding the cells always has a higher concentration of water (it is a more dilute solution of chemicals) than the cytoplasm of the cells. This keeps osmosis working in the right direction.

But sometimes plant and animal cells need to move substances such as glucose against a concentration gradient. For this there is another method of transport known as **active transport** which uses energy from respiration.

When the concentration of your body fluids is the same as in your red blood cell contents, equal amounts of water enter and leave the cell by random movement and the cell keeps its shape

If the concentration of the solution around the red blood cells is higher than the concentration of substances inside the cell, water will leave the cell by osmosis. This makes it shrivel and shrink so it can no longer carry oxygen around your body.

If the concentration of your body fluids is lower than in your red blood cell contents, water enters the cells by osmosis so your red blood cells swell up, lose their shape and eventually burst!

Figure 2 The impact of osmosis on your red blood cells can be devastating – so keeping your body fluids at the right concentration is vital

GET IT RIGHT!

Take care with your definition of osmosis. Make it clear that it is only water which is moving across the membrane, and get your concentrations right!

SUMMARY QUESTIONS

1 Define the following words: **diffusion**; **osmosis**; **partially permeable membrane**

2 Explain using a diagram what would happen:

a) if you set up an experiment with a partially permeable bag containing strong sugar solution in a beaker full of pure water.

b) if you set up an experiment using a partially permeable bag containing pure water in a beaker containing strong sugar solution.

3 Animals that live in fresh water have a constant problem with their water balance. The single-celled organism called *Amoeba* has a special vacuole in its cell. It fills with water and then moves to the outside of the cell and bursts. A new vacuole starts forming straight away. Explain in terms of osmosis why the *Amoeba* needs one of these vacuoles.

KEY POINTS

1 Osmosis is a special case of diffusion.
2 Osmosis is the diffusion/movement of water from a high water concentration (dilute solution) to a low water concentration (concentrated solution) through a partially permeable membrane.

B2 1.5   Cell issues

Discovering cells

Over the past three centuries our ideas about cells have developed as our ability to see them has improved. In 1665, the English scientist Robert Hooke designed the first working microscope and saw cells in cork.

At around the same time a Dutchman, Anton van Leeuwenhoek, also produced a microscope. It enabled him to see bacteria, microscopic animals and blood cells for the first time ever.

Almost two centuries later, by the 1840s, scientists had accepted that cells are the basic units of all living things. From then on, as optical microscopes improved, more details of the secret life inside a cell were revealed as cells were magnified up to 1000 times.

With the invention of the electron microscope in the 1930s it became possible to magnify things much more. We can now look at cells magnified up 500 000 times!

Anton van Leeuwenhoek (1632–1723)

Cork cells drawn by Robert Hooke

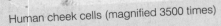

Human cheek cells (magnified 3500 times)

ACTIVITY

Produce a timeline to show how microscopes have developed since they were first invented. Annotate your timeline to show how important our discoveries about cells have been.

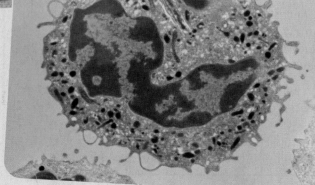

A human white blood cell at high magnification

The ability to see cells and the secret worlds inside them has developed in an amazing way since the days of the early microscopes

Beating osmosis

The cells of all living organisms contain sodium chloride and other chemicals in solution. This means they can always be prone to water moving into them by osmosis. If they are immersed in a solution with a lower concentration of salts than the body cells they will tend to gain water. If in a more concentrated solution, water is lost. Either way can spell disaster. Here are just a few of the different ways in which living things attempt – largely successfully – to beat osmosis!

No contest!

For many marine invertebrates like this jellyfish, osmosis causes no problems because the concentration of solutes in the cells of their bodies is exactly the same as the sea water. So there is no net movement of water in or out of the cells.

Copy cats!

Living on land causes all sorts of problems for the cells, particularly if water is lost and the body fluids get concentrated. Then water will leave the body cells by osmosis fast. Many insects have taken a leaf out of the plant's book – they have a tough, waterproof outer layer which prevents water loss from the body surface. They even have breathing holes known as *spiracles*. These can be closed up when they aren't needed – very like the stomata on the leaves of plants.

Flooding in

Fish that live in fresh water have a real problem. They need a constant flow of water over their gills to get the oxygen they need for respiration. But water moves into their gill cells and blood by osmosis at the same time. Like all vertebrates, fish have kidneys which play a big part in using osmosis to regulate their internal environment. So freshwater fish produce huge amounts of very dilute urine, which gets rid of the excess water that gets into their bodies. They also have special salt-absorbing glands. These use active transport to move salt against the concentration gradient from the water into the fish – rather like the situation in plant root cells.

The big ones

Marine vertebrates like this whale are constantly drinking salty water. The salt loading would cause water to move out of their body cells and kill them if they couldn't deal with it. Fortunately whales have extremely efficient kidneys. When a whale drinks 1000 cm³ of sea water, it produces 670 cm³ of very concentrated urine – and gains 330 cm³ of pure water.

SUMMARY QUESTIONS

1

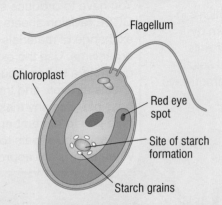

Chlamydomonas is a single-celled organism which lives under water. It can move itself to the light to photosynthesise, and stores excess food as starch.

a) What features does it have in common with most plant cells?

b) What features are not like plant cells and what are they used for?

c) Would you class *Chlamydomonas* as a plant cell or an animal cell? Explain why.

2

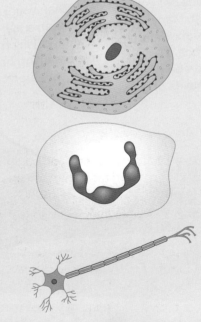

Each of these cells is specialised for a particular function in your body.

a) Copy each of these diagrams and label the cells carefully. Carry out some research if necessary.

b) Describe what you think is the function of each of these cells.

c) Explain how the structure of the cell is related to its function.

EXAM-STYLE QUESTIONS

1 The diagram is of a cell from the leaf of a plant.

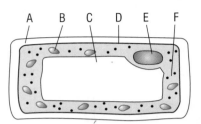

(a) Name the structures **D**, **E** and **F**. (3)

(b) (i) What is the name of structure A? (1)

   (ii) What material is structure **A** made of? (1)

(c) (i) What is the name of structure **C**? (1)

   (ii) What is the liquid it contains called? (1)

(d) Structure **B** is a chloroplast. What is its function? (2)

(e) Name two different structures that are found within the material labelled **F**. (2)

(f) (i) A different type of plant cell is a root hair cell. What is the function of this type of cell? (1)

   (ii) State one way in which a root hair cell differs from the leaf cell shown in the diagram. (1)

2 Copy the table below. Look at the structures listed in the first column. Fill in the empty columns by putting a tick (✓) if you think it is present and a cross (✗) if you think it is absent. (6)

Structure	Animal cell	Plant cell
Nucleus		
Cytoplasm		
Cell wall		
Cell membrane		
Chloroplast		
Permanent vacuole		

3 A student noticed that different trees give different amounts of shade on a sunny day. She decided to investigate three species of tree – oak, sycamore and ash. She thought that the more shading, the better the tree was at gathering light for photosynthesis. She would use a light meter to record the light levels. The student had many things to consider when deciding on a method.

(a) Should she take readings in direct sunlight as well as under the trees? Explain your answer. (2)

(b) Describe the weather that would be most appropriate when collecting the data. (1)

(c) Should the student collect data from one or more than one position? Explain your answer. (1)

(d) Explain why it would be necessary for the student to take as many readings as she could under the trees. (1)

(e) What type of independent variable has the student decided to use? (1)

(f) What type of dependent variable has she decided to use? (1)

(g) How should the student calculate the mean for each set of results? (1)

(h) Suggest how she should present her data. (1)

4 List **A** gives the names of different types of cells found in plants and animals. List **B** gives one special feature of each of these cells. Match each cell type with its feature by writing the relevant letter and number next to one another. (6)

List A	List B
A Fat cell	**1** Has a long tail with muscle-like proteins
B Root hair cell	**2** Can divide and change into many different types of cell
C Sperm cell	**3** Contains chloroplasts
D Leaf cell	**4** Can expand up to 1 000 times its original size
E Stem cell	**5** Contains a chemical called visual pigment
F Cone cell (in eye)	**6** Has extension to increase its surface area

HOW SCIENCE WORKS QUESTIONS

Spinning cells!

It is possible to separate the different parts of a cell using a centrifuge. Your teacher might be able to show you one of these. They really are very simple. They spin around rather like a very fast spin dryer.

They are used to separate structures that might be mixed together in a liquid. One of their uses is to separate the different parts of a cell.

The cells are first broken open so that the contents spill out into the liquid. The mixture is then put into the centrifuge. The centrifuge starts to spin slowly and a pellet forms at the bottom of the tube. This is removed. The rest is put back into the centrifuge at a higher speed and the next pellet removed and so on.

Here are some results:

Centrifuge speed (rpm)	Part of cell in pellet
3 000	Nuclei
10 000	Mitochondria
12 000	Ribosomes

(rpm = revolutions per minute)

a) From these observations can you suggest a link between the speed of the centrifuge and the size of the part of the cell found in the pellet? (1)

b) What apparatus would you need to test your suggestion? (1)

c) i) What was your independent variable? (1)
 ii) Is your independent variable best described as categoric, discrete or continuous? (1)

d) What was your dependent variable? (1)

e) If your suggestion is correct, what results would you expect? (1)

f) What would be the easiest measurement to make to show the size of the mitochondria? (1)

g) Suggest how many mitochondria you might measure. (1)

h) How would you calculate the mean for the measurements you have taken? (2)

B2 2.1 Photosynthesis

Like all living organisms, plants need food. It provides them with the energy for respiration, growth and reproduction. But plants aren't like us – they don't need to eat.

Plants can make their own food! They do it by **photosynthesis**. This takes place in the green parts of plants (especially the leaves) when it is light.

The process of photosynthesis

Photosynthesis can be summed up in the following equation:

carbon dioxide + water (+ light energy) → glucose + oxygen

The cells in the leaves of a plant are full of small green parts called **chloroplasts**. They contain a green substance called **chlorophyll**.

During photosynthesis, light energy is absorbed by the chlorophyll in the chloroplasts. This energy is then used to convert carbon dioxide from the air plus water from the soil into a simple sugar called **glucose**. The chemical reaction also produces oxygen gas. This is released into the air.

a) What is the word equation for photosynthesis?

Some of the glucose produced during photosynthesis is used immediately by the cells of the plant. However, a lot of the glucose made is converted into starch for storage.

Iodine solution is a yellowy-brown liquid which turns dark blue when it reacts with starch. You can use this *iodine test for starch* to show that photosynthesis has taken place in a plant.

PRACTICAL

Producing oxygen

You can show a plant is photosynthesising by collecting the oxygen given off as a by-product. It is very difficult to see oxygen, a colourless gas, being given off by land plants. But if you use water plants you can collect the gas which they give off when they are photosynthesising. It will relight a glowing splint, showing that it is oxygen gas.

PRACTICAL

Testing for starch

Chlorophyll is vital for photosynthesis to take place. It absorbs the light which provides the energy for the plant to make glucose and convert it into starch.

Take a leaf from a variegated plant (partly green and partly white). After treating the leaves, you use iodine solution to show how important chlorophyll is. (See Figure 1.)

● What happens in the test? Explain your observations

b) What is chlorophyll?

The leaves of plants are perfectly adapted because:

● most leaves are broad, they have a big surface area for light to fall on,
● they contain chlorophyll in the chloroplasts to absorb the light energy,
● they have air spaces which allow carbon dioxide to get to the cells, and oxygen to leave them,
● they have veins, which bring plenty of water to the cells of the leaves.

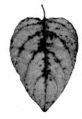

Figure 1 These leaves came from a plant which had been kept in the light for several hours. Leaves have to be specially prepared so the iodine solution can reach the cells. The one on the right has been tested for starch, using iodine solution. Only the green parts of the leaf made their own starch which turns the iodine solution blue-black.

All of these adaptations mean the plant can carry out as much photosynthesis as possible whenever there is light available.

c) How does the broad shape of leaves help photosynthesis to take place?

PRACTICAL

Observing leaves

Look at a whole plant leaf and then a section of a leaf under a microscope. You can see how well adapted it is.

- Compare what you can see with Figure 2 below.
- What magnification did you use?

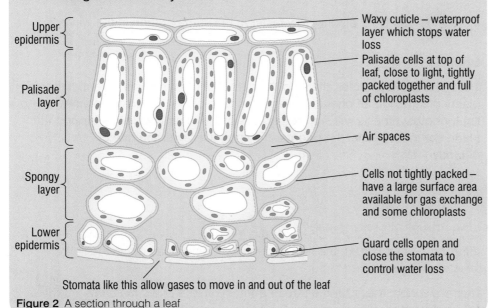

Upper epidermis

Palisade layer

Spongy layer

Lower epidermis

Waxy cuticle – waterproof layer which stops water loss

Palisade cells at top of leaf, close to light, tightly packed together and full of chloroplasts

Air spaces

Cells not tightly packed – have a large surface area available for gas exchange and some chloroplasts

Guard cells open and close the stomata to control water loss

Stomata like this allow gases to move in and out of the leaf

Figure 2 A section through a leaf

NEXT TIME YOU...

. . . breathe in, remember that the oxygen in the air you are breathing was produced as a by-product of photosynthesis by plants. Luckily for us, the world's plants produce about 368 000 000 000 tonnes of oxygen every year!

SUMMARY QUESTIONS

1 Copy and complete using the words below:

carbon dioxide   chlorophyll   energy   gas   glucose light   Oxygen   water

During photosynthesis ...... energy is absorbed by ......, a substance found in the chloroplasts. This ...... is then used to convert .... from the air and ...... from the soil into a simple sugar called .... is also produced and released as a ......

2 a) Where does a plant get the carbon dioxide, water and light that it needs for photosynthesis?

   b) Work out the path taken by a carbon atom as it moves from being part of the carbon dioxide in the air to being part of a starch molecule in a plant.

3 Design experiments to show that plants need a) carbon dioxide and b) light for photosynthesis to take place. For each experiment explain what your control would be and how you would show that photosynthesis has taken place.

KEY POINTS

1 Photosynthesis can be summed up by the equation:

carbon dioxide + water [+ light energy] → glucose + oxygen

2 During photosynthesis light energy is absorbed by the chlorophyll in the chloroplasts. It is used to convert carbon dioxide and water into sugar (glucose). Oxygen is released as a by-product.

3 Leaves are well adapted to allow the maximum photosynthesis to take place.

B2 2.2   Limiting factors

1 What factors limit the rate of photosynthesis in plants?
2 How can we use what we know about limiting factors to grow more food?

You may have noticed that plants grow quickly in the summer, and hardly at all in the winter. Plants need certain things like light, warmth and carbon dioxide if they are going to photosynthesise as fast as they can.

If any of these things are in short supply they may limit the amount of photosynthesis a plant can manage. This is why they are known as **limiting factors**.

a) Why do you think plants grow faster in the summer than in the winter?

Light

The most obvious factor affecting the rate of photosynthesis is light. If there is plenty of light, lots of photosynthesis can take place. If there is very little or no light, photosynthesis will stop regardless of the other conditions around the plant. For most plants, the brighter the light, the faster the rate of photosynthesis.

PRACTICAL

How does the intensity of light affect the rate of photosynthesis?

We can look at this experimentally. (See Figure 1.) At the start, the rate of photosynthesis goes up as the light intensity increases. This tells us that light intensity is a limiting factor.

However, we reach a point when no matter how bright the light, the rate of photosynthesis stays the same. At this point, light is no longer limiting the rate of photosynthesis. Something else has become the limiting factor.

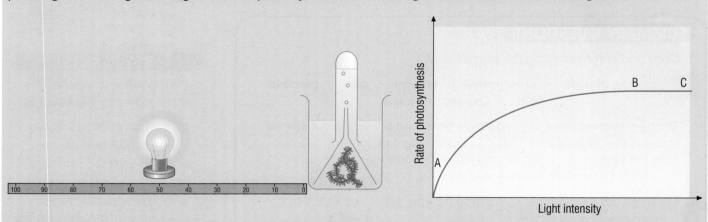

Figure 1 When the light is moved away from this water plant, the rate of photosynthesis falls – shown by a slowing in the stream of oxygen bubbles being produced. If the light is moved closer (keeping the water temperature constant) the stream of bubbles becomes faster, showing an increased rate of photosynthesis. The results can be plotted on a graph like this which shows the effect of light intensity on the rate of photosynthesis.

● Why is light a limiting factor for photosynthesis?
● Name the independent and the dependent variables in this investigation. (See page 276.)

Temperature

Temperature affects all chemical reactions, including photosynthesis. As the temperature rises, the rate of photosynthesis will increase as the reaction speeds up. However, because photosynthesis takes place in living organisms it is controlled by enzymes. Enzymes are destroyed once the temperature rises to around 40 to 50°C. This means that if the temperature gets too high, the rate of photosynthesis will fall as the enzymes controlling it are denatured.

b) Why does temperature affect photosynthesis?

Carbon dioxide levels

Plants need carbon dioxide to make glucose. The atmosphere only contains about 0.04% carbon dioxide, so carbon dioxide levels often limit the amount of photosynthesis which can take place. Increasing the carbon dioxide levels will increase the rate of photosynthesis.

For the plants you see around you on a sunny day, carbon dioxide levels are the most common limiting factor. The carbon dioxide levels around a plant tend to rise in the night as it respires but doesn't photosynthesise. Then as the light and temperature levels increase in the morning, the carbon dioxide all gets used up.

However, in a laboratory or in a greenhouse the levels of carbon dioxide can be increased artificially. This means they are no longer limiting, and the rate of photosynthesis increases with the rise in carbon dioxide.

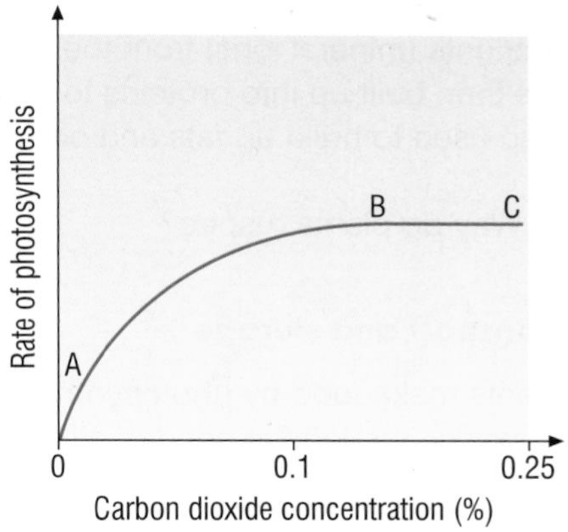

Figure 3 This graph shows the effect of increasing carbon dioxide levels on the rate of photosynthesis at a particular light level and temperature. Eventually one of the other factors becomes limiting.

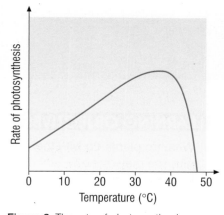

Figure 2 The rate of photosynthesis increases steadily with a rise in temperature up to a certain point. After this the enzymes are destroyed and the reaction stops completely.

> ### DID YOU KNOW?
> There are a few plants that live in very shady areas which have evolved to photosynthesise at their maximum at relatively low levels of light. For them, too much light causes the rate of photosynthesis to drop!

GET IT RIGHT!

Make sure you can explain limiting factors.
Learn to interpret graphs which show the effect of limiting factors on photosynthesis.

SUMMARY QUESTIONS

1. a) What is photosynthesis?
   b) What are the three main limiting factors that affect the rate of photosynthesis in a plant?

2. Which factors do you think would be limiting photosynthesis in the following situations? In each case, explain why the rate of photosynthesis is limited.

   a) Plants growing on a woodland floor in winter.
   b) Plants growing on a woodland floor in summer.
   c) A field of barley first thing in the morning.
   d) The same field later on in the day.

3. Look at the graph in Figure 1.

   a) Explain what is happening between points A and B on the graph.
   b) Explain what is happening between points B and C on the graph.
   c) Look at Figure 2. Explain why it is a different shape to the other two graphs on this spread.

KEY POINTS

1. There are three main factors that limit the rate of photosynthesis – light, temperature and carbon dioxide levels.
2. We can artificially change the environment in which we grow plants. We can use this to observe the effect of different factors on the rate of photosynthesis. We can also use it to control their rate of photosynthesis.

B2 2.3   How plants use glucose

LEARNING OBJECTIVES

1 What do plants do with the glucose they make?
2 How do plants store food?

NEXT TIME YOU...

... tuck into a plate of chips or a pile of mashed potato, remember that you are eating the winter food store of a potato plant! The starch you are enjoying was formed from glucose made in the leaves of the potato plant by photosynthesis. It was transported down from the leaves to the roots to form a tasty tuber!

Plants make glucose when they photosynthesise. This glucose is vital for their survival. Some of the glucose produced during photosynthesis is used immediately by the cells of the plant. They use it for respiration and to provide energy for cell functions, growth and reproduction.

Respiration

Plants cells, like any other living cells, respire all the time. They break down glucose using oxygen to provide energy for their cells. Carbon dioxide and water are the waste products of the reaction.

The energy released in respiration is then used to build up smaller molecules into bigger molecules. Some of the glucose is converted into starch for storage (see below). Plants also build up sugars into more complex carbohydrates like cellulose. They use this to make new plant cell walls.

Plants use some of the energy from respiration to combine sugars with other nutrients (mineral ions) from the soil to make amino acids. These amino acids are then built up into proteins to be used in the cells. Energy from respiration is also used to build up fats and oils to make a food store in the seeds.

a) Why do plants respire?

Transport and storage

Plants make food by photosynthesis in their leaves and other green parts. However, the food is needed all over the plant. It is moved around the plant in a special transport system.

There are two separate transport systems in plants. The **phloem** is made up of living tissue. It transports sugars made by photosynthesis from the leaves to the rest of the plant. They are carried to all the areas of the plant. These include the growing regions where the sugars are needed for making new plant material, and the storage organs where they are needed to provide a store of food for the winter.

The **xylem** is the other transport tissue. It carries water and mineral ions from the soil around the plant.

A vascular bundle. It contains **xylem** and **phloem** with **cambium cells** between them.

Phloem tubes – they have thin walls and living cells

Phloem

Xylem

Cambium cells grow into new xylem and phloem

Xylem vessels – they have thick, strong walls and are not living

Figure 1 A look at a section of a plant stem shows you how the transport system of a plant is arranged

GET IT RIGHT!

Remember:

- Plants respire 24 hours a day to release energy.
- Glucose is soluble in water, but starch is insoluble.

Plants convert some of the glucose produced in photosynthesis into starch to be stored. Glucose is **soluble** (it dissolves in water). If it was stored in plant cells it could affect the way water moves into and out of the cells. Large amounts of glucose stored in the plant cells could affect the water balance of the whole plant. Starch is **insoluble** (it doesn't dissolve in water). This means that plants can store large amounts of starch in their cells without it having any effect on the water balance of the plant.

So the main energy store in plants is starch and it is found all over a plant. It is stored in the leaves to provide an energy store for when it is dark or when light levels are low.

PRACTICAL

Making starch

You can use the presence of starch in a leaf as evidence that photosynthesis has been taking place. It is no good just adding iodine to a leaf – the waterproof cuticle and the green chlorophyll will prevent it reacting clearly with the starch. But once you have treated the leaf, adding iodine will show you clearly if the leaf has been photosynthesising or not. Look at Figure 2.

Figure 2 We use the iodine test for the presence of starch to show us that photosynthesis has taken place. The leaf on the right has been kept in the dark. It has made no glucose to turn into starch, and has used up any starch stores it had for respiration. The leaf on the left has been in the light and been able to photosynthesise. The glucose has been converted to starch which is clearly visible when it reacts with iodine and turns blue-black. The colour is removed from the leaves before testing by boiling them in ethanol.

Starch is also stored in special storage areas of a plant. Many plants produce tubers and bulbs to help them survive through the winter. These are full of stored starch. We often take advantage of these starch stores and eat them ourselves. Potatoes, carrots and onions are all full of starch to keep a plant going until spring comes again!

b) What is the main storage substance in plants?

Figure 3 Trees like this giant redwood can be up to 30 metres tall – and then the roots spread out in all directions underground. Plants need a very effective transport system to move the food they make in their leaves distances like these.

SUMMARY QUESTIONS

1 Copy and complete using the words below:

> **energy   glucose   growth   photosynthesise   respiration
> reproduction   starch   storage   twenty-four**

Plants make ...... when they .... Some of the glucose produced is used by the cells of the plant for ...... which goes on .... hours a day. It provides ...... for cell functions, ... and .... Some is converted to ...... for ....

2 List as many ways as possible in which a plant uses the glucose produced by photosynthesis.

3 a) Why is the glucose made by photosynthesis converted to starch to be stored in the plant?
  b) Where might you find starch in a plant?
  c) How could you show that a potato is a store of starch?

KEY POINTS

1 Plant cells use some of the glucose they make during photosynthesis for respiration.
2 Some of the soluble glucose produced during photosynthesis is converted into insoluble starch for storage.

B2 2.4 Why do plants need minerals?

If you put a plant in a pot of water, and give it plenty of light and carbon dioxide, it won't survive for very long! Although plants can make their own food by photosynthesis, they cannot survive long on photosynthesis alone.

Just as you need minerals and vitamins for healthy growth, so plants need more than simply carbon dioxide, water and light to thrive. They need mineral salts from the soil to make the chemicals needed in their cells.

Why do plants need nitrates?

The problem with the products of photosynthesis is that they are all carbohydrates. Carbohydrates are very important. Plants use them for energy, for storage and even for structural features like cell walls. However, a plant can't function without proteins as well. It needs proteins to act as enzymes and to make up a large part of the cytoplasm and the membranes.

a) What are the products of photosynthesis?

Figure 1 The plants on the left of this picture have been grown in a mixture containing all the minerals they need. The experimental plants on the right have been grown without nitrates. The difference in their rate of growth is clear to see.

Glucose and starch are made up of carbon, hydrogen and oxygen. Proteins are made up of amino acids which contain carbon, hydrogen, oxygen and **nitrogen**. Plants need **nitrates** from the soil to make proteins.

These nitrates, dissolved in water, are taken up from the soil by the plant roots. If a plant is deficient in nitrates (doesn't have enough) it doesn't grow properly. It is small and stunted. So nitrates are necessary for healthy growth.

When plants die and decay the nitrates and other minerals are returned to the soil to be used by other plants.

b) Why do plants need nitrates?

Why do plants need magnesium?

It isn't only nitrates that plants need to grow well. There is a whole range of *mineral ions* they need. For example, plants need **magnesium** to make chlorophyll.

Chlorophyll is vital to plants. It is chlorophyll which absorbs the energy from light which makes it possible for plants to photosynthesise. So if the plant can't make chlorophyll, it can't make food and it will die. This is why magnesium ions are so important for plants – they make up part of the chlorophyll molecule.

Plants only need a tiny amount of magnesium. However, if they don't get enough, they have pale, yellowish areas on their leaves where they cannot make chlorophyll.

c) Why do plants need magnesium ions?

If any of the mineral salts that a plant needs are missing it will begin to look very sickly. This is true in the garden and for houseplants just as much as for crops in a farmer's field.

PRACTICAL

Investigating the effect of minerals

You can grow young plants in water containing different combinations of minerals and see the effect on their growth.

- Why are some plants grown in water with no minerals added and some with all the minerals they need?

Figure 2 The leaf on the right came from a plant that had received all the minerals it needed. The plant on the left was grown without magnesium. It is easy to see which is which – just look for the yellow patches!

If there are not enough mineral ions in the soil, your plants cannot grow properly. They will show the symptoms of mineral deficiencies. If you can pick up the symptoms soon enough and give them the mineral ions that they need, all will be well. If not, your plants will die!

Mineral ion	Why needed?	Deficiency symptoms
nitrate	making protein	stunted growth
magnesium	making chlorophyll	pale, yellow leaves

The most recent development in growing crops is **hydroponics**. You don't plant your crops in soil. Instead you plant them in water to which you add the minerals your plants need to grow as well as possible.

Hydroponic crops are usually grown in massive greenhouses where all the other factors can be controlled as well. Everything is monitored and controlled by computers 24 hours a day. The crops are very clean – no mud on the roots! And you can grow crops very quickly, and even out of their usual season.

All this means you get a good price for them. The downside is that it is an expensive way to farm, and it uses a lot of resources.

SUMMARY QUESTIONS

1. a) Why do plants need mineral ions?
   b) Where do they get mineral ions from?
   c) Which mineral ion is needed by plants to form proteins?

2. a) Look at the plants in Figure 1. Describe how the plants grown without nitrates differ from the plants grown with all the mineral ions they need. Why are they so different?
   b) Look at the plants in Figure 2. Describe how the plants grown without magnesium differ from the plants grown with all the mineral ions they need. Why are they so different?

3. Explain the following in terms of the mineral ions needed by plants and how they are used in the cells:

   a) Farmers spread animal manure on their fields.
   b) Gardeners recommend giving houseplants a regular mineral feed containing nitrates and magnesium ions.
   c) If the same type of crop is grown in the same place every year it will gradually grow less well and becomes stunted, with pale, patchy leaves.

GET IT RIGHT!

Make sure you know the roles of nitrate and magnesium ions – and the deficiency symptoms of each of them.

Figure 3 If you are a farmer you harvest the crops that you grow and sell them. They are not left to die and decay naturally, returning minerals to the soil. So farmers add fertiliser to the soil to replace the minerals lost, ready for the next crop. The fertiliser may be a natural one like manure or an artificial mixture of the minerals that plants need to grow.

KEY POINTS

1. Plant roots absorb mineral salts including nitrate needed for healthy growth.
2. Nitrates and magnesium are two important mineral ions needed for healthy plant growth.
3. If mineral ions are deficient, a plant develops symptoms because it cannot grow properly.

B2 2.5   Plant problems?

Smallholder

'In days gone by most farms were small. Farmers fed their own families and hoped to make enough profit to survive. Different crops had to be grown each year (crop rotation) and the land was rested between crops. Fields lay fallow (no crops were grown) every few years to let the land recover. Manure from their own animals was the main fertiliser.

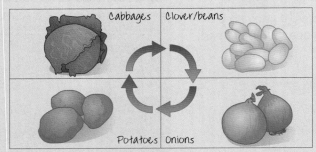

'We're trying to stick to the old ways on our little small-holding. We rotate our crops – you can see from my field plan how I do it. It helps to make sure that the minerals in the soil don't all get used up. It helps keep diseases at bay too.

'We feed our family well, and sell our extra produce to the village shop. Of course, I earn most of my money through my computer business.'

Arable farmer

'We farm a pretty big area. I grow wheat and oil seed rape. After we have harvested, I plough the stubble back into the soil. We used to burn it off but that's not allowed now. I think it's better to plough the stuff in anyway – puts something back!

'My farm is a big business – I can't afford to have land doing nothing. So we add fertiliser to keep the mineral levels right. We need to get the best crop we can every time! Modern fertilisers mean I can plant one crop straight after the other, and I avoid fallow years altogether.

'I have to get the balance right – if I spend too much on fertiliser, I don't make enough profit. But if I don't put enough fertiliser on the fields, I don't grow enough crops! I manage to support the family pretty well with the farm, and we employ one local man as well.'

Hydroponics grower

'In the laboratory you can isolate different factors and see how they limit the rate of photosynthesis. However, for most plants a mixture of these factors affects them. Early in the morning, light levels and temperature probably limit the rate of photosynthesis. Then as the level of light and the temperature rise, the carbon dioxide becomes limiting. On a bright, cold winter day, temperature probably limits the rate of the process. There is a constant interaction between the different factors.

'In commercial greenhouses we can take advantage of this knowledge of limiting factors and leave nothing to chance. We can control the temperature and the levels of light and carbon dioxide to get the fastest possible rates of photosynthesis. This makes sure our plants grow as quickly as possible. We even grow our plants in a nutritionally balanced solution rather than soil to make sure nothing limits their rate of photosynthesis and growth.'

ACTIVITY

The National Farmers Union (NFU) wants to produce a resource for schools to show how arable (crop) farming has changed over the years. Your job is to design *either* one large poster *or* a series of smaller posters that they can send out free to science departments in schools around the country. You need to explain how plants grow, and how farmers give them what they need to grow as well as possible. Use the information on this spread and in the rest of the chapter to help you.

By controlling the temperature, light and carbon dioxide levels in a greenhouse like this we can produce the biggest possible crops – fast!

'We invested in all the computer software and control systems about two years ago. It cost us a lot of money – but we are really reaping the benefits. We can change the carbon dioxide levels in the greenhouses during the day. We control the temperature and the light levels very carefully. What's more we can change the mineral content of the water as the plants grow and get bigger.

'We sell all our stuff to one of the big supermarket chains. Our lettuces are always clean, big and crisp – and we have a really fast turnover. No more ploughing fields for us!

'Of course we don't need as many staff now. We just have lots of alarm systems in our house. Then if anything goes wrong in one of the greenhouses, day or night, we know about it straight away. The monitoring systems and computers are vital to our way of growing. As far as our plants are concerned, limiting factors are a thing of the past!'

SUMMARY QUESTIONS

1 a) Match each word related to photosynthesis to its description:

A Carbon dioxide gas	1 ...... is produced and released into the air
B Water	2 ......provides energy
C Sunlight	3 ...... from the roots moves up to the leaf through the stem
D Glucose	4 ...... is absorbed from the air
E Oxygen	5 ...... is made in the leaf and provides the plant with food

b) Write a word equation for photosynthesis.

c) Much of the glucose made in photosynthesis is turned into an insoluble storage compound. What is this compound?

2

Year	Mean height of seedlings grown in 85% full sunlight (cm)	Mean height of seedlings grown in 35% full sunlight (cm)
2000	12	10
2001	16	12.5
2002	18	14
2003	21	17
2004	28	20
2005	35	21
2006	36	23

The figures in the table show the mean growth of two sets of oak seedlings. One set was grown in 85% full sunlight, the other set in only 35% full sunlight.

a) Plot a graph to show the growth of both sets of oak seedlings.

b) Using what you know about photosynthesis and limiting factors, explain the difference in the growth of the two sets of seedlings.

3 Plants make food in one organ and take up water from the soil in another organ. But both the food and the water are needed all over the plant.

a) Where do plants make their food?

b) Where do plants take in water?

c) There are two transport tissues in a plant. One is the phloem. What is the other one?

d) Which transport tissue carries food around the plant?

e) Which transport tissue carries water around the plant?

EXAM-STYLE QUESTIONS

1 Jenny carried out an investigation to show the rate of photosynthesis in two species of plant at different light intensities.

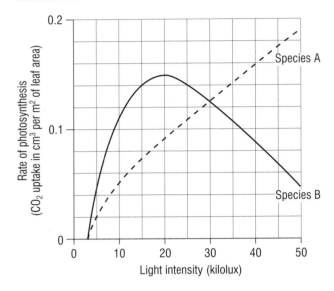

This investigation had two independent variables.

(a) Name the categoric independent variable. (1)

(b) Name the continuous independent variable. (1)

(c) Describe the pattern shown by species B. (3)
The results for species B were as follows:

Light intensity (kilolux)	CO_2 uptake (cm³/m²)
5	0.04
10	0.11
20	0.15
30	0.125
40	0.09
50	0.04

(d) Jenny was not sure where the peak of the graph should be drawn. Which extra measurements should she take to be sure of this? (1)

(e) At what light intensity do both species photosynthesise at the same rate? (1)

(f) If species **A** has a total leaf area of 100 m², how many cm³ of carbon dioxide will it take up at a light intensity of 10 kilolux? Show your working. (2)

(g) Which species shows the best adaptation to shade conditions? Using the information in the graph give reasons for your answer. (2)

(h) What is the name of the sugar produced during photosynthesis? (1)

(i) What is the name of the process by which this sugar is broken down to provide energy for the plant? (1)

2 The diagram below represents a section through a plant leaf showing the arrangement of cells as seen under a microscope.

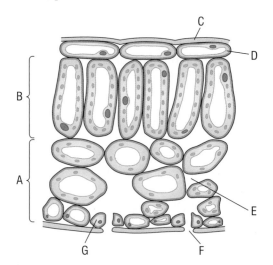

(a) Name the parts labelled **E**, **F** and **G**. (3)

(b) Give one function of the parts labelled
   (i) **C**
   (ii) **G** (2)

(c) List the four letters that indicate structures that contain chloroplasts. (4)

(d) The diagram shows only a small section through a leaf. State **FOUR** ways in which the **whole leaf** is adapted to carry out photosynthesis. In each case show how this feature helps the plant to carry out photosynthesis. (8)

3 Plants need to obtain mineral salts in order to survive.

(a) Name two mineral salts that are essential to plants and in each case give a reason why they are needed. (4)

(b) How do plants obtain the minerals they need? (2)

(c) If crops are grown for long periods on the same piece of land, they may use up some of the minerals in the soil. State two ways in which farmers can avoid these crops dying due to lack of minerals. (2)

HOW SCIENCE WORKS QUESTIONS

Water gardens – or rather hydroponics!

Ed had seen some entrepreneurs make a fortune by growing lettuce in the middle of winter. He wanted some of the action! He knew that he would have to provide heat and light as well as the nutrients and the correct pH. He knew that the plants required water and oxygen to their roots.

None of the books told him how often he should water the lettuce. Water them too often and they would not get enough oxygen. Leave them too long without watering and they would dry out. He decided on an investigation.

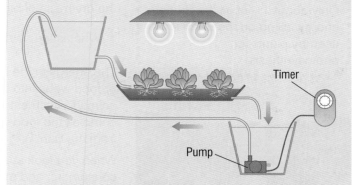

Ed set up five different trays and buckets. He set the timer differently for each tray. The lettuce would now be watered for a different number of times each day. He could therefore work out which was the best for his lettuce.

a) Suggest some time intervals for Ed to water his lettuce. (1)

b) Suggest a dependent variable he could measure. (1)

c) Explain why you have chosen this variable. (1)

d) Describe how Ed might measure this dependent variable. (1)

e) Suggest three control variables he should use. (3)

f) Explain why it would be sensible for Ed to repeat his results. (2)

Ed's first set of results showed very little difference. It did not seem to matter how often he watered them.

g) Suggest a problem he had with the design of his investigation. (1)

h) Why was it important that Ed did his own research and not ask advice from those already growing the lettuce? (2)

B2 3.1   Pyramids of biomass

LEARNING OBJECTIVES

1 Where does biomass come from?
2 What is a pyramid of biomass?

DID YOU KNOW?

Only about 1% of all the Sun's energy falling on the Earth is used by plants for photosynthesis!

Figure 1 Plants produce a huge mass of biological material in just one growing season

Figure 2 This food chain cannot be accurately represented using a pyramid of numbers. Using biomass shows us the amount of biological material involved at each level in a way that simple numbers cannot do.

As you saw in the previous chapter, radiation from the Sun is the source of energy for all the groups of living things on Earth.

Light energy pours out continually onto the surface of the Earth. Green plants capture a small part of this light energy using chlorophyll. It is used in photosynthesis. So some of the energy from the Sun is stored in the substances which make up the cells of the plant. This new plant material adds to the **biomass**.

Biomass is the mass of living material in an animal or plant. Ultimately all biomass is built up using energy from the Sun. Biomass is often measured as the dry mass of biological material in grams.

a) What is the source of all the energy in the living things on Earth?

The energy in the biomass made by plants is passed on through food chains or food webs into the animals which eat the plants. It then passes on into the animals which eat other animals. No matter how long the food chain or complex the food web, the original source of all the biomass involved is energy from the Sun.

When you look at a food chain, there are usually more producers than primary consumers, and more primary consumers than secondary consumers. If you count the number of organisms at each level you can compare them. You can show this using a **pyramid of numbers**. However, in many cases a pyramid of numbers does not accurately reflect what is happening.

b) What is a pyramid of numbers?

Pyramids of biomass

To show what is happening in food chains more accurately we can use biomass. We can draw the total amount of biomass in the living organisms at each stage of the food chain to scale and show it as a pyramid of biomass.

Organism	Number	Biomass – dry mass in g
Oak tree	1	500 000
Aphids	10 000	1000
Ladybirds	200	50

Pyramid of numbers   Pyramid of biomass

c) What is a pyramid of biomass?

Interpreting pyramids of biomass

The biomass found at each stage of a food chain is less than it was at the previous stage.

This is because:

- Not all organisms at one stage are eaten by the stage above.
- Some material taken in is passed out as waste.
- When a herbivore eats a plant, it turns some of the plant material into new herbivore. But much of the biomass from the plant is used by the herbivore in respiration to release energy for living. It does not get passed on to the carnivore when the herbivore is eaten.

So at each stage of a food chain the amount of energy in the biomass which is passed on gets less. A large amount of plant biomass supports a smaller amount of herbivore biomass. This in turn supports an even smaller amount of carnivore biomass.

In general, pyramids of biomass are drawn in proportion. Sometimes, when the biomass of one type of organism is much, much bigger than the others, this doesn't work and so the diagram can only give a rough idea.

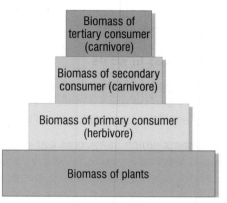

Figure 3 Any food chain can be turned into a pyramid of biomass like this

SUMMARY QUESTIONS

1 a) What is biomass?
   b) Why is a pyramid of biomass more useful for showing what is happening in a food chain than a pyramid of numbers?

2

Organism	Biomass, dry mass (g)
Grass	100 000
Sheep	5000
Sheep ticks	30

   a) Draw a pyramid of biomass for this grassland ecosystem.
   b) What would you expect the pyramid of numbers for this food chain to look like?
   c) Draw the pyramids of numbers and the pyramids of biomass you would expect from the following two food chains:
      i) stinging nettles → caterpillars → robin
      ii) marine plants → small fish → large fish → seals → polar bear

3 a) Explain simply why the biomass from one stage of a pyramid of biomass does not all become biomass in the next stage of the pyramid.
   b) Using the data in Figure 2, calculate the percentage biomass passed on from:
      i) the producers to the primary consumers,
      ii) the primary consumers to the secondary consumers.

KEY POINTS

1 Radiation from the Sun is the main source of energy for all living things. The Sun's energy is captured and used by plants during photosynthesis.

2 The mass of living material at each stage of a food chain is less than at the previous stage. The biomass at each stage can be drawn to scale and shown as a pyramid of biomass.

B2 3.2

Energy losses

LEARNING OBJECTIVES

1 How do we lose energy to the environment?
2 What is the effect of maintaining a constant body temperature?

Figure 1 The amount of biomass in a lion is a lot less than the amount of biomass in the grass which feeds the zebra it preys on. But where does all the biomass go?

An animal like a zebra eats grass and other small plants. It takes in a large amount of plant biomass, and converts it into a much smaller amount of zebra biomass. This is typical of a food chain.

The amounts of biomass and energy contained in living things always gets less at each stage of a food chain from plants onwards. Only a small amount of the biomass taken in gets turned into new animal material. The question is – what happens to the rest?

Energy loss in waste

The biomass which an animal eats is a source of energy, but not all of the energy can be used. Firstly, herbivores cannot digest all of the plant material they eat. The material they can't digest is passed out of the body in the faeces.

The meat which carnivores eat is easier to digest than plants, so they tend to need feeding less often and they produce less waste. But even carnivores often cannot digest hooves, claws, bones and teeth, so some of the biomass that they eat is always lost in their faeces.

When an animal eats more protein than it needs, the excess is broken down and passed out as urea in the urine. So biomass – and energy – are lost from the body.

a) Why is biomass lost in faeces?

Figure 2 Animals like horses eat very large amounts of biomass every day. However they also produce very large quantities of dung made up of all the biomass they couldn't actually digest!

Energy loss due to movement

Part of the biomass eaten by an animal is used for respiration in its cells. This supplies all the energy needs for the living processes taking place within the body.

Movement uses a great deal of energy. The muscles use energy to contract. So the more an animal moves about the more energy (and biomass) it uses from its food. The muscles produce heat as they contract.

b) Why do animals that move around a lot use up more of the biomass they eat than animals which don't move much?

Keeping a constant body temperature

Much of the energy animals produce from their food in cellular respiration is eventually lost as heat to the surroundings. Some of this heat is produced by the muscles as the animals move.

Heat losses are particularly large in mammals and birds because they are 'warm-blooded'. This means they keep their bodies at a constant temperature regardless of the temperature of the surroundings. They use up energy all the time, to keep warm when it's cold or to cool down when it's hot. Because of this, warm-blooded animals need to eat far more food than cold-blooded animals, such as fish and reptiles, to get the same increase in biomass.

c) What do we mean by a 'warm-blooded animal'?

PRACTICAL

Investigating the heat released by respiration

Even plants produce heat by cellular respiration. You can investigate this using germinating peas in a vacuum flask.

● What would be the best way to monitor the temperature continuously?
● Plan the investigation.

Figure 3 Only between 2% and10% of the biomass eaten by an animal such as this horse will get turned into new horse – the rest of the stored energy will be used or lost in other ways

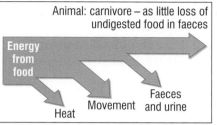

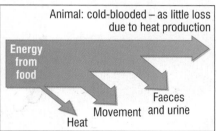

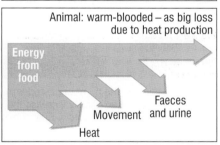

Figure 4 Sankey diagrams show how energy is transferred in a system. We can use them to look at the energy which goes in to and out of an animal and predict whether it eats plants or is a carnivore. You can even tell if it is warm-blooded or cold-blooded!

SUMMARY QUESTIONS

1 Copy and complete using the words below:

**biomass   body temperature   energy   food chain   growth
movement   producers   respiration   waste**

The amounts of ...... and ...... contained in living things always gets less at each stage of a .... from ...... onwards. Biomass is lost as ...... products and used to produce energy in .... This is used for ...... and to control .... Only a small amount is used for ....

2 Explain why so much of the energy from the Sun which lands on the surface of the Earth is not turned into biomass in animals.

3 Why do warm-blooded animals need to eat more food than cold-blooded ones of the same size if they are to put on weight?

KEY POINTS

1 The amount of biomass and energy gets less at each successive stage in a food chain.
2 This is because some material is always lost in waste, and some is used for respiration to supply energy for movement and for maintaining the body temperature.

31

B2 3.3

Energy in food production

LEARNING OBJECTIVES

1 Why do short food chains make food production more efficient?

2 How can we manage food production to reduce energy losses?

Figure 1 Reducing the number of stages in food chains could dramatically increase the efficiency of our food production. Eating less meat would mean more food for everyone.

GET IT RIGHT!

Make sure you can use data on food production and explain both the pros and the cons.

Pyramids of biomass clearly show us that the organisms at each stage of a food chain contain less material and therefore less energy. This has some major implications for the way we human beings feed ourselves.

Food chains in food production

In the developed world much of our diet consists of meat or other animal products such as eggs, cheese and milk. The cows, goats, pigs and sheep that we use to produce our food eat plants. By the time it reaches us, much of the energy from the plant has been used up.

In some cases we even feed animals to animals. Ground up fish, for example, is often part of commercial pig and chicken feed. This means we have put another extra layer into the food chain – plant to fish, fish to pig, pig to people. What could have been biomass for us has been used as energy by other animals in the chain.

a) Name three animals which we use for food.

There is only a limited amount of the Earth's surface that we can use to grow food. The most energy-efficient way to use this food is to grow plants and eat them directly. If we only ate plants, then in theory at least, there would be more than enough food for everyone on the Earth. As much of the biomass produced by plants as possible would be used to feed people.

But every extra stage we introduce – feeding plants to animals before we eat the food ourselves – means less energy getting to us at the end of the chain. In turn this means less food to go round the human population.

b) Why would there be more food for everyone if we all ate only plants?

Artificially managed food production

As you saw on the previous page, animals don't turn all of the food they eat into new animal. Apart from the food which can't be digested and is lost as waste, energy is used in moving around and maintaining a constant body temperature.

Farmers apply these ideas to food production. People want meat, eggs and milk – but they want them as cheaply as possible. So farmers want to get the maximum possible increase in biomass from animals without feeding them any more. There are two ways of doing this:

● Limiting the movement of food animals. Then they lose a lot less energy in moving their muscles and so will have more biomass available from their food for growth.

● Controlling the temperature of their surroundings. Then the animals will not have to use too much energy keeping warm. Again this leaves more biomass spare for growth.

This means keeping the animals inside with restricted room to move, and a constant temperature. This is exactly what happens in the massive poultry rearing sheds where the majority of the chickens that we eat are produced.

Keeping chickens in these conditions means relatively large birds can be reared to eat in a matter of weeks. When animals are reared in this way they can appear more like factory products than farm animals. That's why these intensive methods are sometimes referred to as factory farming.

Intensive farming methods are used because there has been a steady increase in demand for cheap meat and animal products. This is the only way farmers can meet those demands from consumers.

On the other hand, these animals live very unnatural and restricted lives. More people are now aware of how our cheap meat and eggs are produced. So there has been a backlash against the conditions in which intensively reared animals live.

Many people now say they would be willing to eat meat less often and pay more if the animals they eat are raised more naturally.

Figure 2 These chickens are provided with an ideal temperature, plenty of food and very little opportunity to move. They will produce meat and lay more eggs far faster than if they were moving about and keeping themselves warm.

Figure 3 Intensively reared pigs live in small stalls in a warm building with food delivered regularly for maximum growth. It makes life relatively easy for the farmer but costs money to run. Animals reared outside grow more slowly, but seem to have a much better quality of life. The farmer needs land, and has to cope with horrible weather – but it's cheaper as there is no artificial heating or lighting to pay for.

FOUL FACTS

Veal crates are one of the most extreme ways of rearing animals to reduce energy losses. They are narrow, solid-sided wooden boxes used for rearing calves to produce veal. They are so narrow the calves cannot turn round. They are fed an all-liquid, iron-deficient diet to produce pale, white meat. The calves are slaughtered at 4 to 6 months old having never seen the light of day. Veal crates were banned in the UK in 1990, but they are still used in Europe. They will be banned there from 2007.

KEY POINTS

1 Biomass and energy are lost at each stage of a food chain. The efficiency of food production can be improved by reducing the number of stages in our food chains. It would be most efficient if we all just ate plants.
2 If you stop animals moving about and keep them warm, they lose a lot less energy. This makes food production much more efficient.

SUMMARY QUESTIONS

1 The world population is increasing and there are food shortages in many parts of the world. Explain, using pyramids of biomass to help you, why it would make better use of resources if people everywhere ate much less meat and more plant material.

2 Why are animals prevented from moving much and kept indoors in intensive farming?

3 a) What are the costs for a farmer of rearing animals intensively?
   b) What are the advantages of intensive rearing for a farmer?
   c) What are the advantages of less intensive rearing methods?
   d) What are the disadvantages of these more natural methods?

B2 3.4 Decay

GET IT RIGHT!

You need to know the type of organisms that cause decay, the conditions needed for decay and the importance of decay in recycling nutrients.

Figure 1 These tomatoes are slowly being broken down by the action of decomposers. You can see the fungi clearly, but the bacteria are too small to be seen.

FOUL FACTS

There is a forensic research site in the USA known as the Body Farm where scientists have buried or hidden human bodies in many different conditions. They are studying every stage of human decay. The information is used by police forces all over the world when a body is found. It can help to pinpoint when a person died, and show if they were the victim of a crime.

Plants take minerals from the soil all the time. These minerals are then passed on into animals through the food chains and food webs which link all living organisms. If this was a one-way process the resources of the Earth would have been exhausted long ago!

Many trees shed their leaves each year, and most animals produce droppings at least once a day. Animals and plants eventually die as well. Fortunately all these materials are recycled and returned to the environment. We can thank a group of organisms known as the **decomposers** for this.

a) Which group of organisms take materials out of the soil?

The decay process

The decomposers are a group of microorganisms which include bacteria and fungi. They feed on waste droppings and dead organisms.

Detritus feeders, such as maggots and some types of worm, often start the process, eating dead animals and producing waste material. The bacteria and fungi then digest everything – dead animals, plants and detritus feeders plus their waste. They use some of the nutrients to grow and reproduce. They also release waste products.

The waste products of the decomposers are carbon dioxide, water, and minerals which plants can use. When we say that things decay, they are actually being broken down and digested by microorganisms.

The recycling of materials through the process of decay makes sure that the soil remains fertile and plants can grow. It is also thanks to the decomposers that you aren't wading through the dead bodies of all the animals and plants that have ever lived!

b) Which type of organisms are the decomposers?

Conditions for decay

The speed at which things decay depends partly on the temperature. The chemical reactions in microorganisms are like those in most other living things. They work faster in warm conditions. (See Figure 3.) They slow down and even stop if conditions are too cold. Because the reactions are controlled by enzymes, they will stop altogether if the temperature gets too hot as the enzymes are denatured. You can investigate this in a simple experiment.

PRACTICAL

Investigating decay

Plan an investigation into the effect of temperature on how quickly things decay.
● Name the independent variable in this investigation. (See page 276.)

Most microorganisms also grow better in moist conditions. The moisture makes it easier to dissolve their food and also prevents them from drying out. So the decay of dead plants and animals – as well as leaves and dung – takes place far more rapidly in warm, moist conditions than it does in cold, dry ones.

Although some microbes work without oxygen, most decomposers respire like any other organism. This means they need oxygen to release energy, grow and reproduce. This is why decay takes place more rapidly when there is plenty of oxygen available.

c) Why are water, warmth and oxygen needed for the process of decay?

The importance of decay in recycling

Decomposers are vital for recycling resources in the natural world. What's more, we can take advantage of the process of decay to help us recycle our waste.

In **sewage treatment plants** we use microorganisms to break down the bodily waste we produce. This makes it safe to be released into rivers or the sea. These sewage works have been designed to provide the bacteria and other microorganisms with the conditions they need. That includes a good supply of oxygen.

Another place where the decomposers are useful is in the garden. Many gardeners have a **compost heap**. You put your grass cuttings, vegetable peelings and weeds on the compost heap. Then you leave it to let decomposing microorganisms break all the plant material down. It forms a fine, rich powdery substance known as compost. This can take up to a year.

The compost produced is full of mineral nutrients released by the decomposers. Once it is made you can dig your compost into the soil to act as a fertiliser.

Figure 2 The decomposers cannot function at low temperatures so if an organism – like this 4000 year old man – is frozen as it dies, it will be preserved with very little decay

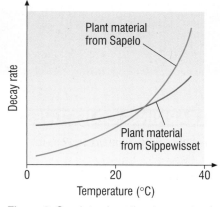

Figure 3 Graph to show the decay rate of plant material (leaves) from two different areas of the USA. The effect of temperature can be seen clearly.

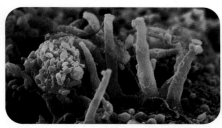

Figure 4 The decomposers are all microorganisms and so they are vulnerable to drying out. Moisture is vital for decay, along with warm temperatures and plenty of oxygen.

SUMMARY QUESTIONS

1 Copy and complete using the words below:

> **bacteria   carbon dioxide   dead   decomposers   digest   fungi   microorganisms   minerals   nutrients   waste droppings   water**

The ...... are a group of ...... which includes ...... and .... They feed on .... and ...... organisms. They ...... them and use some of the .... They also release waste products which include ...., ... and ...... which plants can use.

2 The following methods are all ways of preserving foods to prevent them from decaying. Use your knowledge of the decomposing microorganisms to explain how each method works:

a) Food may be frozen.
b) Food may be cooked – cooked food keeps longer than fresh food.
c) Food may be stored in a vacuum pack – with all the air sucked out.
d) Food may be tinned – it is heated and sealed in an airtight container.

KEY POINTS

1 Living organisms remove materials from the environment as they grow. They return them when they die through the action of the decomposers.

2 Dead materials decay because they are broken down (digested) by microorganisms.

3 Decomposers work more quickly in warm, moist conditions. Many of them also need a good supply of oxygen.

4 The decay process releases substances which plants need to grow.

5 In a stable community the processes that remove materials (particularly plant growth) are balanced by the processes which return materials.

B2 3.5   The carbon cycle

Figure 1 Within the natural cycle of life and death in the living world, mineral nutrients are cycled between living organisms and the physical environment

Imagine a stable community of plants and animals. The processes which remove materials from the environment are balanced by processes which return materials. Materials are constantly cycled through the environment. One of the most important of these is carbon.

All of the main molecules that make up our bodies (carbohydrates, proteins, fats and DNA) are based on carbon atoms combined with other elements.

The amount of carbon on the Earth is fixed. Some of the carbon is 'locked up' in fossil fuels like coal, oil and gas. It is only released when we burn them.

Huge amounts of carbon are combined with other elements in carbonate rocks like limestone and chalk. There is a pool of carbon in the form of carbon dioxide in the air. It is also found dissolved in the water of rivers, lakes and oceans. All the time a relatively small amount of available carbon is cycled between living things and the environment. We call this the **carbon cycle**.

a) What are the main sources of carbon on Earth?

Photosynthesis

Green plants use carbon dioxide from the atmosphere in photosynthesis. They use it to make carbohydrates which in turn make biomass. This is passed on to animals which eat the plants. The carbon goes on to become part of the carbohydrates, proteins and fats in their bodies.

This is how carbon is taken out of the environment. But how is it returned?

b) What effect does photosynthesis have on the distribution of carbon levels in the environment?

Respiration

Animals and plants respire all the time. They use oxygen to break down glucose, providing energy for their cells. Carbon dioxide is produced as a waste product and is returned to the atmosphere.

Also when plants and animals die their bodies are broken down by the decomposers. These decomposers release carbon dioxide into the atmosphere as they respire. All of the carbon dioxide released by the various types of living organisms is then available again. It is ready to be taken up by plants in photosynthesis.

Combustion

Fossil fuels contain carbon, which was locked away by photosynthesising plants millions of years ago. When we burn fossil fuels, we release some of that carbon back into our atmosphere:

Photosynthesis: carbon dioxide + water (+ light energy) → glucose + oxygen
Respiration: glucose + oxygen → carbon dioxide + water (+ energy)
Combustion: fossil fuel or wood + oxygen → carbon dioxide + water (+ energy)

The constant cycling of carbon is summarised in Figure 2.

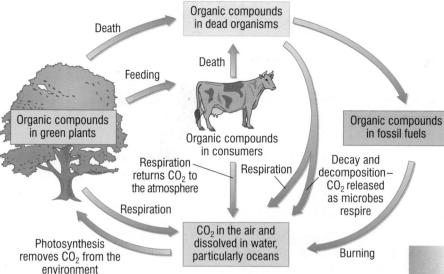

Figure 2 The carbon cycle in nature

For thousands of years the carbon cycle has regulated itself. However, as we burn more fossil fuels we are pouring increasing amounts of carbon dioxide into the atmosphere. Scientists fear that the carbon cycle may not cope. If the levels of carbon dioxide in our atmosphere increase it may lead to global warming.

Energy transfers

It isn't just carbon that passes through all the living organisms. The energy from the Sun also passes through all the different types of organisms. It starts with photosynthesis in plants, and is then transferred into animals. It is then transferred into the detritus feeders and decomposing microorganisms. They recycle the materials as plant nutrients.

All of the energy originally captured by green plants is eventually either:

• transferred into the decomposers, or

• transferred as heat into the environment by respiration.

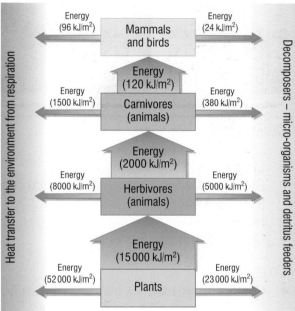

Figure 3 Energy is transferred from one type of organism to another. Along the way large amounts are transferred as heat to the environment through the process of respiration.

This represents the energy flow through 1 m² of an ecosystem – the figures in brackets are those recorded for one particular area

SUMMARY QUESTIONS

1. a) What is the carbon cycle?
   b) What are the main processes involved in the carbon cycle?
   c) Why is the carbon cycle so important for life on Earth?

2. Explain carefully how a) carbon, and b) energy are transferred through an ecosystem.

KEY POINTS

1. The constant cycling of carbon in nature is known as the carbon cycle.

2. Carbon dioxide is removed from the atmosphere by photosynthesis. It is returned to the atmosphere through respiration and combustion.

3. The energy originally captured by green plants is eventually transferred into consumers, into decomposers or as heat into the environment.

B2 3.6   Farming – intensive or free range?

Intensive farming – costs and benefits	'Free-range' farming – costs and benefits
Chickens for meat and eggs 	

Benefits:
- Lots of chickens in small space
- Little or no food wastage
- Energy wasted in movement/heat loss kept to a minimum
- Maximum weight gain/number of eggs laid
- Cheap eggs/chicken meat

Costs:
- Chickens unable to behave naturally – may be debeaked and cannot perch
- Large barns need heating and lighting
- Chickens' legs may break as bones unable to carry weight of rapidly growing bodies
- Risk of disease with many birds closely packed together

Benefits:
- Chickens live a more natural life
- No heating/lighting costs
- Less food needs supplying as they find some for themselves
- Can charge more money for free-range eggs/chickens

Costs:
- Chickens more vulnerable to weather and predators
- More land needed for each bird
- Eggs cannot be collected automatically
- Fewer eggs laid, especially in the winter when it is cold and dark for longer periods of time

ACTIVITIES

1 Choose either cattle or chickens. Produce a leaflet to be handed out in your local shopping centre either supporting intensive farming methods or supporting free-range farming methods. In each case back up your arguments with scientific reasoning.

2 You are going to take part in a debate on animal welfare and farming methods. You have been chosen to speak *either* FOR intensive farming *or* AGAINST 'free-range' farming.
   You have to think carefully about the benefits to the animals of intensive methods, and the disadvantages of free-range farming.

Intensive farming – costs and benefits	'Free-range' farming – costs and benefits

Cattle for beef

Benefits:

- Uses the male calves produced by dairy cows
- Weaning takes place by about 8 weeks and then farmers know exactly how much food each calf eats
- Balance of nutrients in food changed as calf grows to maximise growth
- Kept largely indoors, energy loss through movement and heat loss is kept to a minimum – can get weight gains of 1.5 kg a day!
- Cheap meat

Costs:

- Feedstuff must be bought and can be expensive
- Cowsheds need care and cleaning
- Cowsheds have to be heated and lit

Benefits:

- Calves are weaned naturally and stay with their mothers for up to 6 months
- Feeding on grass or food grown by farmer means no contamination, such as that which led to BSE, is possible
- Cattle behave and live relatively naturally

Costs:

- Animals may take slightly longer to gain weight as they are moving more actively
- More land is needed to provide grazing, hay and silage

ACTIVITY

3 Design a poster for the school gardening club explaining how to make compost and why it is important for the soil. Use the information in this chapter to help you get your facts right!

SUMMARY QUESTIONS

1

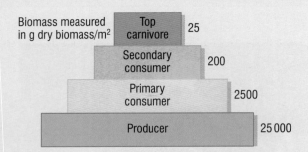

Biomass measured in g dry biomass/m²

Top carnivore	25
Secondary consumer	200
Primary consumer	2500
Producer	25 000

a) From this table calculate the percentage biomass passed on
   i) from producers to primary consumers,
   ii) from primary to secondary consumers,
   iii) from secondary consumers to top carnivores.

b) In any food chain or food web, the biomass of the producers is much larger than that of any other level of the pyramid. Why is this?

c) In any food chain or food web there are only a small number of top carnivores. Use your calculations to help you explain why.

d) All of the animals in the pyramid of biomass shown here are cold-blooded. What difference would it have made to the average percentage of biomass passed on between the levels if mammals and birds had been involved? Explain the difference.

2 Chicks grown for food arrive in the broiler house as one-day-old chicks. They are slaughtered at 42 days of age when they weigh about 2 kg. The temperature, amount of food and water and light levels are carefully controlled. About 20 000 chickens are reared together in one house. The table below shows their weight gain.

Age (days)	1	7	14	21	28	35	42
Mass (g)	36	141	404	795	1180	1657	1998

a) Plot a graph to show the growth rate of one of these chickens.

b) Explain why the temperature is so carefully controlled in the broiler house.

c) Explain why so many birds are reared together in a relatively small area.

d) Why are birds for eating reared like this?

e) Draw a second line to show how you would expect a chicken reared outside in a free-range system to gain weight, and explain the difference.

EXAM-STYLE QUESTIONS

1 The diagram below shows a part of a food web for organisms in a lake.

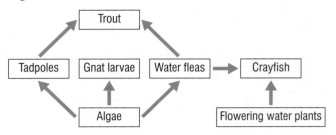

(a) Which organisms feed on algae? (1)

(b) Which organisms are producers? (1)

(c) Which organism is both a primary consumer and a secondary consumer? (1)

(d) Draw and label a pyramid of biomass for the food chain below:

Algae → Tadpole → Trout (1)

(e) If a disease suddenly killed all the water fleas explain how the population of the algae might be affected. (2)

2 The diagram below is a version of the carbon cycle.

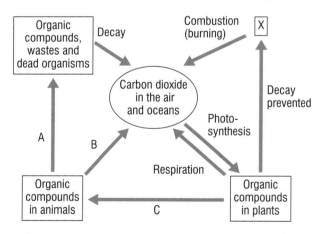

(a) Name the three processes indicated by the three arrows labelled with the letters **A**, **B** and **C**. (3)

(b) In what form is the carbon in the box labelled **X**? (1)

(c) The organic compounds of plants and animals are mostly in the form of three groups of substances that make up the **majority** of the bodies of these organisms. What are the three groups of organic compounds? (3)

(d) The table shows the percentage of carbon cycled by some of the processes involved in the carbon cycle.

Process	Percentage of total carbon cycled
Photosynthesis	50
Respiration by animals	20
Respiration by plants	20
Respiration by microorganisms	5
Combustion/absorbed by oceans	5

(i) Draw a pie chart of these proportions. (3)

(ii) If the total amount of carbon that is cycled in one year across the Earth is 165 gigatonnes, calculate how much carbon is cycled by the respiration of plants. Show your working. (2)

(e) Respiration is an important process in recycling carbon. The word equation for respiration is shown below, with most words replaced by the letters **A**, **B**, **C** and **D**. Give the names of **A**, **B**, **C** and **D**. (4)

$$\mathbf{A} + \mathbf{B} \rightarrow \mathbf{C} + \mathbf{D} + energy$$

(f) The concentration of carbon dioxide in the atmosphere has increased over the past 200 years. Suggest one human activity that might have contributed to this increase. (1)

3   A factory which packaged shrimps produced tonnes of waste shrimp heads. It cost money to dump these in the local tip. The managers decided to investigate the decay of shrimp heads to see if they might be used as fertiliser. They used 80 shrimp heads in 4 sealed jars. Each jar had a different amount of water. They measured the length of the shrimp heads, left them for 60 days and then measured them again:

Amount of water (cm³)	% loss in length
40	68
50	61
60	59
70	56

(a) Explain why they decided to measure the length of shrimp heads. (1)

(b) How many shrimp heads would they have put into each jar? (1)

(c) They predicted that the more water they added the greater the breakdown of the shrimp heads. Is their prediction supported? Explain your answer. (1)

Can this be true?

A scientist claims to have bred a featherless chicken.

The scientist says that it was the result of natural selective breeding and not genetic engineering. He claims that it will be ideal for warmer climates where the intensive breeding of chickens requires expensive air conditioning to keep the chickens at around 25°C. It will therefore be cheaper for farmers to rear these featherless chickens.

They will also be cheaper to feed as they will not need to use energy to grow feathers. Also they will cut down on the pollution caused by having to dump feathers before they are prepared for market.

'I looked to see if the date was April 1st when I read about this story,' said a geneticist.

A biologist said, 'The birds would probably find it difficult to breed without feathers.' Others claimed that it was 'ugly science' and should not be allowed.

a) Why do you think the scientist is so keen to promote his research? (1)

b) Do you think that the scientist was wrong to do the research? (1)

c) Which groups are likely to oppose such research? (1)

d) Who should make the final decision whether farmers should breed these featherless chickens or not? (1)

e) Do we know if the chickens are suffering? How could we find out? (1)

B2 4.1

Enzyme structure

LEARNING OBJECTIVES

1 What is an enzyme?
2 How do enzymes speed up reactions?

DID YOU KNOW?

The lack of just one enzyme in your body can have disastrous results. If you don't make the enzyme phenylalanine hydroxylase you can't break down the amino acid phenylalanine. It builds up in your blood and causes serious brain damage. All UK babies are tested for this condition soon after birth. If they are given a special phenylalanine-free diet right from the start, the risk of brain damage can be avoided.

The cells of your body are like tiny chemical factories. Hundreds of different chemical reactions are taking place all the time. These reactions have to happen fast – you need energy for your heart to beat and to hold your body upright *now*! They also need to be very controlled. The last thing you need is for your cells to start exploding!

Chemical reactions can only take place when different particles collide. The reacting particles don't just have to bump into each other. They need to collide with enough energy to react.

The minimum amount of energy particles must have to be able to react is known as the **activation energy**. So you will make the reaction more likely to happen if you can make it:

- more likely that reacting particles bump into each other,
- increase the energy of these collisions, or
- reduce the activation energy needed.

a) What is the activation energy of a reaction?

Controlling the rate of reactions

In everyday life we control the rates of chemical reactions all the time. When you cook food, you increase the temperature to speed up the chemical reactions. You lower the temperature to slow reactions down in your fridge or freezer. And sometimes we use special chemicals known as **catalysts** to speed up reactions for us.

A catalyst changes the rate of a chemical reaction, usually speeding it up. Catalysts are not used up in the reaction so you can use them over and over again. Different types of reactions need different catalysts. Catalysts work by bringing reacting particles together and lowering the activation energy needed for them to react.

b) What is a catalyst?

Enzymes – the biological catalysts

In your body chemical reaction rates are controlled by **enzymes**. These are special *biological catalysts* which speed up reactions.

Enzymes do not change the overall reaction in any way except to make it happen faster. Each one catalyses a specific type of reaction.

Enzymes are involved in:

- building large molecules from lots of smaller ones,
- changing one molecule into another, and
- breaking down large molecules into smaller ones.

Inorganic catalysts and enzymes both lower the activation energy needed for a reaction to take place.

GET IT RIGHT!

Remember that the way an enzyme works depends on the shape of the active site which allows it to bind with the substrate.

PRACTICAL

Breaking down hydrogen peroxide

Investigate the effect of i) manganese(IV) oxide, and ii) raw liver on the breakdown of hydrogen peroxide solution.

● Describe your observations and interpret the graph below.

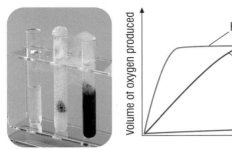
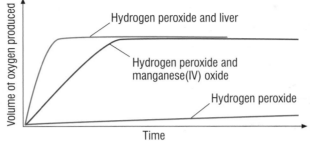

Hydrogen peroxide and liver

Hydrogen peroxide and manganese(IV) oxide

Hydrogen peroxide

Volume of oxygen produced

Time

Figure 1 Hydrogen peroxide is a colourless liquid which slowly breaks down to form oxygen and water. The decomposition reaction goes much faster using manganese(IV) oxide as a catalyst. Raw liver contains an enzyme (catalase) which also speeds up the breakdown of hydrogen peroxide.

Your enzymes are large protein molecules. They are made up of long chains of amino acids, folded and coiled to give a molecule with a very special shape. The enzyme molecule usually has a hole or indentation in it. This special shape allows other molecules to fit into the enzyme. We call this the **active site**. The shape of an enzyme is vital for the way it works.

How do enzymes work?

The substrate (reactant) of the reaction fits into the shape of the enzyme. You can think of it like a lock and key. Once it is in place the enzyme and the substrate bind together. This is called the **enzyme–substrate complex**.

Then the reaction takes place rapidly and the products are released from the surface of the enzyme. (See Figure 3.) Remember that enzymes can join together small molecules as well as breaking up large ones.

Enzymes usually work best under very specific conditions of temperature and pH. This is because anything which affects the shape of the active site also affects the ability of the enzyme to speed up a reaction.

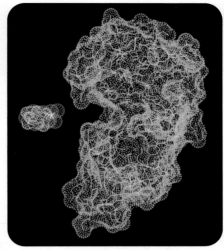

Figure 2 Enzymes have a very complex structure made up of chains of amino acids folded and coiled together. This computer-generated image shows just how complicated the structure really is!

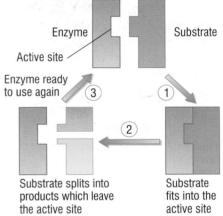

Enzyme   Substrate

Active site

Enzyme ready to use again   ③   ①

②

Substrate splits into products which leave the active site

Substrate fits into the active site

Figure 3 Enzymes have their effect as catalysts using the 'lock-and-key' mechanism shown here. You can see that anything which changes the shape of the protein molecule might change the shape of the active site and stop the enzyme from working.

SUMMARY QUESTIONS

1 Match the words and the definitions:

a) catalyst	A The special site in the structure of an enzyme where the substrate binds.
b) enzyme	B The energy needed for a chemical reaction to take place.
c) activation energy	C A substance which changes the rate of a chemical reaction without being changed itself.
d) active site	D A biological catalyst.

2 a) What is an enzyme?   c) Why is their structure so important?
   b) What are enzymes made of?

3 a) How do enzymes act to speed up reactions in your body?
   b) Why are enzymes so important in your body?

KEY POINTS

1 Catalysts increase the rate of chemical reactions. Enzymes are biological catalysts
2 Enzymes are protein molecules made up of long chains of amino acids. The chains are folded to form the active site. This is where the substrate of the reaction binds with the enzyme.

B2 4.2   Factors affecting enzyme action

LEARNING OBJECTIVES

1 How does increasing the temperature affect your enzymes?
2 What effect does a change in pH have on your enzymes?

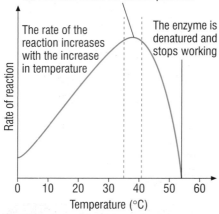

Optimum temperature – this is when the reaction works as fast as possible

The rate of the reaction increases with the increase in temperature

The enzyme is denatured and stops working

Rate of reaction

0 10 20 30 40 50 60
Temperature (°C)

Figure 1 Like most chemical reactions, the rate of an enzyme-controlled reaction increases as the temperature rises – but only until the point where the complex protein structure of the enzyme breaks down

Leave a bottle of milk at the back of your fridge for a week or two and you'll find it is pretty disgusting. The milk will have gone off as enzymes in bacteria break down the protein structure.

Leave your milk in the Sun for a day and the same thing will happen – but much faster. Temperature affects the rate at which chemical reactions take place even when they are controlled by biological catalysts.

Biological reactions are affected by the same factors as any other chemical reactions – concentration, temperature and particle size all affect them. But in living organisms an increase in temperature only works up to a certain point.

a) Why does milk left in the Sun go off quickly?

The effect of temperature on enzyme action

The chemical reactions which take place in living cells happen at relatively low temperatures. Like most other chemical reactions, the rate of enzyme-controlled reactions increases with an increase in temperature. The enzyme and substrate particles move faster as the temperature increases, so this makes them more likely to collide with enough energy to react.

However this is only true up to temperatures of about 40°C. After this the protein structure of the enzyme is affected by the temperature. The long amino acid chains begin to unravel. As a result the shape of the active site changes. We say the enzyme has been **denatured**. It can no longer act as a catalyst, so the rate of the reaction drops dramatically. Most human enzymes work best at 37°C.

b) What does it mean if an enzyme is denatured?

PRACTICAL

Investigating the effect of temperature

You can show the effect of temperature on the rate of enzyme action using simple practicals like the one shown opposite.

The enzyme amylase (found in your saliva) breaks down starch into simple sugars. You mix starch solution and amylase together and keep them at different temperatures. Then you test samples from each temperature with iodine solution at regular intervals.

In the presence of starch, iodine solution turns blue-black. But when there is no starch present, the iodine stays yellowy-brown. When the iodine solution no longer changes colour you know all the starch has been broken down.

This gives you some clear evidence of the effect of temperature on the rate of enzyme controlled reactions.

● How does iodine solution show you if starch is present?
● Why do we test starch solution without amylase added?
● What conclusion can you draw from the results?

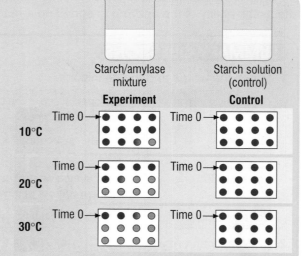

Starch/amylase mixture   Starch solution (control)

Experiment   **Control**

10°C   Time 0   Time 0

20°C   Time 0   Time 0

30°C   Time 0   Time 0

Figure 2 In each case the starch amylase mixture and the control are kept in a water bath at a given temperature. Samples are taken every five minutes and tested with iodine solution on a spotting tile.

Effect of pH on enzyme action

Enzymes have their effect by binding the reactants to a specially shaped **active site** in the protein molecule. Anything which changes the shape of this active site stops the enzyme from working. Temperature is obviously one thing which changes the shape of the protein molecule. The surrounding pH is another.

The shape of enzymes is the result of forces between the different parts of the protein molecule which hold the folded chains in place. A change in the pH affects these forces and changes the shape of the molecule. As a result, the active site is lost, so the enzyme can no longer act as a catalyst.

Different enzymes have different pH levels at which they work at their best – and a change in the pH can stop them working completely.

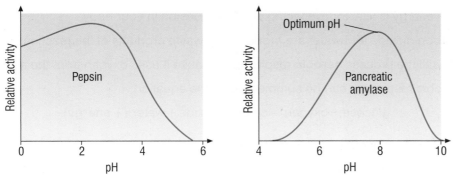

Figure 3 These two enzymes are found in quite different parts of the human gut, and they need very different conditions of pH to work at their maximum rate. Pepsin is found in the stomach, along with hydrochloric acid, while pancreatic amylase is in the small intestine along with alkaline bile.

The role of enzymes

Enzymes are vital to all living cells. They catalyse a huge range of reactions. Without them respiration, photosynthesis and protein synthesis would be impossible. This also applies to all the other reactions which take place in your cells. For the enzymes to work properly the temperature and pH must be just right. This is why it is so dangerous if your temperature goes very high when you are ill and run a fever. Once your body temperature reaches about 41°C, your enzymes start to be denatured and you will soon die.

GET IT RIGHT!

The rate of enzyme-controlled reactions increases as the temperature goes up to about 40°C because the particles are moving faster. So substrate molecules collide with enzymes more often. Once the temperature goes much over 40°C most enzymes are denatured and no longer work as catalysts.
Enzymes aren't killed (they are molecules, not living things themselves) – use the term denatured.

Figure 4 The magical light display of a firefly is caused by the action of a very special enzyme called luciferase

KEY POINTS

1 Enzyme activity is affected by temperature and pH.
2 High temperatures and the wrong pH can affect the shape of the active site of an enzyme and stop it working.
3 Enzymes catalyse processes such as respiration, photosynthesis and protein synthesis in living cells.

SUMMARY QUESTIONS

1 Copy and complete using the words below:

> **active site   cells   denatured   enzyme   increases**
> **protein   reactions   shape   temperatures   40°C**

The chemical …… which take place in living …… happen at relatively low …… . The rate of these …… controlled reactions …… with an increase in temperature. However this is only true up to temperatures of about …… . After this the …… structure of the enzyme is affected and the …… of the …… …… is changed. The enzyme has been …… .

2 Look at Figure 3.

a) At which pH does pepsin work best?
b) At which pH does amylase work best?
c) What happens to the activity of the enzymes as the pH increases?
d) Explain why this change in activity happens.

B2 4.3

Aerobic respiration

1 What is aerobic respiration?
2 Where in your cells does respiration take place?

The average energy needs of a teenage boy are 11 510 kJ of energy every day – but teenage girls only need 8830 kJ a day. This is partly because on average girls are smaller than boys but also because boys have more muscle cells, which means more mitochondria demanding fuel for aerobic respiration.

One of the most important enzyme-controlled processes in living things is **aerobic respiration**.

Your digestive system, lungs and circulation all work to provide your cells with what they need for respiration to take place.

During aerobic respiration glucose (a sugar produced as a result of digestion) reacts with oxygen. This reaction releases energy which your cells can use. This energy is vital for everything else that goes on in your body.

Carbon dioxide and water are produced as waste products of the reaction.

We call the process **aerobic** respiration because it uses oxygen from the air.

Aerobic respiration can be summed up by the equation:

glucose + oxygen → carbon dioxide + water (**+ energy**)

a) Why is aerobic respiration so important?

PRACTICAL

Investigating respiration

Animals and plants – even bacteria – all respire. To show that cellular respiration is taking place, you can either deprive a living organism of the things it needs to respire, or show that waste products are produced from the reaction.

Depriving a living thing of food and/or oxygen would kill it – so this would be an unethical investigation. So we concentrate on the waste products of respiration. Carbon dioxide and energy in the form of heat are the easiest to identify.

Lime water goes cloudy when carbon dioxide bubbles through it. The higher the concentration of carbon dioxide, the quicker the lime water goes cloudy. This gives us an easy way of demonstrating that carbon dioxide has been produced. We can also look for a rise in temperature to show that energy is being produced during respiration.

● Plan an ethical investigation into aerobic respiration in living organisms.

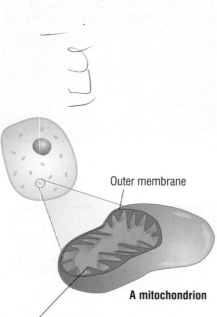

Outer membrane

A mitochondrion

Folded inner membrane gives a large surface area where the enzymes which control cellular respiration are found

Figure 1 Mitochondria are the powerhouses which provide energy for all the functions of your cells

Mitochondria – the site of respiration

Aerobic respiration involves lots of chemical reactions, each one controlled by a different enzyme. Most of these reactions take place in the **mitochondria** of your cells.

Mitochondria are tiny rod-shaped bodies (**organelles**) which are found in all plant and animal cells. They have a folded inner membrane which provides a large surface area for the enzymes involved in aerobic respiration.

Cells which need a lot of energy – like muscle cells and sperm – have lots of mitochondria. Cells which use very little energy – like fat cells – have very few mitochondria.

b) Why do mitochondria have folded inner membranes?

Reasons for respiration

- Respiration releases energy from the food we eat so that the cells of the body can use it.

- Both plant and animal cells need energy to carry out the basic functions of life. They build up large molecules from smaller ones to make new cell material. Much of the energy released in respiration is used for these 'building' activities (synthesis reactions). For example in plants, the sugars, nitrates and other nutrients are built up into amino acids which are then built up into proteins.

- Another important use of the energy from respiration in animals is in making muscles contract. Muscles are working all the time in our body, whether we are aware of them or not. Even when you sleep your heart beats, you breathe and your gut churns – and these muscular activities use energy.

- Finally, mammals and birds are 'warm-blooded'. This means that our bodies are the same temperature inside almost regardless of the temperature around us. On cold days we use energy to keep our body warm, while on hot days we use energy to sweat and keep our body cool.

Figure 2 Warm-blooded animals like this bird use up some of the energy they produce by aerobic respiration just to keep a steady body temperature. When the weather is cold, they use up a lot more energy to keep warm. Giving them extra food supplies can mean the difference between life and death.

> **GET IT RIGHT!**
>
> Make sure you know the equation for respiration. Remember that aerobic respiration takes place in the mitochondria.

SUMMARY QUESTIONS

1 Copy and complete these sentences, matching the pairs.

a) Energy is released from glucose ……	A …… energy is released.
b) During respiration chemical reactions take place ……	B …… because it uses oxygen from the air.
c) When glucose reacts with oxygen …….	C …… are formed as waste products.
d) Carbon dioxide and water ……	D …… by a process known as respiration.
e) The process is known as aerobic respiration ……	E …… inside the mitochondria in the cells of your body.

2 Why are mitochondria so important and how is their structure adapted for the job that they do?

3 You need a regular supply of food to provide energy for your cells. If you don't get enough to eat you become thin and stop growing. You don't want to move around and you start to feel cold. There are three main uses of the energy released in your body during aerobic respiration. What are they and how does this explain the symptoms of starvation described above?

4 Suggest an experiment to show that a) oxygen is taken up, and b) carbon dioxide is released, during aerobic respiration.

> **KEY POINTS**
>
> 1 Aerobic respiration involves chemical reactions which use oxygen and sugar and release energy. The reaction is summed up as:
>
> glucose + oxygen →
> carbon dioxide + water
> (+ **energy**).
>
> 2 Most of the reactions in aerobic respiration take place inside the mitochondria.

B2 4.4

Enzymes in digestion

The food you eat is made up of large insoluble molecules which your body cannot absorb. They need to be broken down or *digested* to form smaller, soluble molecules. These can then be absorbed and used by your cells. This chemical breakdown is controlled by your digestive enzymes.

Most of your enzymes work *inside* the cells of your body. Your digestive enzymes are different – they work *outside* of your cells. They are produced by specialised cells which are found in glands (like your salivary glands and your pancreas), and in the lining of your gut.

The enzymes then pass out of these cells into the gut itself. It is here that they get mixed up with your food molecules and break them down.

Your gut is a hollow muscular tube which squeezes your food. The gut:

- helps to break up your food into small pieces with a large surface area for your enzymes to work on,
- mixes your food with your digestive juices so that the enzymes come into contact with as much of the food as possible, and
- uses its muscles to move your food along its length from one area to the next.

a) How do your digestive enzymes differ from most of your other enzymes?

Digesting carbohydrates

Enzymes which break down carbohydrates are known as **carbohydrases**. Starch is one of the most common carbohydrates that you eat. It is broken down into **sugars** like glucose. This reaction is catalysed by the carbohydrase called *amylase*.

Amylase is produced in your salivary glands, so the digestion of starch starts in your mouth. Amylase is also made in your pancreas and your small intestine. No digestion takes place in the pancreas. All the enzymes made there flow into your small intestine, which is where most of the starch you eat is digested.

b) What is the name of the enzyme which breaks down starch in your gut?

Digesting proteins

The breakdown of protein food like meat, fish and cheese into amino acids is catalysed by **protease** enzymes. Proteases are produced by your stomach, your pancreas and your small intestine. The breakdown of proteins into **amino acids** takes place in your stomach and small intestine.

c) Which enzymes breaks down protein in your gut?

Digesting fats

The **lipids** (fats and oils) that you eat are broken down into **fatty acids** and **glycerol** in your small intestine. The reaction is catalysed by *lipase* enzymes which are made in your pancreas and your small intestine. Yet again the enzymes made in the pancreas are passed into the small intestine.

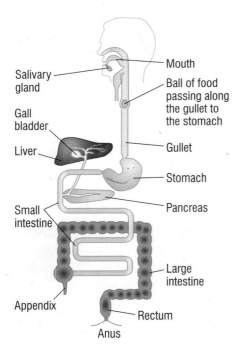

Salivary gland
Mouth
Ball of food passing along the gullet to the stomach
Gall bladder
Liver
Gullet
Stomach
Small intestine
Pancreas
Large intestine
Appendix
Rectum
Anus

Figure 1 The human digestive system

Once your food molecules have been completely digested into soluble glucose, amino acids, fatty acids and glycerol, they leave your small intestine. They pass into your blood supply to be carried around the body to the cells which need them.

d) Which enzymes break down fats in your gut?

PRACTICAL

Investigating digestion

You can make a model gut using a bag of special membrane containing starch and amylase enzymes. When the enzyme has catalysed the breakdown of the starch, you can detect the presence of sugar on the outside of the 'gut'!

● How can you test for sugars?

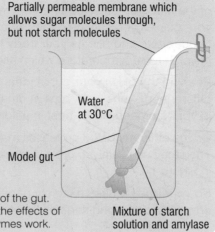

Figure 2 This apparatus provides you with a model of the gut. You can use it to investigate how the gut works and the effects of factors like temperature and pH on how the gut enzymes work.

Using the digested food

● The glucose produced by the action of amylase and other carbohydrases is used by the cells of your body in respiration.
● Fatty acids and glycerol may be used as a source of energy or to build cell membranes, make hormones and as fat stores.
● The amino acids produced when you digest protein are not used as fuel. Once inside your cells, amino acids are built up into all the proteins you need. These synthesis reactions are catalysed by enzymes. In other words, your enzymes make new enzymes as well as all the other proteins you need in your cells. This **protein synthesis** takes place in the **ribosomes**.

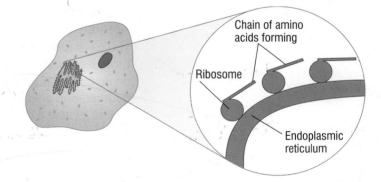

Figure 3 Ribosomes are very small. They can only be seen using the most powerful microscopes. However their role in protein synthesis means they are vital to the working of your cells and your whole body!

SUMMARY QUESTIONS

1 Copy and complete using the words below:

> **absorbed   broken down   cells   digestive enzymes**
> **food   insoluble   soluble**

The ...... you eat is made up of large ...... molecules which need to be .... to form smaller, ... molecules. These can be ...... by your body and used by your .... This chemical breakdown is controlled by your ....

2 Make a table which shows amylase, protease and lipase. For each enzyme show where it is made, which reaction it catalyses and where it works in the gut.

3 Why is digestion of your food so important? Explain in terms of the molecules involved.

B2 4.5

Speeding up digestion

LEARNING OBJECTIVES

1 Why does your stomach contain hydrochloric acid?
2 What is bile and why is it so important in digestion?

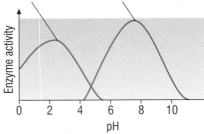

Pepsin – protease from the stomach   Trypsin – protease from the small intestine

Figure 1 Both of these enzymes catalyse the breakdown of proteins. But as these graphs show, the enzyme found in the stomach works best at a very different pH to the one made in the pancreas and used in the small intestine.

Your digestive system produces many enzymes which speed up the breakdown of the food you eat. However enzymes aren't the only important chemicals in your gut. As you saw on pages 44 and 45, enzymes are very sensitive to temperature and pH. As your body is kept at a fairly steady 37°C, your enzymes have an ideal temperature which allows them to work as fast as possible.

Keeping the pH in your gut at ideal levels isn't quite so easy. That's because different enzymes work best at different pH levels. The protease enzyme found in your stomach works best in acidic conditions.

On the other hand, the proteases made in your pancreas need alkaline conditions. Then they can catalyse protein breakdown as fast as they can. Look at the graph in Figure 1.

So your body makes a variety of different chemicals which help to give your enzymes ideal conditions all the way through your gut.

a) Why do your enzymes almost always have the right temperature to work at their best?

Changing pH in the gut

You have around 35 million glands in the lining of your stomach secreting protease enzymes to digest the protein you eat. These enzymes work best in an acid pH. So your stomach also produces a concentrated solution of hydrochloric acid from the same glands. In fact your stomach produces around 3 litres of acid a day!

This acid allows your stomach protease enzymes to work very effectively. It also kills most of the bacteria which you take in with your food.

Finally, your stomach also produces a thick layer of mucus which coats your stomach walls and protects them from being digested by the acid and the enzymes!

b) How does your stomach avoid digesting itself?

FOUL FACTS

Pigments from your bile are largely responsible for the brown colour of your faeces. If you have a disease which stops bile getting into your gut, your faeces will be white or silvery grey!

PRACTICAL

Breaking down protein

You can see the effect of acid on pepsin, the protease found in the stomach, quite simply. Set up three test tubes, one containing pepsin only, one containing only hydrochloric acid and one containing a mixture of the two. Keep them at body temperature in a water bath. Add a similar sized chunk of meat to all three of them. Set up a web cam and watch for a few hours to see what happens!

● What conclusions can you make?

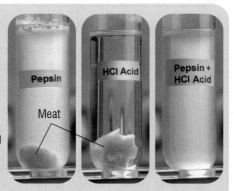

Figure 2 These test tubes show clearly the importance of protein-digesting enzymes *and* hydrochloric acid in your stomach. Meat was added to each tube at the same time.

After a few hours – depending on the size and type of the meal you have eaten – your food leaves your stomach and moves on into your small intestine. Some of the enzymes which catalyse digestion in your small intestine are made in your pancreas. Some are also made in the small intestine itself. They all work best in an alkaline environment.

The acidic liquid coming from your stomach needs to become an alkaline mix in your small intestine! So how does it happen?

Your liver carries out many important jobs in your body and one of them is producing bile. Bile is a greenish-yellow alkaline liquid which is stored in your gall bladder until it is needed.

As food comes into the small intestine from the stomach, bile is squirted onto it. The bile neutralises the acid from the stomach and then makes the semi-digested food alkaline. This provides the ideal conditions for the enzymes in the small intestine.

c) Why does the food coming into your small intestine need neutralising?

Altering the surface area

It is very important for the enzymes of the gut to have the largest possible surface area of food to work on. This is not a problem with carbohydrates and proteins. However, the fats that you eat do not mix with all the watery liquids in your gut. They stay as large globules – think of oil in water – which makes it difficult for the lipase enzymes to act.

This is the second important function of the bile. It **emulsifies** the fats in your food. This means it physically breaks up large drops of fat into smaller droplets. This provides a much bigger surface area for the lipase enzymes to act on. The larger surface area helps them chemically break down the fats more quickly into fatty acids and glycerol.

GET IT RIGHT!

Remember food is not digested in the liver or the pancreas.
Bile is **not** an enzyme and it does **not** break down fat molecules.
Bile emulsifies fat droplets to increase the surface area, which in turn increases the rate of fat digestion by lipase.

SUMMARY QUESTIONS

1 Copy and complete using the words below:

**alkaline   emulsifies   gall bladder   liver   neutralises
small intestine**

Bile is an…… liquid produced by your ……. It is stored in the …… …… and released onto food as it comes into the …… ……. It …… the acid food from the stomach and makes it alkaline. It also …… fats.

2 Look at Figure 1.

a) At what pH does the protease from the stomach work best?
b) How does your body create the right pH in the stomach for this enzyme?
c) At what pH does the protease from the intestine work best?
d) How does your body create the right pH in the small intestine for this enzyme?

3 Draw a diagram to explain how bile produces a big surface area for lipase to work on and explain why this is important.

KEY POINTS

1 The enzymes of the stomach work best in acid conditions.
2 The enzymes made in the pancreas and the small intestine work best in alkaline conditions.
3 Bile produced by the liver neutralises acid and emulsifies fats.

B2 4.6 Making use of enzymes

Figure 1 More and more homes now have a dishwasher – and dishwasher powders contain enzymes. They digest the cooked-on proteins like eggs which are often hard to remove even in a dishwasher.

Figure 2 Learning to eat solid food isn't easy. Having some of it pre-digested by protease enzymes can make it easier to get the goodness you need to grow!

Enzymes were first isolated from living cells in the 19th century, and ever since we have found more and more ways of using them in industry. Some microorganisms produce enzymes which pass out of the cells and are easy for us to use. In other cases we use the whole microorganism.

Enzymes in the home

In the past, people boiled and scrubbed their clothes to get them clean – and did it all by hand. Now we not only have washing machines to do the washing for us, we also have enzymes ready and waiting to digest the stains.

Many people use **biological detergents** to remove stains from their clothes from substances such as grass, sweat, food and blood. Biological washing powders contain proteases and lipases which break down the proteins and fats in the stains. They help provide us with a cleaner wash. We also use them at the lower temperatures that enzymes need to work best, so we use less electricity too.

a) What is a biological washing powder?

PRACTICAL

Investigating biological washing powder

Weigh a chunk of cooked egg white and leave it in a strong solution of biological washing powder.

- What do you think will happen to the egg white?
- How can you measure just how effective the protease enzymes are?
- How could you investigate the effect of surface area in enzyme action?

Enzymes in industry

Pure enzymes have many uses in industry.

Proteases are used in the manufacture of baby foods. They 'pre-digest' some of the protein in the food. When babies first begin to eat solid foods they are not very good at it. Treating the food with protease enzymes makes it easier for a baby's digestive system to cope with. It is easier for them to get the amino acids they need from their food.

Carbohydrases (carbohydrate digesting enzymes) are used to convert starch into sugar (glucose) syrup. We use huge quantities of sugar syrup in food production – just have a look at the ingredients labels on all sorts of foods.

Starch is made by plants like corn, and it is very cheap. Using enzymes to convert this plant starch into sweet sugar provides a cheap source of sweetness for food manufacturers.

It is also important for the process of making fuel (ethanol) from plants.

b) Why does the starch need to be converted to sugar before it is used to make ethanol?

Sometimes the glucose syrup made from starch is passed into another process which uses a different set of enzymes. **Isomerase** enzyme is used to convert glucose syrup into **fructose syrup** by rearranging the atoms in the glucose molecule.

Glucose and fructose contain exactly the same amount of energy (1700 kJ or 400 kcal per 100 g) but fructose is much sweeter than glucose. This means much smaller amounts of it are needed to make food taste sweet. So fructose is widely used in 'slimming' foods. The food tastes sweet but contains fewer calories.

Figure 3 The market for slimming foods is enormous and growing all the time. Enzyme technology is being used to convert more and more glucose syrup into fructose syrup to make so-called 'slimming' foods.

The advantages and disadvantages of using enzymes

In an industrial process, many of the reactions need high temperatures and pressures to make them fast enough to produce the products needed. Supplying heat and building chemical plants which can stand high pressures costs a lot of money.

However, enzymes can provide the perfect answer to industrial problems like these. They catalyse reactions at relatively low temperatures and normal pressures. Enzyme-based processes are therefore often fairly cheap to run.

The main problem with enzymes is that they are very sensitive to their surroundings. For enzymes to function properly the temperature must be kept down (usually below 45°C). The pH also needs to be kept within carefully monitored limits which suit the enzyme. It costs money to control these conditions.

Whole microbes are relatively cheap, but need to be supplied with food and oxygen and their waste products removed. What's more, they use some of the substrate to grow more microbes. Pure enzymes use the substrate more efficiently, but they are also more expensive to produce.

GET IT RIGHT!

Remember that most enzyme names end in -ase. Some enzymes used in industry work at quite high temperatures – so don't be put off if a graph shows an optimum temperature well above 45°C!

SUMMARY QUESTIONS

1 List three enzymes and the ways in which we use them in the food industry.

2 Biological washing powders contain enzymes in tiny capsules. Explain why:

  a) they are more effective than non-biological powders at lower temperatures,

  b) they are not more effective at high temperatures.

3 Make a table to show the advantages and disadvantages of using enzymes in industry.

KEY POINTS

1 Some microorganisms produce enzymes which pass out of the cells and can be used in different ways.

2 Biological detergents may contain proteases and lipases.

3 Proteases, carbohydrases and isomerase are all used in the food industry.

B2 4.7 High-tech enzymes

The washing powder debate

> I've got three children and they are all messy eaters! Their clothes get lots of mud and grass stains as well. I always use biological detergents because they get my washing really clean.

> I've got very sensitive skin. When my mum changed to a biological detergent I got dermatitis so we never use biological detergents now.

> When we first started manufacturing our biological detergent we found a lot of our factory staff developed allergies. We realised they were reacting to enzyme dust in the air – proteins often trigger allergies. But once we put the enzymes in tiny capsules all the allergy problems stopped. Unfortunately it got some bad publicity and lots of people still seem to think biological detergents cause allergies.

> I try to be as green as possible in my lifestyle but I'm not sure about biological detergents. Enzymes are natural, after all – but I've heard they can cause allergies. On the other hand, biological powders use a lot less electricity because they clean at lower temperatures. That's good for the environment and cheaper for me!

ACTIVITY

You are part of a team producing an article for a lifestyle magazine about biological washing powders. Create a double-page article – make it lively, interesting to look at, scientifically accurate and informative!

> Allergies aren't really a problem with biological detergents. However, if the clothes aren't rinsed really thoroughly, protein-digesting enzymes can get left in the fabric. Then the enzymes may digest some of the protein in your skin and set up dermatitis. But if the detergent is used properly, there shouldn't be a problem.

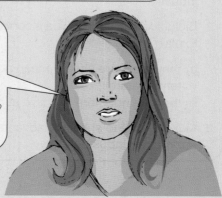

Enzymes and medicine

Here are just some of the ways in which enzymes are used in medicine:

To diagnose disease

If your liver is damaged or diseased, some of your liver enzymes may leak out into your blood. If your symptoms suggest your liver isn't working properly, doctors can test your blood for these enzymes to find out if your liver really is damaged.

To diagnose and control disease

People who have diabetes often have too much sugar in their blood. As a result, they also get sugar in their urine. One common test for sugar in the urine relies on a colour change on a test strip.

The test strip contains a chemical indicator and an enzyme. It is placed in a urine sample. The enzyme catalyses the breakdown of any glucose found in the urine. The products of the reaction then make the indicator change colour if glucose is present.

To cure disease

- If your pancreas is damaged or diseased it cannot make enzymes. So you have to take extra enzymes – particularly lipase – to allow you to digest your food. The enzymes are in special capsules to stop them being digested in your stomach!
- If you have a heart attack, an enzyme called streptokinase will be injected into your blood as soon as possible. It dissolves clots in the arteries of the heart wall and reduces the amount of damage done to your heart muscle.
- An enzyme from certain bacteria is being used to treat a type of leukaemia in children. The cancer cells cannot make one particular amino acid, so they need to take it from your body fluids. The enzyme catalyses the breakdown of this amino acid, so the cancer cells cannot get any and they die. Your normal cells can make the amino acid so they are not affected. Doctors hope something similar may work against other types of cancer.

Dodgy science

Health special

IN THE RAW!

WILL YOU TRY THE NEW DIET SENSATION?

The latest food craze to sweep the US is to eat your food – including meat – completely raw. And now it's coming to the UK!

It has been reported that there are lots of health benefits to this new way of eating. It is claimed that raw food contains live enzymes which will help to give you more energy. Apparently when food is cooked these enzymes die.

One of the owners of a new raw food restaurant has been quoted as saying,

'It is an amazingly interesting way of preparing food, it is good to have live enzymes in your system and, most importantly, it is yummy.'

SUMMARY QUESTIONS

1 a) Copy and complete the following sentences, matching the parts of the sentences.

i)	A catalyst will speed up or slow down a reaction ……	1	…… could not occur without enzymes.
ii)	Living organisms make very efficient catalysts ……	2	…… made of protein.
iii)	All enzymes are ……	3	…… binds to the active site.
iv)	The reactions which keep you alive ……	4	…… known as enzymes.
v)	The substrate of an enzyme ……	5	…… a specific type of molecule.
vi)	Each type of enzyme affects ……	6	…… but is not changed itself.

b) Explain how an enzyme catalyses a reaction. Use diagrams if they make your explanation clearer.

2 Use Figure 2 on page 44 to help you answer this question.

a) What effect does the enzyme amylase have on starch?

b) What do these results tell you about the effect of temperature on the action of the amylase?

c) Why is one tube of starch solution kept at each temperature without the addition of the enzyme?

d) How could you improve this investigation?

e) What do you predict would happen to the activity of the enzyme if acid from the stomach were added to the mixture?

3 The table gives some data about the relative activity levels of an enzyme at different pH levels.

pH	Relative activity
4	0
6	3
8	10
10	1

a) Plot a graph of this data.

b) Does this enzyme work best in an acid or an alkaline environment?

c) This is a protein-digesting enzyme. Where in the gut do you think it might be found? Explain your answer.

EXAM-STYLE QUESTIONS

1 (a) In the summary of aerobic respiration shown below, choose a word from each of the boxes that best completes the equation. (2)

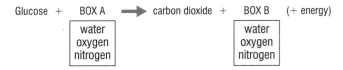

Glucose + BOX A → carbon dioxide + BOX B (+ energy)

BOX A: water / oxygen / nitrogen
BOX B: water / oxygen / nitrogen

(b) (i) State two ways in which the energy released during respiration is used in **all** animals. (2)

(ii) How else might the energy released be used in mammals and birds only? (1)

(iii) Give a further use of the energy released that applies to plants rather than animals. (1)

2 **A, B, C, D** and **E** are the names of enzymes or groups of enzymes. The numbers **1, 2, 3, 4** and **5** refer to the functions or uses of each of these enzymes.

Match each letter with the appropriate number. (5)

A	Lipase	1	Used in the manufacture of baby foods
B	Amylase	2	Group of enzymes that act on carbohydrates
C	Proteases	3	Its substrate is starch
D	Isomerase	4	Used in the production of slimming foods
E	Carbohydrases	5	The products of its catalytic action are glycerol and fatty acids

3 Amylase is an enzyme that catalyses the conversion of starch into sugar.

(a) To which of the following groups of food does starch belong? (1)

carbohydrates   fats   protein   vitamins

(b) Give the names of the **three** organs in the human body that secrete the enzyme amylase. (3)

The graph on the next page shows the effect of temperature on the activity of amylase.

(c) (i) At what temperature did the amylase work fastest? (1)

(ii) Why did the amylase not work above 56°C? (1)

(iii) State one other factor apart from temperature that will affect the rate of reaction of amylase. (1)

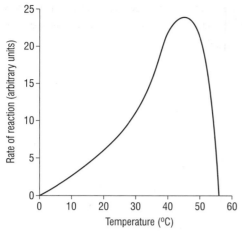

4 In the making of cheese, a commercially prepared form of an enzyme called rennin is used to make the protein in milk more solid. Rennin is an enzyme that is produced naturally in the stomachs of young mammals. The owner of a cheese making factory wanted to use a different source of rennin. She needed to find out the best temperature to use for the new rennin. She planned to set up 20 test tubes. All would have 20 cm³ of milk in them: half with the rennin added (A) and half to be left without rennin (B). One tube of each type would be left in a water bath until one of them clotted. When this happened, the time taken would be recorded.

(a) Construct a table that could be used by the owner. (3)

(b) Fill in the table to show the range of temperatures she might use. (1)

(c) Fill in the table to show the interval for the independent variable. (1)

(d) Suggest how the owner might know when the milk is clotted. (1)

(e) Would you suggest that she repeats her results? Explain your answer. (1)

(f) Why do you think she used tubes A and B at each temperature? (1)

5 Bile is a greenish liquid that plays an important role in the digestion of food.

(a) In which organ is bile produced? (1)

(b) Where is bile stored in the body? (1)

(c) Into which region of the digestive system is bile released? (1)

(d) Describe how bile is involved in the digestion of fats. (3)

(e) What is the name of the enzyme that digests fats? (1)

(f) Name two places where this enzyme is produced in the body. (2)

HOW SCIENCE WORKS QUESTIONS

Najma had carried out a 'rates of reaction' investigation in chemistry. Her results are in Table 1 below.

Table 1 Chemistry investigation

Temperature (°C)	Time taken (secs)
20	106
30	51
40	26
50	12
60	5

When asked in biology to do a 'rates of reaction' investigation she expected to get the same results. She reasoned that in both cases she was collecting the oxygen produced from hydrogen peroxide. The only difference was that she used manganese(IV) oxide in chemistry and she was using mashed up plant cells in biology! Her results from biology are in Table 2.

Table 2 Biology investigation

Temperature (°C)	Time taken (secs)
20	114
30	96
40	80
50	120
60	No reaction

a) What was Najma's prediction for the biology investigation? (1)

b) Was her prediction supported, refuted or should she rethink the prediction? (2)

c) Najma checked her results against some results in a textbook. Why was this a good idea? (1)

d) Najma was feeling happier now that she had been supported by other scientists' results. She had also learned that enzymes had a temperature at which they worked best. How could she change her investigation so that she could find the best temperature for this enzyme? (1)

e) Najma also learned that this enzyme was called catalase and that it occurs in nearly all organisms, even those living in hot water springs. How could she change her investigation to find the best temperature for catalase in hot water spring organisms? (2)

B2 5.1

Controlling internal conditions

LEARNING OBJECTIVES

1 How do you keep conditions inside your body constant?
2 How do you get rid of the waste products of your cells?

Figure 1 Whatever you choose to do in life, the conditions inside your body will stay more-or-less exactly the same. When you think of the range of things you can do, it is amazing how the balance is maintained.

For your body to work properly the conditions surrounding your millions of cells must stay as constant as possible. On the other hand, almost everything you do tends to change things.

As you move you produce heat, as you respire you produce waste, when you digest food you take millions of molecules into your body. Yet you somehow keep your internal conditions constant within a very narrow range. How do you manage this?

The answer is through **homeostasis**. As you saw in topic B1a1.5, many of the functions in your body help to keep your internal environment as constant as possible. Now you are going to find out more about some of them.

a) What is homeostasis?

Removing waste products

No matter what you are doing, even sleeping, the cells of your body are constantly producing waste products as a result of the chemical reactions which are taking place. The more extreme the conditions you put yourself in, the more waste products your cells will make. There are two main poisonous waste products which would cause major problems for your body if the levels built up. These are carbon dioxide and urea.

Carbon dioxide

Carbon dioxide is produced during cellular respiration.

Every cell in your body respires, and so every cell produces carbon dioxide. It is vital that you remove this carbon dioxide. That's because if it all remained dissolved in the cytoplasm of your cells it would affect the pH. Dissolved carbon dioxide produces an acidic solution – and a lower pH would affect the working of all the enzymes in your cells!

PRACTICAL

Investigating breathing

Find out the capacity of your lungs or the effect of exercise on breathing.

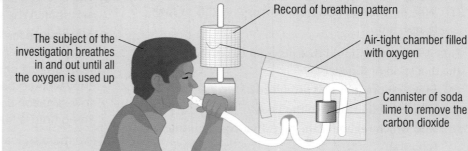

Record of breathing pattern

The subject of the investigation breathes in and out until all the oxygen is used up

Air-tight chamber filled with oxygen

Cannister of soda lime to remove the carbon dioxide

Figure 2 Because you breathe in and out of the machine all the time, you can't get rid of your waste carbon dioxide in the normal way. There has to be a special filter to remove the carbon dioxide so it doesn't poison you!

● How can we improve the reliability of investigations involving living organisms?

The carbon dioxide moves out of the cells into your blood. Your blood stream carries it back to your lungs. Almost all of the carbon dioxide you produce is removed from your body via your lungs when you breathe out. The air you breathe in contains only 0.04% carbon dioxide, but the air you breathe out contains about 4% carbon dioxide!

b) How do you remove carbon dioxide from your body?

Urea

The other main waste product of your body is **urea**.

Urea is produced in your **liver** when excess amino acids are broken down. When you eat more protein than you need, or when body tissues are worn out, the extra protein has to be broken down. Amino acids cannot be used as fuel for your body. But in your liver the amino group is removed and converted into urea.

The rest of the amino acid molecule can then be used in respiration or to make other molecules. The urea passes from the liver cells into your blood.

Urea is poisonous and if the levels build up in your blood it will cause a lot of damage. Fortunately the urea is filtered out of your blood by your **kidneys**. It is then removed in your **urine**, along with any excess water and salt.

Urine is produced all the time by your kidneys. It leaves your kidneys and is stored in your **bladder** which you then empty from time to time!

c) Where is urea made?

Maintaining body balance

Water and ions enter your body when you eat or drink. The water and ion content of your body are carefully controlled to prevent damage to your cells. Water is lost through breathing, through sweating and in the urine, while ions are lost in the sweat and in the urine.

If the water or ion content of your body is wrong, too much water may move into or out of your cells. That's why control is vital.

It is also very important to control your body temperature and the levels of sugar in your blood. So homeostasis plays a very important role in your body.

GET IT RIGHT!

Don't confuse urea and urine. Urea is made in the liver; urine is produced by the kidney. Urine contains urea.

KEY POINTS

1 The internal conditions of your body have to be controlled to maintain a constant internal environment.

2 Poisonous waste products are made all the time and need to be removed.

3 Carbon dioxide is produced during respiration and leaves the body via the lungs when you breathe out.

4 Urea is produced by your liver as excess amino acids are broken down, and it is removed by your kidneys in the urine.

SUMMARY QUESTIONS

1 Copy and complete using the words below:

**blood   carbon dioxide   constant   controlled   environment
enzymes   homeostasis   sugar   temperature   urea   water**

The internal ...... of your body is kept relatively ...... by a whole range of processes which make up .... Waste products such as .... and ...... have to be removed from your ...... all the time. The ...... and ion concentration of your blood are constantly ...... and so is your blood ...... level. Your body ...... is kept the same so your ...... work effectively.

2 There are two main waste products which have to be removed from the human body – carbon dioxide and urea. For each waste product, describe:

a) how it is formed, b) why it has to be removed, c) how it is removed from the body.

3 Explain briefly a) how a period of exercise would affect the internal conditions of your body, and b) how the conditions would be returned to normal.

B2 5.2 Controlling body temperature

LEARNING OBJECTIVES

1 How does your body monitor its temperature?
2 How does your body stop you getting too hot? [Higher]
3 How does your body keep you warm? [Higher]

Figure 1 People in different parts of the world live in conditions of extreme heat and extreme cold and still maintain a constant internal body temperature

Wherever you go and whatever you do it is vital that your body temperature is maintained at around 37°C. This is the temperature at which your enzymes work best. Your skin temperature can vary enormously without causing harm. It is the temperature deep inside your body, known as the core body temperature, which must be kept stable.

At only a few degrees above or below normal body temperature your enzymes cannot function properly. All sorts of things can affect your internal body temperature, including:

● heat produced in your muscles during exercise,
● fevers caused by disease, and
● the external temperature rising or falling.

People can control some aspects of their own temperature. We can change our clothing, light a fire, and turn on the heating or air-conditioning. But it is our internal control mechanisms which are most important in controlling our body temperature.

a) Why is control of your body temperature so important?

Control of the temperature relies on the **thermoregulatory centre** in the brain. This centre contains receptors which are sensitive to temperature changes. They monitor the temperature of the blood flowing through the brain itself.

Extra information comes from the temperature receptors in the skin. These send impulses to the thermoregulatory centre giving information about the skin temperature. The receptors are so sensitive they can detect a difference of as little as 0.5°C!

Sweating helps to cool your body down. So the loss of salt and water when you sweat can affect your water and ion balance. If you are sweating a lot you need to take in more drink or food to replace the water and ions you have lost – just watch a marathon runner!

Cooling the body down

If you get too hot, your enzymes denature and can no longer catalyse the reactions in your cells. When your core body temperature begins to rise, impulses are sent from the thermoregulatory centre to the body so more heat is lost:

● The blood vessels, which supply your skin capillaries, **dilate** (open wider). This lets more blood flow through the capillaries. Your skin flushes, so you lose more heat by radiation.
● Your rate of sweating goes up. Sweat (made up mainly of water, salt and a little protein) oozes out of your sweat glands and spreads over your skin. As the water evaporates it cools the skin, taking heat from your body. In very humid conditions, when the sweat doesn't evaporate very easily, it is very difficult to cool down.

HIGHER

HIGHER

Reducing heat loss

It is just as dangerous for your core temperature to drop as it is to rise. If you get very cold, the rate of the enzyme-controlled reactions in your cells falls too low. You don't make enough energy and your cells begin to die. If your core body temperature starts to get too low, impulses are sent from your thermoregulatory centre to the body to conserve and even generate more heat.

- The blood vessels which supply your skin capillaries **constrict** (close up) to reduce the flow of blood through the capillaries. This reduces the heat lost through the surface of the skin, and makes you look pale.
- Shivering begins – your muscles contract and relax rapidly which involves lots of cellular respiration. This releases some energy as heat which you use to raise your body temperature. As you warm up, shivering stops.
- Sweat production is reduced.

b) Why is a fall in your core body temperature so dangerous?

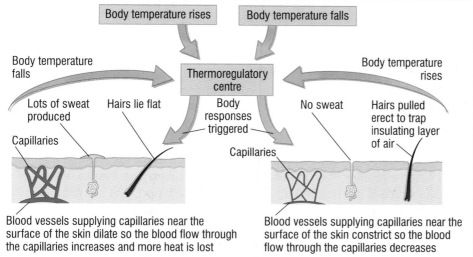

Figure 2 Changes in your core body temperature set off automatic responses to oppose the changes and maintain a steady internal environment.

PRACTICAL

Body temperature

Use a temperature sensor and data logger to record your skin and core body temperature on one hand as you plunge the other into icy water.

- Explain your observations.

GET IT RIGHT!

Use the terms dilate and constrict for the changes which take place in the blood vessels supplying the capillaries near the surface of the skin.
Remember sweating only cools your body when the sweat actually evaporates.

SUMMARY QUESTIONS

1 Here is a jumbled list of some of the events by which your body temperature is controlled when it starts to go up. Sort them out into the right order and then copy them out.

A Her body temperature starts to rise.
B Sally takes a long, cool drink to replace the liquid she has lost through sweating.
C Her temperature returns to normal.
D Her skin goes red and her rate of sweating increases so the amount of heat lost through her skin goes up.
E Sally exercises hard.

2 a) Why is it so important to maintain a body temperature of about 37°C?
  b) Explain the role of i) the thermoregulatory centre in the brain and ii) the temperature sensors in the skin in maintaining a constant core body temperature.

3 Explain how the body responds to both an increase and a decrease in core temperature to return its temperature to normal levels. [Higher]

KEY POINTS

1 Your body temperature must be maintained at the level at which enzymes work best.
2 Your body temperature is monitored and controlled by the thermoregulatory centre in your brain.
3 Your body responds to cool you down if you are overheating and to warm you up if your core body temperature falls. [Higher]

B2 5.3   Controlling blood sugar

It is very important that your cells have a constant supply of the glucose they need for cellular respiration. Glucose is transported around your body to all the cells by your blood. However you don't spend all of your time eating to keep your blood sugar levels high. Instead the level of sugar in your blood is controlled by hormones produced in your pancreas.

a) Why are the levels of glucose in your blood so important?

The pancreas and the control of blood sugar levels

When you digest a meal, large amounts of glucose pass into your blood. Without a control mechanism your blood glucose levels would vary wildly. After a meal they would soar to a point where glucose would be removed from the body in the urine. A few hours later the levels would plummet and cells would not have enough glucose to respire.

This internal chaos is prevented by your **pancreas**. The pancreas is a small pink organ found under your stomach. It constantly monitors your blood glucose concentration and controls it using two hormones known as **insulin** and **glucagon**.

When your blood glucose concentration rises above the ideal range after you have eaten a meal, insulin is released. Insulin causes your liver to remove any glucose which is not needed at the time from the blood. The soluble glucose is converted to an insoluble carbohydrate called **glycogen** which is stored in your liver.

When your blood glucose concentration falls below the ideal range, the pancreas secretes glucagon. Glucagon makes your liver break down glycogen, converting it back into glucose. In this way the stored sugar is released back into the blood.

By using these two hormones and the glycogen store in your liver, your pancreas keeps your blood glucose concentration fairly constant. Its normal concentration is usually about 90 mg glucose per 100 cm³ of blood.

b) Which two hormones are involved in the control of your blood sugar levels?

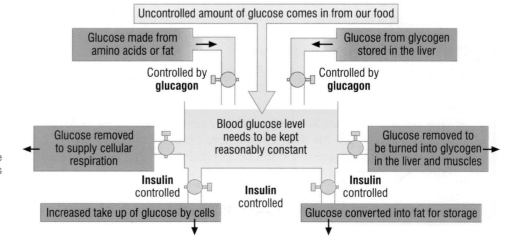

Figure 1 This model of your blood glucose control system shows the blood glucose as a tank. It has both controlled and uncontrolled inlets and outlets. In every case the control is given by the hormones insulin and glucagon.

What causes diabetes?

Most of us never think about our blood sugar levels because they are perfectly controlled by our pancreas. But for some people life isn't quite this simple. Unfortunately, their pancreas does not make enough – or any – insulin.

Without insulin your blood sugar levels get higher and higher after you eat food. Eventually your kidneys produce glucose in your urine. You produce lots of urine and feel thirsty all the time.

Without insulin, glucose cannot get into the cells of your body, so you lack energy and feel tired. You break down fat and protein to use as fuel instead, so you lose weight.

Before there was any treatment for diabetes, people would waste away. Eventually they would fall into a coma and die. Fortunately there are now some very effective ways of treating diabetes!

c) Why do people with untreated diabetes feel very tired and lack energy?

Treating diabetes

If you have a mild form of diabetes, managing your diet is enough to keep you healthy. Avoiding carbohydrate-rich foods keeps the blood sugar levels relatively low. So your reduced amount of insulin can cope with small amounts of glucose.

However, other people with diabetes need replacement insulin before meals. Insulin is a protein which would be digested in your stomach. So it is usually given as an injection to get it into your blood.

This injected insulin allows glucose to be taken into your body cells and converted into glycogen in the liver. This stops the concentration of glucose in your blood from getting too high.

Then as the blood glucose levels fall, natural glucagon makes sure glycogen is converted back to glucose. As a result your blood glucose levels are kept as stable as possible. (See graphs on page 65.)

Insulin injections treat diabetes successfully but they do not cure it. Until a cure is developed, someone with diabetes has to inject insulin several times every day of their life.

d) How can people with mild diabetes control the disease?

Figure 2 The treatment of diabetes involves regular blood sugar tests and insulin injections. These could become a thing of the past if some of the new treatments being developed work as well as scientists hope!

KEY POINTS

1 Your blood glucose concentration is monitored and controlled by your pancreas.
2 The pancreas produces the hormone insulin which allows glucose to move from the blood into the cells.
3 In diabetes, the blood glucose may rise to fatally high levels because the pancreas does not secrete enough insulin. It can be treated by injections of insulin before meals.

SUMMARY QUESTIONS

1 Define the following words:
   hormone;
   insulin;
   diabetes;
   glycogen.

2 a) Explain how your pancreas keeps the blood glucose levels of your body constant.
   b) Why is it so important to control the level of glucose in your blood?

3 What is diabetes and how can it be treated?

B2 5.4   Homeostasis matters!

HYPOTHERMIA = THE SILENT KILLER

If your core body temperature falls too low you suffer from hypothermia. About 30 000 people die of it every year in the UK alone. Here is some more information about hypothermia:

- Hypothermia is when your body temperature drops below 35°C and the normal working of your body is affected.
- Old people, small children and people exposed in bad weather conditions are most at risk.
- Young people on outdoor expeditions are often at risk if they do not wear the right clothing. Wet weather and wind make you lose heat faster.
- The first signs of hypothermia are extreme tiredness and not wanting to move – you may not realise how cold you are.
- Up to 20% of your body heat is lost through your head.
- Warm clothing, adequate heating, regular food and warm drinks, together with exercise all help to prevent hypothermia.
- People with hypothermia have greyish-blue, puffy faces and blue lips. Their skin feels very cold to the touch. They will be drowsy, with slurred speech. As it gets worse, they will stop shivering. If the body temperature falls too low the sufferer will become unconscious and may die.
- It has been estimated that every time the temperature drops one degree Celsius below average in the winter, 8000 more elderly people will die of hypothermia.

ACTIVITY

If more people were aware of the risks of hypothermia, fewer people would die from it. Use the information to help you design **either** a poster **or** a leaflet informing people about the dangers of hypothermia and ways to avoid it.

HEAT WAVE KILLS SEVEN

The latest spell of very hot weather has led to seven deaths this week. As Britain sizzles in the latest heat-wave, with temperatures of over 33℃, people are dropping like flies.

Heat stroke and other heat-related illnesses are hitting the elderly, small babies and people with existing heart problems particularly hard.

The World Health Organisation along with the World Meteorological Organisation have suggested that a hot weather warning is added to our weather forecasts along with pollen levels, air pollution and flood warnings.

To reduce your risk of heat stroke as Britain continues to fry, stay in air-conditioned rooms where possible, drink plenty of water and take cool baths.

ACTIVITY

Climate change may well result in colder winters and hotter summers. Write an article for the lifestyle pages of a newspaper on:
- how your body copes with changes in temperature,
- the dangers to health of hot summers and cold winters, and
- the best ways to avoid any problems.

THE DIABETES DEBATE

The treatment of diabetes has changed a great deal over the years. For centuries nothing could be done. Then in the early 1920s Frederick Banting and Charles Best realised that extracts of animal pancreas could be used to keep people with diabetes alive. For many years insulin from pigs and cows was used to treat affected people. This saved millions of lives.

In recent years, bacteria have been developed using genetic engineering which produce pure human insulin. This is now injected by the majority of people affected by diabetes.

Scientists are trying to find easier ways – like nasal sprays – to get insulin into the body. Transplanting working pancreas cells from both dead and living donors has been shown to work for some people. And for the future, scientists are hoping to use embryonic stem cells to provide people affected by diabetes with new, functioning pancreas cells which can make their own insulin.

The difference these treatments have made to the lives of people with diabetes and their families is enormous. If a cure is found, it will be even better. But most of these developments have some ethical issues linked to them.

- Banting and Best did their experiments on dogs. They made some of the dogs diabetic by removing most of their pancreas, and they extracted insulin from the pancreases of other dogs. Many dogs died in the search for a successful treatment – but the scientists found a treatment to a disease which has killed millions of people over the centuries.
- Human insulin is now mass-produced using genetically engineered bacteria. The gene for human insulin is stuck into the bacterial DNA and the bacteria make pure human protein.
- There are not enough dead donors to give pancreas transplants to the people who need them. However, in living donor transplants there is a risk to the health of the donor as they have to undergo surgery.
- Stem cell research promises a possible cure – but the stem cells come from human embryos which have been specially created for the process.

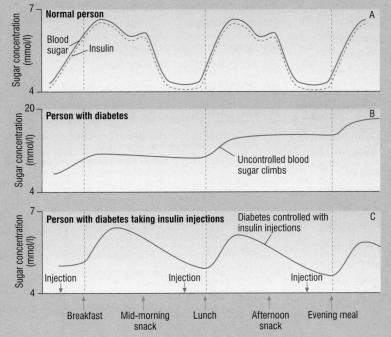

ACTIVITY

a) You are to plan a three-minute speech for a debate. The title of the debate is:

'Ethical concerns are less important than a cure for diabetes.'

You can argue for or against the motion, but your arguments must be clear and sensible and backed up by scientific evidence.

b) Work in groups of 9 and set up a role play involving the following characters:
- Frederick Banting who first showed that animal insulin could be used to treat humans with diabetes.
- A spokesperson from a pharmaceutical company manufacturing human insulin.
- A daughter who has been cured of diabetes by receiving pancreas tissue from her mother, and her mother who donated the tissue.
- A scientist working on the development of insulin-producing cells from embryonic stem cells.
- Someone who has had diabetes since they were 10 years old.
- An animal rights activist.
- A 'pro-life' activist who is against any use of stem cells.
- A representative of a group opposed to genetic engineering.
- The chair of the discussion. Each character must explain to the chair why research into diabetes should – or should not – continue.

Figure 1 These graphs show the impact insulin injections have on people affected by diabetes. The injections keep the blood sugar level within safe limits. They cannot mimic the total control given by the natural production of the pancreas – but they work well enough to let people lead a full and active life.

SUMMARY QUESTIONS

1 a) Draw and annotate a diagram explaining the basic principles of homeostasis.

   b) Write a paragraph explaining why control of the conditions inside your body is so important.

2 We humans maintain our body temperature at a constant level over a wide range of environmental temperatures. Many other animals – fish, amphibians and reptiles as well as the invertebrates – cannot do this. Their body temperature is always very close to the environmental temperature.

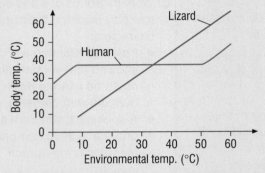

   a) What is the body temperature of a person and a lizard at an atmospheric temperature of 20°C?

   b) From the graph, at what external temperature does the human core temperature become dangerously low? Why is it dangerous?

   c) At what external temperature does the human core temperature become dangerously high? Why is it dangerous?

   d) Explain how a person maintains a constant core body temperature as the external temperature falls.

   e) Explain how a person maintains a constant core body temperature as the external temperature rises.
   [Higher]

3 Use Figure 1 on page 65 to answer this question.

   a) Look at graph A. Why does the level of insulin increase after a meal?

   b) Graph B shows the blood sugar pattern of someone who has just developed diabetes and is not yet using injected insulin. What differences are there between this pattern and the one shown in A?

   c) Graph C shows the effect of regular insulin injections on the blood sugar level of someone with diabetes. Why are the insulin injections so important to their health?

   d) People who are mildly diabetic and those who inject insulin all have to watch the amount of carbohydrate in their diet. Explain why.

EXAM-STYLE QUESTIONS

1 Complete the passage below by choosing the correct terms from the box and matching them with the numbers in the passage.

sweating	dilate	shivering
thermoregulatory	radiation	constrict

Body temperature is controlled by the ....1.... centre in the brain. On a hot day it causes blood vessels in the skin to ...2... and so lose heat by ....3.... Heat may also be lost by ...4... . On a cold day the blood vessels ....5.... to conserve heat. When cold, ...6.... may also occur to create some heat.   [Higher] (6)

2 The table shows the daily water loss from a typical human being.

Water lost in	Volume of water (cm³ per day)
Urine	1500
X	400
Evaporation from the skin	350
Faeces	150
Sweat	100

   (a) One way in which water is lost from the body has been missed out and replaced by the letter **X**. What does **X** represent? (1)

   (b) These figures were taken on a cool day with the person at rest. State two ways in which the figures would be different if the person had been exercising on a hot day. (2)

   (c) Apart from water, what other two substances are typically found in urine? (2)

   (d) Where is urine stored in the body? (1)

3 (a) What is the name of the hormone that causes the liver to remove glucose from the blood? (1)

   (b) Where in the body is this hormone produced? (1)

   (c) Two people drank a solution that contained 100 g of glucose. The blood sugar level of each person was measured over the next three hours. The results are shown in the table on the next page.

      (i) On a piece of graph paper, draw a line graph of the data in the table opposite. (5)

      (ii) One of the two persons is diabetic. From the graph suggest which one and give two reasons for your answer. (2)

Time in minutes	Blood sugar level (mg/100 cm³ blood)	
	Person X	Person Y
0 (glucose drunk)	90	90
30	160	140
60	220	90
90	200	80
120	150	70
150	130	80
180	110	90

4 Read the following passage about diabetes.

Diabetes is a metabolic disorder in which there is an inability to control blood glucose levels due to the lack of the hormone insulin. Diabetes was a fatal disease until in 1921 Banting and Best succeeded in isolating insulin from the pancreases of pigs and cows, having first carried out experiments on dogs. Insulin is a small protein of 51 amino acids, the sequence of which was determined in the 1950s by Sanger. More recently the gene for human insulin has been isolated and the hormone can now be produced by bacteria as a result of genetic engineering. Diabetics must test their blood sugar levels regularly and inject insulin if they are to lead normal lives.

(a) Why do diabetics inject insulin rather than taking it by mouth? (2)

(b) What would happen to the blood sugar level of a diabetic who failed to inject insulin? (1)

(c) Suggest one other symptom of diabetes other than changes to blood sugar. (1)

(d) Give three advantages of using genetically engineered insulin rather than extracting the hormone from animal pancreases. (3)

(e) Injecting insulin only *treats* diabetes. In future it may be possible to replace the damaged pancreas by transplantation.
 (i) What would be the benefits to the person with diabetes of such treatment?
 (ii) State the drawbacks of this treatment. (4)

HOW SCIENCE WORKS QUESTIONS

You have probably heard the weatherman, during winter, tell you about the 'wind chill factor'. This is to give you a better idea of how cold your skin might feel if you were to go out whilst the temperature was low and it was windy. Remember that wind will cool the skin by evaporating moisture from it and therefore make it feel colder than the actual air temperature.

Until recently the wind chill factor was calculated by measuring temperatures of some water in a container in the Arctic. The tank of water was 10 metres above the ground.

a) Explain why this was a poor way to calculate the effect of wind chill on humans. (2)

Recently some investigations were carried out to get a better measure of the effect of wind chill on humans. The tests were carried out on humans dressed in protective clothing, except their cheeks were left exposed, so that their cheek skin temperature could be measured.

b) Why do you think the cheeks were chosen? (1)

c) The people were tested at different temperatures and wind speeds. What would have been a suitable sensitivity for the thermometer? (1)

d) How many people would have been chosen? (1)

e) How would these people have been chosen? (1)

f) Imagine you were carrying out these tests. Draw up a table that would let you fill in the results as you did the tests on just one person. (2)

g) Now fill in the table with some temperatures and some wind speeds that you think might be useful. (5)

B2 6.1 Cell division and growth

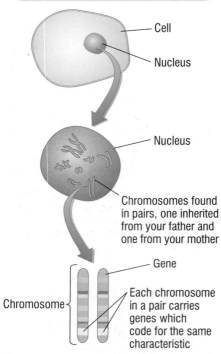

Figure 1 The nucleus of your cell contains the chromosomes that carry the genes which control the characteristics of your whole body

Cell
Nucleus
Nucleus
Chromosomes found in pairs, one inherited from your father and one from your mother
Gene
Chromosome
Each chromosome in a pair carries genes which code for the same characteristic

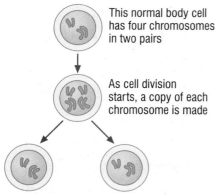

This normal body cell has four chromosomes in two pairs

As cell division starts, a copy of each chromosome is made

The cell divides in two to form two daughter cells. Each daughter cell has a nucleus containing four chromosomes identical to the ones in the original parent cell.

New cells are needed for an organism, or part of an organism, to grow. They are also needed to replace cells which become worn out and repair damaged tissue. However the new cells must have the same genetic information in them as the originals, so they can do the same job.

Each of your cells has a nucleus containing the instructions for making whole new cells and even an entire new you! These instructions are carried in the form of genes.

A gene is a small packet of information which controls a characteristic, or part of a characteristic, of your body. The genes are grouped together on chromosomes. A chromosome may carry several hundred or even thousands of genes.

You have 46 chromosomes in the nucleus of your cells (except your gametes – sperm or ova). They come in 23 pairs. One of each pair is inherited from your father, and one from your mother.

a) Why are new cells needed?

Mitosis

Body cells divide to make new cells. The cell division which takes place in the normal body cells and produces identical daughter cells is called **mitosis**. As a result of mitosis all your body cells have the same genetic information.

In asexual reproduction, the cells of the offspring are produced by mitosis from cells of their parent. This is why they contain exactly the same genes with no variety.

How does mitosis work? Before a cell divides it produces new copies of the chromosomes in the nucleus. This means that when division takes place two genetically identical **daughter cells** are formed.

In some areas of the body of an animal or plant, cell division like this carries on rapidly all of the time. Your skin is a good example – cells are constantly being lost from the surface and new cells are constantly being formed by cell division to replace them.

b) What is mitosis?

Differentiation

In the early development of animal and plant embryos the cells are very unspecialised. Each one of them (known as **stem cells**) can become any type of cell which is needed.

In many animals, the cells become specialised very early in life. By the time a human baby is born most of its cells have become specialised for a particular job, such as liver cells, skin cells and muscle cells. They have **differentiated**. Some of their genes have been switched on and others have been switched off.

Figure 2 Identical daughter cells are formed by the simple division that takes place during mitosis. It supplies all the new cells needed in your body for growth, replacement and repair. Your cells really have 23 pairs of chromosomes – but for simplicity this cell is shown with only two pairs!

This means that when a muscle cell divides by mitosis it can only form more muscle cells. Liver cells can only produce more liver cells. So in adult animals, cell division is restricted because differentiation has occurred. Specialised cells can divide by mitosis, but this can only be used to repair damaged tissue and replace worn out cells. Each cell can only produce identical copies of itself.

In contrast, most plant cells can differentiate all through their life. Undifferentiated cells are formed at active regions of the stems and roots. In these areas mitosis takes place almost continuously.

Plants keep growing all through their lives at these 'growing points'. The plant cells produced don't differentiate until they are in their final position in the plant. What's more, the differentiation isn't permanent. If you move a plant cell from one part of a plant to another, it can re-differentiate and become a completely different type of cell. You just can't do that with animal cells – once a muscle cell, always a muscle cell!

PRACTICAL

Observing mitosis

Make a special preparation of a growing root tip to view under a microscope. Then you can see the actively dividing cells and the different stages of mitosis as it is taking place.

- Describe your observations of mitosis.

We can produce huge numbers of identical plant clones from a tiny piece of leaf tissue. Now you can see why this is possible. In the right conditions a plant cell will become unspecialised and undergo mitosis many times. In different conditions, each of these undifferentiated cells will produce more cells by mitosis. These will then differentiate to form a tiny new plant identical to the original parent.

The reason animal clones cannot be made easily is because animal cells differentiate permanently early in embryo development – and can't change back! Animal clones can only be made by cloning embryos in one way or another.

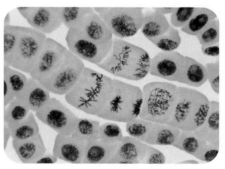

Figure 3 The undifferentiated cells in this onion root tip are dividing rapidly. You can see mitosis taking place, with the chromosomes in different positions as the cells divide.

Cells produced by mitosis have identical genetic information.

SUMMARY QUESTIONS

1 Copy and complete using the words below:

   **chromosomes   genetic information   genes   growth
   mitosis   nucleus   replace**

   New cells are needed for ...... and to ...... worn out cells. The new cells must have the same .... in them as the originals. Each cell has a ...... containing the ...... grouped together on .... The type of cell division which produces identical cells is known as ....

2 Division of the body cells is taking place all the time in living organisms.

   a) Why is it so important?

   b) Explain why the chromosome number must stay the same when the cells divide to make other normal body cells.

3 The process of growth and differentiation is very different in plants and animals.

   a) What is differentiation?

   b) How is differentiation in animal and plant cells so different?

   c) How does this difference affect the cloning of plants and animals?

KEY POINTS

1 In body cells, chromosomes are found in pairs.

2 Body cells divide by mitosis to produce more identical cells for growth, repair, replacement or in some cases asexual reproduction.

3 Most types of animal cells differentiate at an early stage of development. Many plant cells can differentiate throughout their life.

B2 6.2

Stem cells

LEARNING OBJECTIVES

1 What is special about stem cells?
2 How can we use stem cells to cure people?

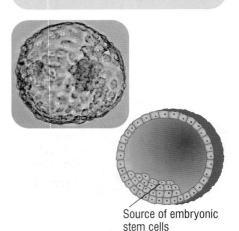

Source of embryonic stem cells

Figure 1 This ball of cells is an early human embryo. In the right conditions these few cells can form all the organs of the human body.

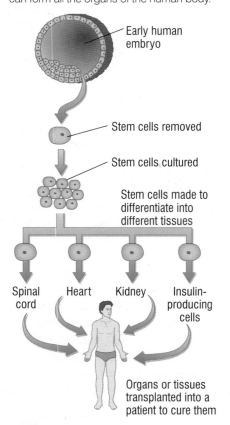

Early human embryo

Stem cells removed

Stem cells cultured

Stem cells made to differentiate into different tissues

Spinal cord   Heart   Kidney   Insulin-producing cells

Organs or tissues transplanted into a patient to cure them

Most of the cells in your body are differentiated. They are specialised and carry out particular jobs. But some of your most important cells are the completely unspecialised **stem cells**. They can differentiate (divide and change) into many different types of cell when they are needed. Human stem cells are found in human embryos and in some adult tissue including bone marrow.

The function of stem cells

Stem cells divide and form the specialised cells of your body which make up your various tissues and organs. When an egg and sperm fuse to form an embryo, they form a single new cell. That cell divides and the embryo is soon a hollow ball of cells. The inner cells of this ball are the stem cells which will eventually give rise to every type of cell in your body.

Even when you are an adult some of your more specialised stem cells remain. Your bone marrow is a good source of stem cells. What's more, scientists now think there may be a tiny number of stem cells in most of the different tissues in your body. This includes your blood, brain, muscle and liver.

The stem cells can stay there for many years until your tissues are injured or affected by disease. Then they start dividing to replace the different types of damaged cells.

a) What are stem cells?

Using stem cells

Many people suffer and even die because various parts of their body stop working properly. For example, spinal injuries can cause paralysis. That's because the spinal nerves do not repair themselves. Millions of people would benefit if we could replace damaged body parts.

In 1998, there was a breakthrough. Two American scientists managed to culture human embryonic stem cells that were capable of forming other types of cells.

Scientists hope that these embryonic stem cells can be encouraged to grow into almost any different type of cell needed in the body. For example, we may be able to grow new nerve cells. If new nerves grown from stem cells could be used to reconnect the spinal nerves, people who have been paralysed could walk again.

With stem cells we might also be able to grow whole new organs which could be used in transplant surgery. These new organs would not be rejected by the body. Conditions from infertility to dementia could eventually be treated using stem cells.

Unfortunately, at the moment no-one is quite sure just how the cells in an embryo are switched on or off. We don't yet know how to form particular types of tissue. Once we know how to do this, we can really start to use stem cells effectively.

b) What was the big scientific breakthrough by American scientists in 1998?

Figure 2 Some of the embryonic stem cells which scientists have produced and grown have formed into adult cells. Unfortunately no-one is quite sure how to control this process at the moment. Hopefully one day the technique shown in this diagram will be used to treat people.

Problems with stem cells

Many embryonic stem cells come from aborted embryos or from spare embryos in fertility treatment. This raises ethical problems. There are people, including many religious groups, who feel it is wrong to use a potential human being as a source of cells, even to cure others.

Some people feel that as the embryo cannot give permission, using it is a violation of its human rights. On top of this, progress with stem cells is slow. There is some concern that embryonic stem cells might cause cancer if they are used to treat sick people. This has certainly been seen in mice. Making stem cells is slow, difficult, expensive and hard to control.

c) What is the biggest ethical concern with the use of embryonic stem cells?

The future of stem cell research

We have found embryonic stem cells in the umbilical cord blood of newborn babies. These may help to overcome some of the ethical concerns.

Scientists are also finding ways of growing adult stem cells. Unfortunately the adult stem cells found so far can only develop into a limited range of cell types. However this is another possible way of avoiding the controversial use of embryonic tissue.

The area of stem cell research known as *therapeutic cloning* could be very useful – but it is proving very difficult.

Therapeutic cloning involves using cells from an adult person to produce a cloned early embryo of themselves as a source of perfectly matched embryonic stem cells. In theory these could then be used to heal the original donor and maybe many others as well.

Most people remain excited by the possibilities of embryonic stem cells in treating many diseases. Just how many of these early hopes will be fulfilled only time will tell!

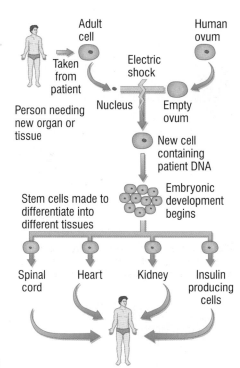

Organs or tissues transplanted into the patient with no risk of rejection

Figure 3 In 2005, a team led by Professor Woo Suk Hwang in South Korea claimed to have produced human embryos from adult cells and developed cloned stem cells from them. This seemed a huge step forward in stem cell research. But sadly, in 2006 the work was shown to be a massive scientific fraud. This was a massive blow to everyone working in stem cell research.

SUMMARY QUESTIONS

1 Copy and complete using the words below:

> **bone marrow   differentiate   embryos   hollow
> inner   stem cells**

Unspecialised cells known as …… …… can …… (divide and change) into many different types of cell when they are needed. Human stem cells are found in human …… and in adult …… …… . The embryo forms a …… ball of cells and the …… cells of this ball are the stem cells.

2 a) Why was the work of the American scientists in 1998 such a breakthrough in stem cell research?

b) How might stem cells be used to treat patients who are paralysed after a spinal injury?

3 a) What are the advantages of using stem cells to treat a wide range of diseases?

b) What are the difficulties with stem cell research?

c) How are scientists hoping to overcome the difficulties of using embryonic stem cells in their research?

KEY POINT

1 Embryonic stem cells (from human embryos) and adult stem cells (from adult bone marrow) can be made to differentiate into many different types of cells.

B2 6.3   Cell division in sexual reproduction

LEARNING OBJECTIVES

1 What happens to your chromosomes when your gametes are formed? [Higher]
2 How does sexual reproduction give rise to variation?

DID YOU KNOW?

About 80% of fertilised eggs never make it to become a live baby – in fact about 50% never even implant into the lining of the womb.

GET IT RIGHT!

Be careful with the spelling of mitosis and meiosis. Make sure you know the differences between the two processes.

DID YOU KNOW?

One testis can produce over 200 million sperm each day. As most boys and men have two working testes, that gives a total of 400 million sperm produced by meiosis every 24 hours! Only one sperm is needed to fertilise an egg. However as each tiny sperm needs to travel 100 000 times its own length to reach the ovum, less than one in a million ever completes the journey – so it's a good thing that plenty are made!

Mitosis is taking place all the time, in tissues all over your body. But mitosis is not the only type of cell division. There is another type which takes place only in the reproductive organs of animals and plants. **Meiosis** results in sex cells with only half the original number of chromosomes.

Meiosis

The reproductive organs in people, like most animals, are the **ovaries** and the **testes**. This is where the sex cells (the gametes) are made. The female gametes or **ova** are made in the ovaries. The male gametes or **sperm** are made in the testes.

The gametes are formed by meiosis, which is a special form of cell division where the chromosome number is reduced by half. When a cell divides to form gametes, the first stage is very similar to normal body cell division. The chromosomes are copied so there are four sets of chromosomes. The cell then divides twice in quick succession to form four gametes, each with a single set of chromosomes.

Why is meiosis so important?

Your normal body cells have 46 chromosomes in two matching sets – 23 come from your mother and 23 from your father. If two 'normal' body cells joined together in sexual reproduction, the new cell would have 92 chromosomes, which simply wouldn't work!

Fortunately, as a result of meiosis, your sex cells contain only one set of chromosomes, exactly half of the full chromosome number. So when the gametes join together at fertilisation, the new cell formed contains the right number of 46 chromosomes.

a) What are the names of the male and female gametes and how do they differ from normal body cells?

A cell in the reproductive organs looks just like a normal body cell before it starts to divide and form gametes

As in normal cell division, the first step is that the chromosomes are copied

The cell divides in two, and these new cells immediately divide again

This gives four sex cells, each with a single set of chromosomes – in this case two instead of the original four

Figure 1 The formation of sex cells in the ovaries and testes involves a special kind of cell division to halve the chromosome number. The original cell is shown with only two pairs of chromosomes to make it easier to follow what is happening.

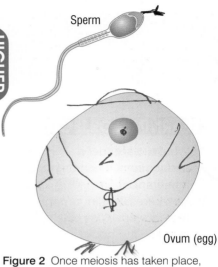

Sperm

Ovum (egg)

Figure 2 Once meiosis has taken place, the male and female gametes develop very differently – they are adapted for very different jobs

In girls, the first stage of meiosis is completed before they are even born. The tiny ovaries of a baby girl contain all the ova she will ever have.

In boys, meiosis doesn't start until puberty when the testes start to produce sperm. It then carries on for the rest of their lives.

Each gamete you produce is slightly different from all the others. The combination of chromosomes will be different. What's more, there is some exchange of genes between the chromosomes during the process of meiosis. This means that no two eggs or sperm are the same. This introduces lots of variety into the genetic mix of the offspring.

b) What type of cell division is needed to produce the gametes?

Fertilisation

More variety is added when fertilisation takes place. Each sex cell has a single set of chromosomes. When two sex cells join during fertilisation the new cell formed has a full set of chromosomes. In humans, the egg cell has 23 chromosomes and so does the sperm. When they join together they produce a new normal cell with the full human complement of 46 chromosomes.

The combination of genes on the chromosomes of every newly fertilised ovum is completely unique. Once fertilisation is complete, the unique new cell begins to divide by mitosis. This will continue long after the fetus is fully developed and the baby is born.

Variation

The differences between asexual and sexual reproduction are a reflection of the different types of cell division involved in the two processes.

In asexual reproduction the offspring are produced as a result of mitosis from the parent cells. (See the start of this chapter.) So they contain exactly the same chromosomes and the same genes as their parents. There is no variation in the genetic material.

In sexual reproduction the gametes are produced by meiosis in the sex organs of the parents. This introduces variety as each gamete is different. Then when the gametes fuse, one of each pair of chromosomes, and so one of each pair of genes, comes from each parent.

The combination of genes in the new pair will contain **alleles** (different forms of the gene) from each parent. This also helps to produce different characteristics in the offspring.

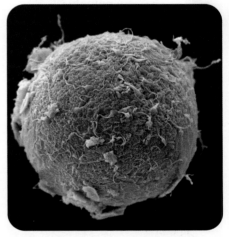

Figure 3 At the moment of fertilisation the chromosomes in the two gametes are combined so the new cell has a complete set, like any other body cell. This cell will then grow and reproduce by mitosis to form a new individual.

KEY POINTS

1 Cells in the reproductive organs divide to form the gametes (sex cells).
2 Body cells have two sets of chromosomes; gametes have only one set.
3 Gametes are formed from body cells by meiosis. [Higher]
4 Sexual reproduction gives rise to variety because genetic information from two parents is combined.

SUMMARY QUESTIONS

1 a) How many pairs of chromosomes are there in a normal human body cell?
   b) How many chromosomes are there in a human egg cell?
   c) How many chromosomes are there in a fertilised human egg cell?

2 Sexual reproduction results in variety. Explain how.

3 a) What is the name of the special type of cell division which produces gametes from ordinary body cells? Describe what happens to the chromosomes in this process.
   b) Where in your body would this type of cell division take place?
   c) Why is this type of cell division so important in sexual reproduction? [Higher]

B2 6.4 | From Mendel to DNA

GET IT RIGHT!

Mendel knew nothing of chromosomes and genes. Make sure you don't confuse modern knowledge with what Mendel knew when he did his experiments.

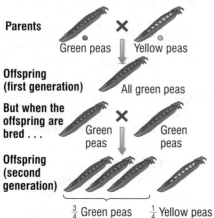

Parents — Green peas × Yellow peas

Offspring (first generation) — All green peas

But when the offspring are bred... Green peas × Green peas

Offspring (second generation) — $\frac{3}{4}$ Green peas $\frac{1}{4}$ Yellow peas

Figure 1 Gregor Mendel, the father of modern genetics. When he died in 1884 he was still hoping that eventually other people would acknowledge his discoveries. In the 21st century, we know just how right he was!

For hundreds of years people had no idea about how information moved from one generation to the next. Yet now we can identify people by the genetic information in their cells!

Mendel's discoveries

Gregor Mendel was born in 1822 in Brunn, Czechoslovakia. Clever but poor, he became a monk to get an education.

He worked in the monastery gardens and became fascinated by the peas growing there. He decided to carry out some breeding experiments, using pure strains of round peas, wrinkled peas, green peas and yellow peas for his work. Mendel cross-bred the peas and counted the different offspring carefully. He found that characteristics were inherited in clear and predictable patterns.

Mendel explained his results by suggesting there were separate units of inherited material. He realised some characteristics were dominant over others and that they never mixed together. This was an amazing idea for the time.

a) Why did Gregor Mendel become a monk?

Mendel kept records of everything he did, and analysed his results. This was almost unheard of in those days! Finally in 1866, when he was 44 years old, Mendel published his findings.

He never saw chromosomes and never heard of genes. Yet he explained some of the basic laws of genetics in a way we still use today.

Sadly Mendel's genius was ahead of his time. As no-one knew about genes or chromosomes, people simply didn't understand his theories. He died twenty years later with his ideas still ignored – but convinced that he was right!

b) What was unusual about Mendel's scientific technique at the time?

Sixteen years after his death, Gregor Mendel's work was finally recognised. By 1900, people had seen chromosomes through a microscope. Three scientists, discovered Mendel's papers and repeated his experiments. When they published their results, they gave Mendel the credit for what they observed! From then on ideas about genetics developed fast. It was suggested that Mendel's units of inheritance might be carried on the chromosomes seen beneath the microscope. And so the science of genetics as we know it today was born.

DNA – the molecule of inheritance

The work of Gregor Mendel was just the start of our understanding of inheritance. Today, we know that our features are inherited on genes carried on our chromosomes. We also know what those chromosomes are made of.

Your chromosomes are made up of long molecules of a chemical known as DNA (**d**eoxyribose **n**ucleic **a**cid). Your genes are small sections of this DNA. The DNA carries the instructions to make the proteins which form most of your cell structures. These proteins also include the enzymes which control your cell chemistry.

HIGHER

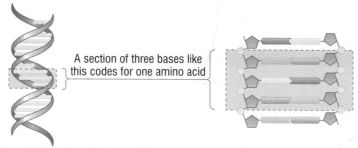

A section of three bases like this codes for one amino acid

Figure 2 It is at this fundamental level of chemistry that your characteristics are determined. A small quirk of chemistry would have resulted in a very different you – a very strange thought.

The long strands of your DNA are made up of combinations of four different chemical bases. (See Figure 2.) These are grouped into threes and each group of three codes form an amino acid.

Each gene is made up of hundreds or thousands of these bases. The order of the bases controls the order in which the amino acids are put together so that they make a particular protein for use in your body cells. Each gene codes for a particular combination of amino acids which make a specific protein.

A change or mutation in a single group of bases can be enough to change or disrupt the whole protein structure and the way it works.

DNA fingerprinting

Unless you have an identical twin, your DNA is unique to you. Other members of your family will have strong similarities in their DNA, but each individual has their own unique blueprint. Only identical twins have the same DNA. That's because they have both developed from the same original cell.

The unique patterns in your DNA can be used to identify you. A technique known as 'DNA fingerprinting' can be applied.

Certain areas of your DNA produce very variable patterns under the microscope. These patterns are more similar between people who are related than between total strangers. The patterns are known as **DNA fingerprints**. They can be produced from very tiny samples of DNA from body fluids such as blood, saliva and semen.

The likelihood of two identical samples coming from different people (apart from identical twins) is millions to one. As a result DNA fingerprinting is enormously useful in solving crimes. It is also used to show who is the biological father of a child when there is doubt.

Figure 3 DNA fingerprints like these can be used to identify the guilty – and the innocent – in a crime investigation

KEY POINTS

1 Gregor Mendel was the first person to suggest separately inherited factors which we now call genes.
2 Chromosomes are made up of large molecules of DNA.
3 A gene is a small section of DNA which codes for a particular combination of amino acids which make a specific protein. [Higher]
4 Everyone (except identical twins) has unique DNA which can be used to identify them using DNA fingerprinting.

SUMMARY QUESTIONS

1 a) How did Mendel's experiments with peas convince him that there were distinct 'units of inheritance' which were not blended together in offspring?
   b) Why didn't people accept his ideas?
   c) The development of the microscope played an important part in helping to convince people that Mendel was right. How?

2 Two men claim to be the father of the same child. Explain how DNA fingerprinting could be used to find out which one is the real father.

3 Explain the saying 'One gene, one protein'. [Higher]

B2 6.5   Inheritance in action

1 How is sex determined in humans?
2 Can you predict what features a child might inherit? [Higher]

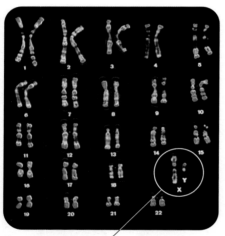

Sex chromosomes

Figure 1 The chromosomes of the human male. The X chromosome carries genes controlling lots of different features. The Y chromosome is much smaller than the X chromosome and carries information mainly about maleness!

Ideas about genetics, chromosomes and genes are everywhere in the 21st century. We read about them in the papers, see them on TV and learn about them in science lessons. The way features are passed from one generation to another follow some clear patterns. We can use these to predict what may be passed on.

How inheritance works

Scientiest have built on the work of Gregor Mendel. We now understand how genetic information is passed from parent to offspring.

Human beings have 23 pairs of chromosomes. In 22 cases, each chromosome in the pair is a similar shape and has genes carrying information about the same things. But one pair of chromosomes may be different – these are the **sex chromosomes**. Two X chromosomes mean you are female. However, one X chromosome and a much smaller one, known as the Y chromosome, give a male.

a) Twins are born. Twin A is XY and twin B is XX. What sex are the two babies?

The chromosomes we inherit carry our genetic information in the form of genes. Many of these genes have different forms, known as alleles. (See page 73.) A gene can be pictured as a position on a chromosome. An allele is the particular form of information in that position on an individual chromosome. For example, the gene for dimples may have the dimple or the no-dimple allele in place.

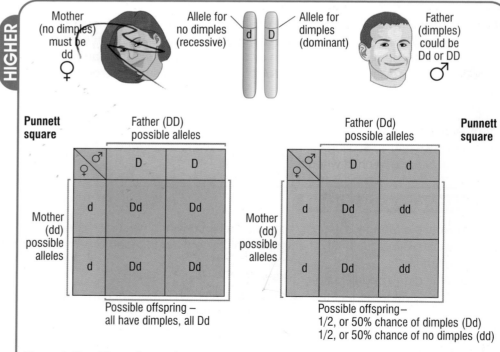

Figure 2 The different forms of genes, known as alleles, can result in the development of quite different characteristics. We can use diagrams like this Punnett square to explain what is happening or predict what the offspring might be like.

Most of your characteristics, like your eye colour and nose shape, are controlled by a number of genes. However, some characteristics, like dimples or having attached earlobes, are controlled by a single gene. Often there are only two possible alleles for a particular feature. However, sometimes you can inherit one from a number of different possibilities.

Some alleles control the development of a characteristic even when they are only present on one of your chromosomes. These alleles are **dominant**, e.g. dimples and dangly earlobes.

Some alleles only control the development of a characteristic if they are present on both alleles – in other words, no dominant allele is present. These alleles are **recessive**, e.g. no dimples and attached earlobes.

HIGHER

How does inheritance work?

We can use a simple model to help us understand how inheritance works. It explains how different features are passed on from one generation to another.

Imagine a bag containing marbles. If you put your hand in and – without looking – picked out two marbles at a time, what pairs might you get? If the bag contained only red marbles or only blue marbles, the pairs would all be the same. But if the bag held a mixture of red and blue marbles you could end up with three possible pairs – two blue marbles, two red marbles or one of each.

This is what happens when you inherit genes from your parents, depending on the different alleles they have. For example, if both of your parents have two alleles for dimples (like the red marbles) you will definitely inherit two dimple alleles – and you will have dimples! If both of your parents have two alleles for no dimples, you will inherit alleles for no dimples and you will be dimple free.

But if your parents both have one allele for dimples and one for no dimples, you could end up with two dimple alleles, two no dimple alleles – or one of each.

DID YOU KNOW?

Sex determination varies from species to species. In birds, females are XY and the males are XX. In some species of reptiles the males are XY and the females XX. In others the males are XX and the females XY. Some reptiles including alligators and tortoises don't have any sex chromosomes at all. The sex of the babies is decided by the temperature of the eggs as they incubate. And there are some species of fish and snails which change sex at different stages of their lives!

SUMMARY QUESTIONS

1 Copy and complete:

   male   sex chromosomes   23   22   X   XX   Y

   Human beings have ...... pairs of chromosomes. In ...... pairs the chromosomes are always the same. The final pair are known as .... If you inherit ...... you will be female, while an ...... and a ...... make you ....

2 a) What is meant by the term 'dominant allele'?
   b) What is meant by the term 'recessive allele'?
   c) Try and discover as many human characteristics as you can which are inherited on a single gene. Which alleles are dominant and which are recessive?

3 Use a Punnett square like the one in Figure 2 to show the possible offspring from a cross between two people who both have dimples and the genotype Dd. [Higher]

KEY POINTS

1 In human body cells the sex chromosomes determine whether you are female (XX) or male (XY).
2 Some features are controlled by a single gene.
3 Genes can have different forms called alleles.
4 Some alleles are dominant and some are recessive.
5 We can construct genetic diagrams to predict features. [Higher]

B2 6.6 — Inherited conditions in humans

Not all diseases are infectious. Sometimes diseases are the result of a problem in your genes and can be passed on from parent to child. They are known as **genetic diseases** or **genetic disorders**.

We can use our knowledge of dominant and recessive alleles to work out the risk of inheriting a genetic disease.

a) How is a genetic disease different from an infectious disease?

Huntington's disease

One example of a very serious, although very rare, genetic disorder is Huntington's disease. This is a disorder of the nervous system. It is caused by a dominant allele and so it can be inherited from one parent who has the disease. If one of your parents is affected by Huntington's you have a 50% chance of inheriting the disease. That's because half of their gametes will contain the faulty allele.

The symptoms of this inherited disease usually appear when you are between 30 and 50 years old. Sadly, the condition is fatal. Because the disease does not appear until middle-age, many people have already had children and passed on the faulty allele before they realise they are affected.

b) You may inherit Huntington's disease even if only one of your parents is affected. Why?

Cystic fibrosis

Another genetic disease which has been studied in great detail is **cystic fibrosis**. This is a disorder which affects many organs of the body, particularly the lungs and the pancreas.

The organs become clogged up by a very thick sticky mucus which stops them working properly. The reproductive system is affected so most people with cystic fibrosis are infertile.

Treatment for cystic fibrosis includes physiotherapy and antibiotics to help keep the lungs clear of mucus and infections. Enzymes are used to replace the ones the pancreas cannot produce and to thin the mucus.

However, although treatments are getting better all the time, there is still no cure.

Cystic fibrosis is caused by a recessive allele so it must be inherited from both parents. Children affected by cystic fibrosis are born to parents who do not suffer from the disease. They have a dominant healthy allele which means their bodies work normally but they carry the cystic fibrosis allele. Because it gives them no symptoms, they have no idea it is there.

People who have a silent disease-causing allele like this are known as **carriers**. In the UK, one person in 25 carries the cystic fibrosis allele. Most of them will never be aware of it, unless they happen to have children with a partner who also carries the allele. Then there is a 25% (one in four) chance that any child they have will be affected.

c) You will only inherit cystic fibrosis if you get the allele from both parents. Why?

Figure 1 Modern medicine and determination mean that many sufferers from cystic fibrosis manage to lead full and active lives. However, the cells in their bodies are still carrying the faulty alleles and cannot function properly.

The genetic lottery

When the genes from parents are combined, it is called a genetic cross. We can show this using a genetic diagram (see Figures 2 and 3). A genetic diagram shows us:

- the alleles for a characteristic carried by the parents,
- the possible gametes which can be formed from these, and
- how these could combine to form the characteristic in their offspring.

When looking at the possibility of inheriting genetic diseases, it is important to remember that every time an egg and a sperm meet it is down to chance which alleles combine. So if two parents who both carry the cystic fibrosis allele have four children, there is a 25% chance (one in four) that each child might have the disease.

But in fact all four children could have cystic fibrosis, or none of them might be affected. They might all be carriers, or none of them might inherit the faulty alleles at all. It's all down to chance!

Both parents are carriers, so Cc

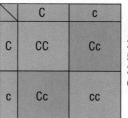

	C	c
C	CC	Cc
c	Cc	cc

25% normal (CC)
50% carriers (Cc)
25% affected by cystic fibrosis (cc)

3/4, or 75% chance normal
1/4, or 25% chance cystic fibrosis

Figure 3 The arrival of a child with cystic fibrosis in a family often comes as a complete shock. The faulty alleles can be covered up by normal alleles for generations until two carriers have a child and by chance both of the cystic fibrosis alleles are passed on.

Parent with Huntington's disease   Hh
Normal parent   hh

	H	h
h	Hh	hh
h	Hh	hh

50% chance Huntington's disease, Hh
50% chance normal, hh

Figure 2 A genetic diagram for Huntington's disease shows us how a dominant allele can affect offspring. It is important to realise that this shows that the chance of passing on the disease allele is 50%, but it cannot tell us which, if any, of the children will actually inherit the allele.

Curing genetic diseases

So far we have no way of curing genetic diseases. Scientists hope that genetic engineering will enable them to cut out faulty alleles and replace them with healthy ones. They have tried this in people affected by cystic fibrosis. But so far they have not managed to cure anyone.

There are genetic tests which can show people in affected families if they carry the faulty allele. This allows them to make choices such as whether to have a family. It is also possible to screen embryos for the alleles which cause these and other genetic disorders. These tests are very useful but raise many ethical issues. (See page 81.)

(See page 81.)

GET IT RIGHT!

If one parent has a characteristic caused by a single dominant allele (e.g. Huntington's disease, dangly earlobes) you have a 50% chance of inheriting it.
If one parent has two dominant alleles (e.g. for Huntington's disease, dangly earlobes) you have 100% chance of inheriting it.
If both parents have a recessive allele for a characteristic (e.g. cystic fibrosis, attached earlobes) you have a 25% chance of inheriting that characteristic.

KEY POINTS

1 Some disorders are inherited.
2 Huntington's disease is caused by a dominant allele of a gene and can be inherited from only one parent.
3 Cystic fibrosis is caused by a recessive allele of a gene and so must be inherited from both parents.

SUMMARY QUESTIONS

1 a) What is Huntington's disease?
     b) Why can one parent carrying the allele for Huntington's disease pass it on to their children even though the other parent is not affected?

2 At the moment, only people who have genetic diseases in their family are given genetic screening. What would be the pros and cons of screening everyone for diseases like cystic fibrosis and Huntington's disease?

3 a) Why are carriers of cystic fibrosis not affected by the disease themselves?
     b) A couple have a baby who has cystic fibrosis. Neither of the couple, nor their parents, have any signs of the disease.
       Draw genetic diagrams of the grandparents and the parents to show how this could happen. [Higher]

B2 6.7 Stem cells and embryos – an ethical minefield

The stem cell dilemma

Doctors have treated people with adult stem cells for many years by giving bone marrow transplants. Now scientists are moving ever closer to treating very ill people using embryonic stem cells. This area of medicine raises many issues. Here are just a few different opinions:

I think it is absolutely wrong to use human embryos in this way. Each life is precious to God. They may only be tiny balls of cells – but they could become people.

The accident happened so quickly. Now I'm stuck in this wheelchair for the rest of my life. I can't walk or even control when I go to the loo. It would be wonderful if they could develop cell stem therapy. I want them to heal my spinal cord so I can walk again!

It may become possible to take stem cells from the umbilical cord of every newborn baby. They could be frozen and stored ready for when the person might need them later in their life.

The embryos we use would all be destroyed anyway. Now we are even making our own embryos from adult cells. We could do so much good for people that we all feel it is very important for the research to continue.

It was terrible to see my husband suffer. By the time he died he didn't know who I was or any of the children. If these stem cells can cure Alzheimer's disease then we should do the research as fast as possible.

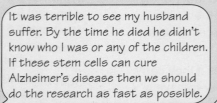

We need to be careful. There are some real problems with these stem cell treatments. We don't want to solve one problem and cause another.

I am going to volunteer to let them use some of my cells for therapeutic cloning. It is too late to help me now, but I'd like to think I could help other people.

ACTIVITY

Here is an opportunity to make your voice heard. Your class is going to produce a large wall display covered with articles both for and against stem cell research. Your display is aimed at students in Years 10 and 11, so make sure the level of content is right for your target group.

Try and carry out a survey or vote of your target group before the display is put up. Find out:

- how many people support stem cell research,
- what proportion are completely against it, and
- how many haven't made up their minds.

Record your findings

Work on your own or in a small group. Each group is to produce one piece of display material. Make sure that some of you give information in favour of stem cell research and others against. Use a variety of resources to help you – the material in this chapter is a good starting point. Make sure that your ideas are backed up with as much scientific evidence as possible.

Once the material has been displayed for a week or two, repeat your initial survey or vote. Analyse the data to see if easy access to information has changed people's views!

Can we know too much?

Today we not only understand the causes of many genetic disorders, we can also test for them. But being able to test for a genetic disorder doesn't necessarily mean we should always do it.

- People in families affected by Huntington's disease can take a genetic test which tells them if they have inherited the faulty gene. If they have, they know that they will develop the fatal disease as they get older and may pass on the gene to their children. Some people in affected families take the test and use it to help them decide whether to marry or have a family. Others prefer not to know.

- If a couple have a genetic disease in their family or already have a child with a genetic disorder, they can have a developing embryo tested during pregnancy. Cells from the embryo are checked. If it is affected, the parents have a choice. They may decide to keep the baby, knowing that it will have a genetic disorder when it is born. On the other hand, they may decide to have an abortion. This prevents the birth of a child with serious problems and allows them to try again to have a healthy baby.

- Some couples who have a genetic disease in the family or who already have a child affected by a genetic disease have their embryos screened before they are implanted in the mother. Embryos are produced by IVF (*in vitro* fertilisation). Doctors remove a single cell from each embryo and screen it for genetic diseases. Only healthy embryos free from genetic disease are implanted back into their mother. Using this method, only healthy babies are born.

ACTIVITY

Many couples who have a genetic disease in the family spend time with a genetic counsellor to help them understand what is happening and the choices they have. Plan a role-play of an interview with a genetic counsellor.

Either: Plan the role of the counsellor. Make sure you have all the information you need to talk to a couple who have already got one child with cystic fibrosis who would like to have another child. You need to be able to explain the chances of another child being affected and the choices that are open to them.

Or: Plan the role of a parent who already has one child with cystic fibrosis and who wants to have another child. Work in pairs to give the views of a couple if you like. Think carefully about the factors which will affect your decision such as: Can you cope with another sick child? Are you prepared to have an abortion? Do you have religious views on the matter? What is fairest to the unborn child – and the child you already have? Is it ethical to choose embryos to implant?

SUMMARY QUESTIONS

1 a) What is mitosis?

   b) Explain, using diagrams, what takes place when a cell divides by mitosis.

   c) Mitosis is very important during the development of a baby from a fertilised egg. It is also important all through life. Why?

2 a) What are stem cells?

   b) It is hoped that many different medical problems may be cured using stem cells. Explain how this might work.

   c) There are some ethical issues about the use of embryonic stem cells. Explain the arguments both for and against their use.

3 a) What is meiosis and where does it take place?

   b) Explain, using labelled diagrams, what takes place when a cell divides by meiosis.

   c) Why is meiosis so important?

[Higher]

4 Hugo de Vries is one of the scientists who made the same discoveries as Mendel several years after his death. Write a letter from Hugo to one of his friends after he has found Mendel's writings. Explain what Mendel did, why no-one took any notice of him and how the situation is so different now for you if you were doing the same sort of experiments.

5 Whether you have a straight thumb or a curved one is decided by a single gene with two alleles. The straight allele **S** is dominant to the curved allele **s**. Use this information to help you answer these questions.
   Josh has straight thumbs but Sami has curved thumbs. They are expecting a baby.

   a) We know exactly what Sami's thumb alleles are. What are they and how do you know?

   b) If the baby has curved thumbs, what does this tell you about Josh's thumb alleles? Fill in a Punnett square to show the genetics of your explanation.

   c) If the baby has straight thumbs, what does this tell us about Josh's thumb alleles? Fill in a Punnett square to show the genetics of your explanation.

[Higher]

EXAM-STYLE QUESTIONS

1 The diagram below is of stages in sexual reproduction in a mammal.

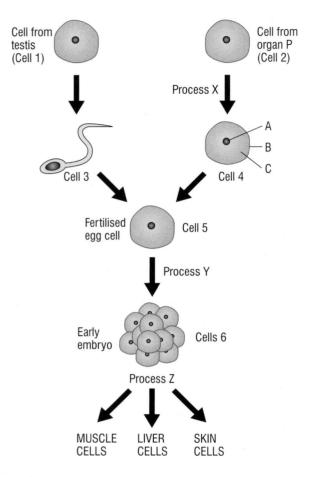

(a) What is the name of organ **P**? (1)

(b) Give the names of parts **A**, **B** and **C** in cell 4. (3)

(c) What is the name of cell 3? (1)

(d) What type of cell division takes place in processes **Y** and **Z**? (1)

(e) Which two of the cells labelled 1–6:

   (i) are genetically identical to one another? (1)

   (ii) are known as gametes? (1)

(f) Cells 6 will in due course change into a range of different cell types.

   (i) What name is given to the type of cell labelled as cells 6? (1)

   (ii) What is the process called by which these cells change into different cell types? (1)

Making connections

Developing ideas about substances

Many people think that Antoine Lavoisier was the father of modern chemistry. If this is so, then his wife, Marie-Anne may well be the mother. She was well educated, and translated documents and illustrated his scientific texts with great skill.

Antoine Lavoisier lived in France between 1743 and 1794. His experiments were some of the first proper chemical experiments involving careful measurements. For example, in chemical reactions he carefully weighed reactants and products. This was an important advance over the work of earlier chemists.

Working with his wife, Lavoisier showed that the quantity of matter is the same at the end as at the beginning of every chemical reaction. Working with other French chemists, Lavoisier invented a system of chemical names which described the structure of chemical compounds. Many of these names are still in use, including names such as sulfuric acid and sulfates.

ACTIVITY

The three scientists described here made enormous contributions to our understanding of the behaviour of matter and chemistry. Using this information, produce a poster with a timeline showing how our understanding of the behaviour of matter changed in the period from the early 18th century to the beginning of the 20th century.

You could research these ideas further using the Internet, especially at www.timelinescience.org.

Michael Faraday came from very humble beginnings, but his work on electricity and chemistry still affects our lives today. His achievements were acknowledged when his portrait was included on the £20 note in 1991.

Born in Yorkshire in 1791, Michael Faraday was one of 10 children. Apprenticed to a bookbinder, Faraday became an assistant to the great chemist Sir Humphry Davy. After hearing some of Davy's lectures in London, he sent him a bound copy of some notes he had made and was taken on.

After much work on electricity, Faraday turned his attention to electrolysis. He produced an explanation of what happens when we use an electric current to split up a chemical compound. Not only did Faraday explain what happens, he also introduced the words we still use today – **electrolysis**, **electrolyte** and **electrode**.

Ernest Rutherford was born in New Zealand in 1871. After his education in New Zealand he worked and studied in England and Canada. Then in 1910 he showed that the structure of the atom consists of a tiny positively charged nucleus that makes up nearly all of the mass of the atom. The nucleus is surrounded by a vast space which contains the electrons – but most of the atom is simply empty space! Rutherford received the Nobel Prize for Chemistry in recognition of his huge contribution to our understanding of the atom.

Ernest Rutherford was responsible for producing the evidence that completely changed our ideas about the structure of atoms

Chapters in this unit

 Structures and bonding

 Structures and properties

 How much?

 Rates of reaction

 Energy and reactions

 Electrolysis

 Acids, alkalis and salts

C2 1.1

Atomic structure

LEARNING OBJECTIVES

1 What is inside atoms?
2 Why is the number of protons in an atom equal to the number of electrons?
3 What is the order in which atoms are arranged in the periodic table?
4 What is the charge on a proton, neutron and electron?

In the middle of an atom is a small nucleus. This contains two types of particles, which we call **protons** and **neutrons**. A third type of particle orbits the nucleus – we call these particles **electrons**. Any atom has the same number of electrons orbiting its nucleus as it has protons in its nucleus.

Protons have a positive charge while neutrons have no charge – they are neutral. So the nucleus itself has an overall positive charge.

The electrons orbiting the nucleus are negatively charged. The size of the negative charge on an electron is exactly the same as the size of the positive charge on a proton. (In other words, the relative charge on a proton is $+1$, while the relative charge on an electron is -1.)

Because any atom contains equal numbers of protons and electrons, the overall charge on any atom is exactly zero. For example, a carbon atom has 6 protons, so we know it also has 6 electrons.

a) What are the names of the three particles that make up an atom?
b) An oxygen atom has 8 protons – how many electrons does it have?

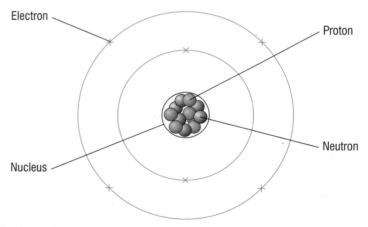

Figure 1 Understanding the structure of an atom gives us important clues to the way chemicals react together

Type of sub-atomic particle	Relative charge
proton	+1
neutron	0
electron	−1

To help you remember the charge on the sub-atomic particles:

Protons are **P**ositive;
Neutrons are **N**eutral;
so that means Electrons must be Negative!

Atomic number

We call the number of protons in the nucleus of an atom its **atomic number** or **proton number**.

As all of the atoms of a particular element have the same number of protons, they also have the same atomic number. So the atomic number of hydrogen is 1 and it has one proton in the nucleus. The atomic number of carbon is 6 and it has 6 protons in the nucleus. The atomic number of sodium is 11 and it has 11 protons in the nucleus.

Each element has its own atomic number. If you are told that the atomic number of an element is 8, you can identify that element from the periodic table. In this case it is oxygen.

c) Which element has an atomic number of 14?

Elements in the periodic table are arranged in order of their atomic numbers.

Figure 2 The elements in the periodic table are arranged in order of their atomic numbers

You read the periodic table from left to right, and from the top down – just like reading a page of writing.

Look at the atomic numbers of the elements in the last group of the periodic table:

d) What do you notice about the atomic numbers going from helium to neon to argon?

You will be able to explain this pattern when you learn more about the arrangement of electrons in atoms later in this chapter.

SUMMARY QUESTIONS

1 Copy and complete using the words below:

   atomic   electrons   negative   neutrons   protons

   In the nucleus of atoms there are …… and …… . Around the nucleus there are …… which have a …… charge. In the periodic table, atoms are arranged in order of their …… number.

2 Use the periodic table in Figure 2 to find the atomic number of the elements lithium, sulfur, magnesium, chlorine and nitrogen.

3 Atoms are always neutral. Explain why this means that an atom must always contain the same number of protons and electrons.

GET IT RIGHT!

In an atom, the number of protons is always equal to the number of electrons. You can find out the number of protons and electrons in an atom by looking up its atomic number in the periodic table.

DID YOU KNOW?

In 1808, a chemist called John Dalton published a theory of atoms, explaining how these joined together to form new substances. Not everyone liked his theory though – one person wrote 'Atoms are round bits of wood invented by Mr Dalton!'

KEY POINTS

1 Atoms are made of protons, neutrons and electrons.
2 Protons and electrons have equal and opposite electric charges. Protons are positively charged, and electrons are negatively charged.
3 Atoms are arranged in the periodic table in order of their atomic number.
4 Neutrons have no electric charge. They are neutral.

C2 1.2

The arrangement of electrons in atoms

GET IT RIGHT!

Make sure that you can draw the electronic structure of the atoms of all of the first 20 elements when you are given their atomic numbers.

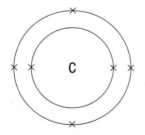

Figure 2 A simple way of representing the electrons in a carbon atom and the energy levels where they are found. We can show this as 2,4. This is called the **electronic structure** (or **electronic configuration**) of the atom.

One model of the atom which we use has electrons arranged around the nucleus in **shells**, rather like the layers of an onion. Each shell represents a different **energy level**. The lowest energy level is shown by the shell which is nearest to the nucleus.

With their negative charge, electrons are attracted to the positively charged nucleus. To move an electron from a shell close to the nucleus to one further away we need to put energy into the atom. The energy is needed to overcome this attractive force. This means that electrons in shells further away from the nucleus have more energy than electrons in shells closer to the nucleus.

a) Where are the electrons in an atom?

b) Which shell represents the lowest energy level in an atom?

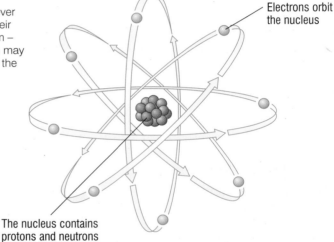

Figure 1 No-one has ever seen the electrons in their energy levels in an atom – this is one model which may help you to understand the structure of atoms

Electrons orbit the nucleus

The nucleus contains protons and neutrons

We could not possibly draw atoms which look like this every time we wanted to show the structure of an atom. It's easier to draw atoms as in Figure 2.

An energy level can only hold a certain number of electrons. The first, and lowest, energy level holds two electrons. The second energy level is filled up by eight electrons. Once there are eight electrons in the third energy level, the fourth begins to fill up, and so on.

Elements whose atoms have a full outer energy level are very stable and unreactive. They are called the **noble gases** – helium, neon and argon are examples.

The most usual way of drawing the arrangement of electrons in an atom is shown in Figure 2. We can also write down the numbers of electrons in each energy level.

The atomic number of an element tells us how many electrons there are in its atoms. For example, for the carbon atom in Figure 2 the atomic number is 6, giving us 6 electrons. This means that we write its **electronic structure** as 2,4.

An atom with the atomic number 13 has an electronic structure 2,8,3. This represents 2 electrons in the first, and lowest, energy level, then eight in the next energy level and 3 in the highest energy level (its outermost shell).

The best way to understand these arrangements is to look at some examples.

c) How many electrons can the first energy level hold?

Filling up the energy levels (shells)

We call the horizontal rows of the periodic table **periods**. As we move across a period of the table, each element has one more electron in its highest energy level (or outer shell) than the element before it. When we start a new period, a new energy level begins to fill with electrons.

The pattern is quite complicated after argon. However, the elements in the main groups all have the same number of electrons in their highest energy level. These electrons are often called the outer electrons because they are in the outer shell.

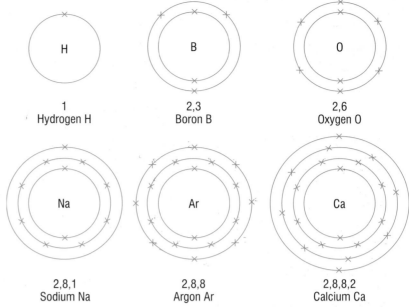

1	2,3	2,6
Hydrogen H	Boron B	Oxygen O
2,8,1	2,8,8	2,8,8,2
Sodium Na	Argon Ar	Calcium Ca

Figure 3 Once you know the pattern, you should be able to draw the energy levels and electrons in any of the first 20 atoms (given their atomic number)

All the elements in Group 1 have one electron in their highest energy level and the noble gases, except for helium, have 8 electrons in their highest energy level.

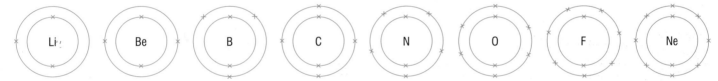

We call the vertical columns of the periodic table **groups**. The chemical properties of an element depend on how many electrons it has. Most importantly, the way an element reacts is determined by the number of electrons in its highest energy level or outer shell. As we have seen, the elements in a particular group all have the same number of electrons in their highest energy levels. This means that they all share similar chemical properties.

Figure 4 As a period builds up, the number of electrons in the outer shell of each element increases by one

---

SUMMARY QUESTIONS

1 Copy and complete using the words below:

   **electron   energy   energy levels   group   nucleus
   period   shells**

   The electrons in an atom are arranged around the ...... in ...... or .... The electrons further away from the nucleus have more ...... than those close to the nucleus. As you go across a ...... of the periodic table, each element has one more ...... than the previous element. All elements in the same ...... have the same number of electrons in their outer shell.

2 Draw the arrangement of electrons in the following atoms:

   a) Li   b) B   c) P   d) Ar.

3 What is special about the electronic structure of neon and argon?

KEY POINTS

1 The electrons in an atom are arranged in energy levels or shells.
2 Atoms with the same number of electrons in their outer shell belong in the same group of the periodic table.
3 The number of electrons in the outer shell of an atom determines the way that the atom behaves in chemical reactions.

C2 1.3   Chemical bonding

LEARNING OBJECTIVES

LEARNING OBJECTIVES

1 How do elements form compounds?
2 Why do the elements in Group 1 react with the elements in Group 7?

You already know that we can mix two substances together without either of them changing. For example, we can mix sand and salt together and then separate them again. No change will have taken place. We can even dissolve sugar in tea and separate it out again. But in chemical reactions the situation is very different.

When the atoms of two or more elements react they make a compound. The compound formed is different to both of them and we cannot get either of the elements back again easily. We can also react compounds together to form other compounds, but the reaction of elements is easier to understand as a starting point.

a) What is the difference between **mixing** two substances and **reacting** them?

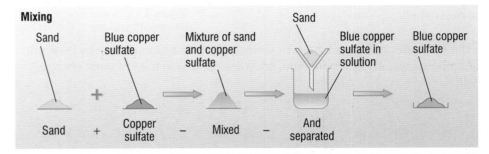

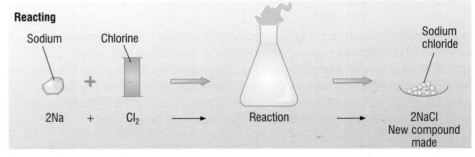

Figure 1 The difference between mixing and reacting. Separating mixtures is usually quite easy, but separating substances once they have reacted can be quite difficult.

Why do atoms react?

When an atom has a full outer shell it is stable and unreactive (like the noble gases in Group 0). However most atoms do not have a full outer shell. When atoms react they take part in changes which give them a stable arrangement of electrons. They may do this by either:

● sharing electrons, which we call **covalent bonding**, or by
● transferring electrons, which we call **ionic bonding**.

In ionic bonding the atoms involved lose or gain electrons so that they have a noble gas structure. So for example, if sodium, 2,8,1 loses one electron it is left with the stable electronic structure of neon 2,8.

However, it is also left with one more proton in the nucleus than there are electrons in orbit around the nucleus. The proton has a positive charge so the sodium atom has now become a positively charged particle. We call this a **sodium ion**. The sodium ion has a single positive charge. We write the formula of a sodium ion as Na^+. The electronic structure of the Na^+ ion is $[2,8]^+$.

b) When atoms join together by **sharing** electrons, what type of bond is this?

c) When atoms join together as a result of **gaining** or **losing** electrons, what type of bond is this?

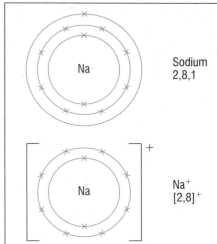

Figure 2 A positive sodium ion (Na^+) is formed when a sodium atom loses an electron during ionic bonding with another element

Similarly some atoms gain electrons during reactions to achieve a stable noble gas structure. Chlorine, for example, has the electronic structure 2,8,7. By gaining a single electron, it gets the stable electronic structure of argon [2,8,8].

In this case there is now one more electron than there are positive protons in the nucleus. So the chlorine atom becomes a negatively charged particle known as a **chloride ion**. This carries a single negative charge. We write the formula of the chloride ion as Cl^-. Its electronic structure is $[2,8,8]^-$.

Representing electron transfer

When atoms react together to form ions, atoms which need to lose electrons react with elements which need to gain electrons. So when sodium reacts with chlorine, sodium loses an electron and chlorine gains that electron so they both form stable ions.

We can show this in a diagram. Look at Figure 4:

The electrons of one atom are represented by dots, and the electrons of the other atom are represented by crosses.

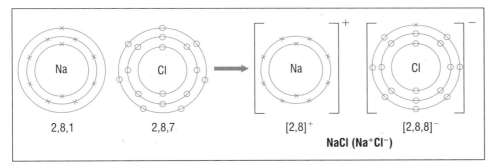

2,8,1   2,8,7 $[2,8]^+$ $[2,8,8]^-$

NaCl (Na^+Cl^-)

Figure 4 The formation of sodium chloride (NaCl) – an example of ion formation by transferring a single electron

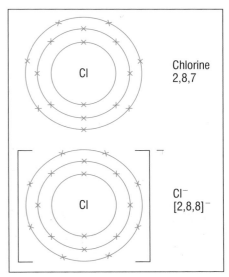

Figure 3 A negative chloride ion (Cl^-) is formed when a chlorine atom gains an electron during ion formation with another element

SUMMARY QUESTIONS

1 Copy and complete using the words below:

covalent   difficult   gaining   ionic   losing   new
noble   sharing

When two substances react together they make a …… substance and it is …… to separate them. Some atoms react by …… electrons – we call this …… bonding. Other atoms react by …… or …… electrons – this leads to …… bonding. When atoms react in this way they tend to get the electronic structure of a …… gas.

2 Draw diagrams to show the ions that would be formed when the following atoms transfer electrons. For each one, state whether electrons have been lost or gained and show the charge on the ions formed.

a) aluminium (Al)   b) fluorine (F)
c) potassium (K)   d) oxygen (O)

KEY POINTS

1 Elements react to form compounds by gaining or losing electrons or by sharing electrons.

2 The elements in Group 1 react with the elements in Group 7 because Group 1 elements can lose an electron to gain a full outer shell. This electron can be given to an atom from Group 7, which then also gains a full outer shell.

C2 1.4

Ionic bonding

You have seen how positive and negative ions form during some reactions. Ionic compounds are usually formed when metals react with non-metals.

The ions formed are held to each other by enormously strong forces of attraction between the oppositely charged ions. This electrostatic force of attraction, which acts in all directions, is called the **ionic bond**.

The ionic bonds between the charged particles results in an arrangement of ions that we call a **giant structure**. If we could stand among the ions they would seem to go on in all directions for ever.

The force exerted by an ion on the other ions in the lattice acts equally in all directions. This is why the ions in a giant structure are held together so strongly.

The giant structure of ionic compounds is very *regular*. This is because the ions all pack together neatly, like marbles in a tin or apples in a box.

a) What name do we give to the arrangement of ions in an ionic compound?
b) What holds the ions together in this structure?

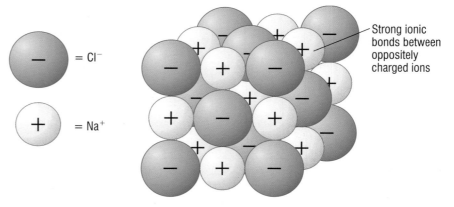

Strong ionic bonds between oppositely charged ions

$= Cl^-$

$= Na^+$

Figure 1 A giant ionic lattice (3D network) of sodium and chloride ions

Other ionic compounds

Sometimes the atoms reacting need to gain or lose two electrons to gain a stable noble gas structure. An example is when magnesium (2,8,2) reacts with oxygen (2,6). When these two elements react they form magnesium oxide (MgO). This is made up of magnesium ions with a double positive charge (Mg^{2+}) and oxide ions with a double negative charge (O^{2-}).

We can represent the atoms and ions involved in forming ions by *dot and cross diagrams*. In these diagrams we only show the electrons in the outermost shell of each atom or ion. So they are quicker to draw than the diagrams on the previous page. Look at Figure 2 on the next page:

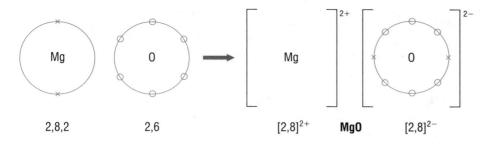

2,8,2   2,6 $[2,8]^{2+}$ **MgO** $[2,8]^{2-}$

Figure 2 When magnesium oxide (MgO) is formed the reacting atoms lose or gain two electrons

In some cases one of the atoms needs to gain or lose more electrons than the other has to lose or gain. In this case, two or more atoms of each element may react.

For example, think about calcium chloride. Each calcium atom needs to lose two electrons but each chlorine atom needs to gain only one electron. This means that two chlorine atoms react with every one calcium atom to form calcium chloride. So the formula of calcium chloride is $CaCl_2$.

DID YOU KNOW?

The structure of ionic lattices is investigated by passing X-rays through them.

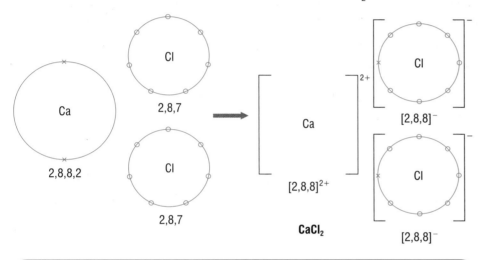

2,8,8,2   2,8,7   2,8,7 $[2,8,8]^{2+}$ **CaCl₂** $[2,8,8]^{-}$

Figure 3 The formation of calcium chloride (CaCl₂)

SUMMARY QUESTIONS

1 Copy and complete the table:

Atomic number	Atom	Electronic structure of atom	Ion	Electronic structure of ion
8	O	c)	e)	$[2,8]^{2-}$
19	a)	2,8,8,1	K^+	g)
17	Cl	d)	Cl^-	h)
20	b)	2,8,8,2	f)	i)

j) Explain why potassium chloride is KCl but potassium oxide is K_2O.

k) Explain why calcium oxide is CaO but calcium chloride is $CaCl_2$.

2 Draw dot and cross diagrams to show how you would expect the following elements to form ions together:

a) lithium and chlorine,
b) calcium and oxygen,
c) aluminium and chlorine.

KEY POINTS

1 Ionic compounds are held together by strong forces between the oppositely charged ions. This is called ionic bonding.

2 Other elements that can form ionic compounds include those in Groups 2 and 6.

C2 1.5 Covalent bonding

LEARNING OBJECTIVES

1 How are covalent bonds formed?
2 What kinds of substances do covalent bonds produce?

Figure 1 Many of the substances which make up the living world are held together by covalent bonds between non-metal atoms

Reactions between metals and non-metals usually result in ionic bonding. However many, many compounds are formed in a very different way. When non-metals react together they share electrons to form molecules. We call this **covalent bonding**.

Simple molecules

The atoms of non-metals generally need to gain electrons to achieve stable outer energy levels. When they react together neither atom can give away electrons, so they get the electronic structure of a noble gas by sharing electrons. The atoms in the molecules are then held together because they are sharing pairs of electrons. We call these strong bonds between the atoms **covalent bonds**.

a) What is the bond called when two atoms share electrons?

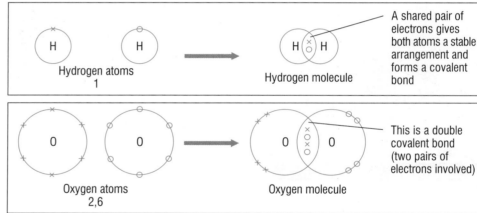

Figure 2 Atoms of hydrogen and oxygen join together to form stable molecules in which the atoms are held together by covalent bonds

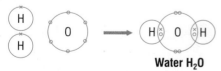

Hydrogen chloride HCl

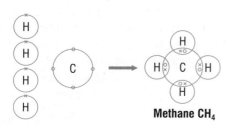

Water H₂O

Sometimes in covalent bonding each atom brings the same number of electrons to the reaction for sharing. But this is not always the case. Sometimes one element will need several electrons, while the other element only needs one more electron for a stable arrangement. In this case, more atoms become involved in the reaction.

b) How many electrons are shared in a covalent bond?

We can represent the covalent bonds in substances such as water, ammonia and methane in a number of ways. Each way of representing them means exactly the same thing – it just depends on what we want to show.

Methane CH₄

Figure 3 The principles of covalent bonding remain the same however many atoms are involved

Water
H₂O

Figure 4 We can represent a covalent compound by showing the highest energy level, the outer electrons or just the fact that there are a certain number of covalent bonds

Giant structures

Many substances containing covalent bonds consist of small molecules, for example, H_2O. However some covalently bonded substances are very different. They have giant structures where huge numbers of atoms are held together by a network of covalent bonds.

Diamonds have a giant covalent structure. In diamond, each carbon atom forms four covalent bonds with its neighbours in a rigid giant covalent lattice.

Silicon dioxide (silica) is another substance with a giant covalent structure.

c) What do we call the structure of a substance held together by a network of covalent bonds?

NEXT TIME YOU...

... see a diamond ring, think about what properties make the diamond suited to its purpose.

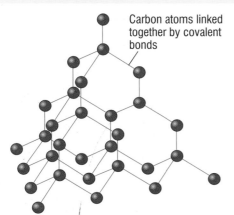

Carbon atoms linked together by covalent bonds

Figure 6 Diamonds owe their hardness and long-lasting nature to the way the carbon atoms are arranged

Figure 5 Part of the giant covalent structure of diamond

SUMMARY QUESTIONS

1 Copy and complete using the words below:

covalent   giant   molecules   shared

When non-metal atoms react together they tend to produce …… bonds. The atoms in these bonds are held together by …… electrons. Most substances held together by covalent bonds consist of ……, but a few have …… structures.

2 Draw diagrams to show the covalent bonds between the following atoms.

a) two hydrogen atoms
b) two chlorine atoms
c) a hydrogen atom and a fluorine atom

3 Draw dot and cross diagrams to show the covalent bonds when:

a) a nitrogen atom bonds with three hydrogen atoms
b) a carbon atom bonds with two oxygen atoms.

KEY POINTS

1 Covalent bonds are formed when atoms share electrons.
2 Many substances containing covalent bonds consist of molecules, but some have giant covalent structures.

C2 1.6   Bonding in metals

LEARNING OBJECTIVES

1 How are the atoms in metals arranged?
2 How are the atoms in metals held together? [Higher]

Metals are another example of giant structures. You can think of metal as a lattice of metal atoms (or positively charged ions), arranged in regular layers.

The outer electrons (in the highest occupied energy level) in each atom can easily move from one atom to the next one. The outer electrons form a 'sea' of free electrons surrounding positively charged metal ions. Strong electrostatic attraction between the negatively charged electrons and positively charged ions bond the metal ions together. The electrons act a bit like a glue!

a) Which electrons do metal atoms use to form metallic bonds?

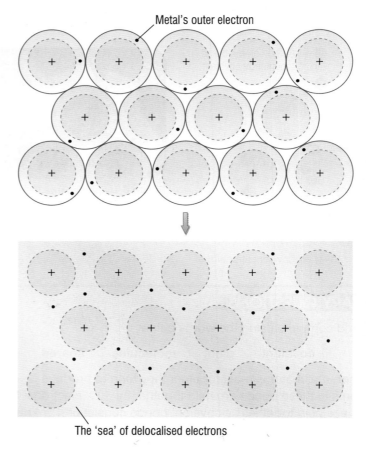

Metal's outer electron

The 'sea' of delocalised electrons

Figure 1 A metal consists of positively charged metal ions surrounded by a 'sea' of electrons

The 'sea' of free electrons are called **delocalised electrons**. These electrons help us explain the properties of metals.

b) What do you think happens to the delocalised electrons when an electric current flows through a metal?

Metal crystals

The giant structure of a metal is not usually the same all through the metal. If you look very closely at a metal surface that has been specially prepared, you can see that the metal is made up of a number of small crystals. We call these **grains**, and the places where they join are the **grain boundaries**.

c) What do we call the crystals in metals?

PRACTICAL

Growing silver crystals

You can grow crystals of silver metal by suspending a length of copper wire in silver nitrate solution. The crystals of silver will appear on the wire quite quickly, but for best results they need to be left for several hours!

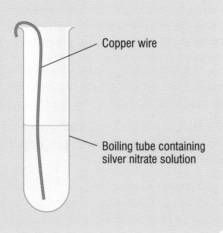

Copper wire

Boiling tube containing silver nitrate solution

Figure 2 Growing silver crystals

● Explain your observations.

Sometimes you can see metal crystals on the surface of steel that has been dipped in zinc to prevent it from rusting. We call this treatment **galvanising**. Galvanised steel is used to make channels for carrying insulated electric wires and many other containers, and is not usually painted.

d) Why do we galvanise steel?

PRACTICAL

Survey of metallic crystals

Take a look round your school to see if you can find any galvanised steel. See if you can spot the metal crystals. You can also look for crystals on brass fittings that have been left outside and not polished.

SUMMARY QUESTIONS

1 Copy and complete using the words below:

   electrons   electrostatic   free   giant   outer   positive

   Metals also have ...... structures. The atoms in these are held together by ...... from the ...... energy levels of the metal atoms. The ...... ions that this produces are held together by strong ...... forces. The electrons in metals are ...... to move throughout the structure.

2 Find out how we can change the grain size in a metal and how this affects its properties.

3 Explain why the electrons in a metal are both like glue and not like glue. [Higher]

KEY POINTS

1 The atoms (or ions) in metals are arranged in regular layers.

2 The positive ions in metals are held together by electrons from the outer shell of each metal atom. These delocalised electrons are free to move throughout the metal lattice. [Higher]

C2 1.7   The history of the atom

John Dalton's atomic theory

John Dalton – the man who gave us atoms

John Dalton was born in 1766 in the Lake District in England. His father was a weaver who taught John at home before sending him to a Quaker school in Eaglesfield, where they lived. John was amazingly clever – by the time he was 12 he was teaching other children!

He was interested in almost everything. He made observations of the weather as well as being the first person to study colour-blindness. (John was colour-blind himself – see the photo below.)

But Dalton is best-remembered for his ideas about chemistry – and in particular his theories about atoms. As a result of a great deal of work, Dalton suggested that:

- All matter is made up of indivisible particles called atoms.
- Atoms of the same element are similar in mass and shape but differ from the atoms of other elements.
- Atoms cannot be created or destroyed.
- Atoms join together to form compound atoms (what we would now call molecules) in simple ratios.

Dalton's statements were backed up with much research, even though not all of it was accurate. For example, he insisted that one hydrogen atom combined with one oxygen atom to form water. However, most of his research reflected the same results as other scientists of the time were getting.

Dalton's atomic theory explained much of what scientists were seeing, and so his idea of atoms was accepted relatively quickly. Some scientists even made wooden models of atoms of different elements, to show their different relative sizes.

By 1850, the atomic theory of matter was almost universally accepted and virtually all opposition had disappeared. Dalton's atomic theory was the basis of much of the chemistry done in the rest of the 19th and early 20th centuries.

John Dalton's eyes (on the watch-glass) were taken out after his death as he requested. He wanted a doctor to check his theory of colour blindness. Unfortunately this theory proved incorrect.

ACTIVITY

Imagine that you are John Dalton and that you have just finished writing a book about your ideas on atoms. Write a letter to someone explaining your ideas. You can choose to write to:

- another scientist,
- a member of your family,
- a journalist who is interested in your ideas and who wants to know more about them in order to write a newspaper article for the general public.

Atoms and the future

Deep underneath the Swiss countryside lies a huge maze of tunnels. Inside these tunnels, scientists are working to puzzle out the structure of the atom. They are searching for the particles that make up the protons and neutrons inside each atom.

To find these tiny particles they need to use huge machines. These accelerate particles like electrons and protons up to speeds close to the speed of light. Then the particles smash into each other in a kind of 'subatomic demolition derby'!

This is a particle detector under construction

It's really important that we know as much as we can about atoms. Although it doesn't seem like this knowledge is very useful at the moment, it could lead to important discoveries in the future. And besides, we should try to find out as much as we can about the world around us!

This shows a section of a particle accelerator

The money that's spent on this kind of research is enormous. We should spend money on APPLIED kinds of scientific research that may be able to help people, not on research that isn't any practical use.

ACTIVITY

Research like this costs a great deal of money. Who do you agree with?

Design a poster to show your ideas.

101

SUMMARY QUESTIONS

1 a) Unscramble the following words to make the names of the three different particles in an atom:

nropto   erontun   lentroce

b) Now show the charge on each of these particles by writing one of the following words next to each name – neutral, positive, negative.

2 Draw the structure of the following atoms showing all the energy levels in each atom:

a) helium (He, atomic number 2),

b) oxygen (O, atomic number 8),

c) potassium (K, atomic number 19),

d) chlorine (Cl, atomic number 17),

e) aluminium (Al, atomic number 13).

3 The diagrams show the energy levels in three atoms: (The letters are NOT the chemical symbols.)

A 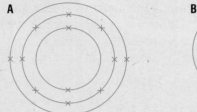   **B**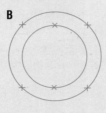

C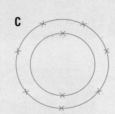

a) Which atom belongs to group 2?

b) To which group does atom C belong?

c) Atom B bonds with four atoms of hydrogen. Draw a dot and cross diagram to show the compound that is formed.

d) Draw dot and cross diagrams to show how atom A bonds with C atoms.

4 Describe, with diagrams, how the particles are held together in the following substances:

a) a molecule of bromine (Br_2),

b) a sample of diamond (carbon).

c) a salt crystal (NaCl).

5 Explain the bonding in sodium metal. You may wish to include a diagram. (The atomic number of sodium is 11.)

EXAM-STYLE QUESTIONS

1 The diagram represents an atom of an element.

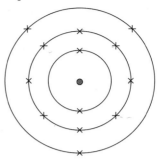

(a) Write the electronic structure of this atom as numbers and commas.   (1)

(b) How many protons are in the nucleus of this atom?   (1)

(c) Name the other particles that are in the nucleus.   (1)

(d) In which group of the periodic table is this element?   (1)

(e) Draw a similar diagram to show the ion formed by this atom in ionic compounds. Show the charge on the ion.   (2)

2 Complete the missing information (a) to (f) in the table.

Atomic number	Symbol	Electronic structure of atom	Formula of ion	Electronic structure of ion
9	F	(a)	(b)	$[2,8]^-$
11	(c)	2,8,1	Na^+	(d)
(e)	S	2,8,6	S^{2-}	(f)

(6)

3 A hydrogen atom can be represented by the diagram:

(a) Draw a similar diagram to show the electrons in the outer shell of a chlorine atom.   (1)

(b) Draw a dot and cross diagram to show the bonding in a molecule of hydrogen chloride.   (2)

(c) Explain why hydrogen and chlorine form a single covalent bond.   (2)

(d) Explain why silicon can form giant structures.   (3)

4 (a) Draw a dot and cross diagram to show the arrangement of electrons in a magnesium ion. Show the charge on the ion. (3)

(b) Draw a dot and cross diagram to show the arrangement of electrons in an oxide ion. (3)

(c) What is the formula of magnesium oxide? (1)

5 Berzelius (1779–1848) carried out experiments to discover the atomic mass of many elements. He wrote about the fact that bodies combine in definite proportions and that led him to suggest the existence of a cause.

(a) Suggest an observation that Berzelius might have made. (1)

(b) Is what Berzelius wrote a prediction or a hypothesis? Explain your answer. (1)

(c) Berzelius gave oxygen the number 100 to represent its relative atomic mass. He then set out to compare the mass of other elements with oxygen. However, he could not measure these directly because they could not be turned into gases – the temperature needed was too high and he did not have the equipment to do this.

   (i) Explain, in general terms, the problem he had. (1)

   (ii) Use this example to explain the relationship between technology and science. (1)

6 The diagram represents atoms of potassium in the solid metal.

(a) What is the electronic structure of a potassium atom? (1)

(b) Explain as fully as you can how the atoms are held together in solid potassium metal. (3)

[Higher]

HOW SCIENCE WORKS QUESTIONS

How the atomic theory was developed

2,500 years ago, Democritus believed that matter could be broken into smaller and smaller pieces until finally there would be particles that were 'indivisible' – the Greek word for this is *atomos*. He thought they looked like this:

Humphry Davy, who went to Truro Grammar School, discovered many of the elements that we are familiar with in chemistry lessons. He separated potassium, sodium and chlorine. As he couldn't break these elements down any further, he said that this must be the definition of an element.

Dalton became convinced that each element was made of a different kind of atom. He can be credited with the first scientific use of the term 'atom', although the Greeks had used the idea thousands of years before.

Dalton believed that

- the atom must be very small,
- all matter is made from atoms, and
- these atoms cannot be destroyed.

He gave hydrogen the atomic weight of 1, because he knew it to be the lightest atom.

He thought water was made of 1 hydrogen and 1 oxygen atom and therefore predicted that oxygen must have an atomic weight of 7.

Berzelius, a Swedish chemist, tested Dalton's theory experimentally. He correctly found the atomic weights of 40 elements.

a) When was the first theory of the atom put forward? (1)

b) What observation led to the definition of an element? (1)

c) What hypothesis did Dalton come up with? (1)

d) What prediction was made by Dalton? (1)

e) Check in the periodic table whether Dalton's prediction was correct. (1)

f) What was Berzelius' contribution to the atomic theory? (1)

g) Is Dalton's atomic theory completely true? Explain your answer. (1)

C2 2.1   Ionic compounds

LEARNING OBJECTIVES

1 Why do ionic compounds have high melting points?
2 Why do ionic compounds conduct electricity when we melt them or dissolve them in water?

We have already seen that an ionic compound consists of a giant structure of ions arranged in a lattice. The attractive electrostatic forces between the oppositely charged ions act in all directions and they are also very strong. This holds the ions in the lattice together very tightly.

a) What type of force holds the ions together in an ionic compound?

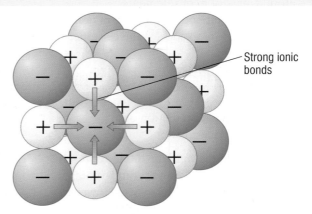

Figure 1 The attractive forces between the oppositely charged ions in an ionic compound are very strong

GET IT RIGHT!

Remember that all ionic compounds have giant structures. The oppositely charged ions in these structures are held together by strong electrostatic forces of attraction.

Because the attractive forces between the oppositely charged ions in the lattice are very strong, and there are lots of them to overcome, it takes a lot of energy to break the lattice apart. This means that ionic compounds have high melting points and boiling points. Look at the graph in Figure 2.

b) Why do ionic compounds have high melting points and boiling points?

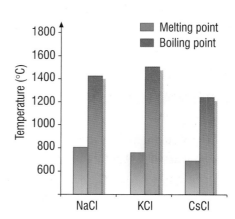

Figure 2 The strong attractive forces in a lattice of ions mean that ionic compounds have high melting points and boiling points

Once we have supplied enough energy to separate the ions from the lattice, they are free to move, and the ionic solid becomes a liquid. The ions are free to move anywhere in this liquid, so they are able to carry electrical charge through the molten liquid. A solid ionic compound cannot conduct electricity like this, because each ion is held in a fixed position in the lattice and cannot move around. They can only vibrate in their fixed positions.

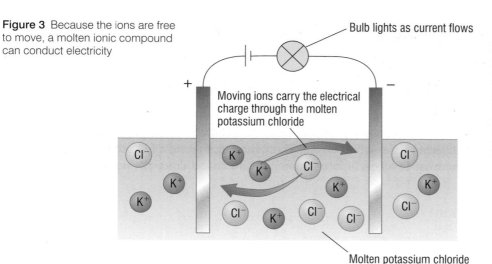

Figure 3 Because the ions are free to move, a molten ionic compound can conduct electricity

Bulb lights as current flows

Moving ions carry the electrical charge through the molten potassium chloride

Molten potassium chloride

Many ionic compounds will dissolve in water. When we dissolve an ionic compound in water the lattice is split up by the water molecules, and the ions are free to move. In the same way as molten ionic compounds will conduct electricity, solutions of ionic compounds will also conduct electricity. The ions in the solution are able to move around.

c) Why can ionic compounds conduct electricity when they are molten or dissolved in water?

Ionic solid	Molten ionic compound	Ionic compound in solution
Ions fixed in lattice – does not conduct electricity	High temperature provides energy to overcome strong attractive forces between ions. Ions free to move – will conduct electricity.	Water molecules separate ions from the lattice. Ions free to move – will conduct electricity.

PRACTICAL

Testing conductivity

Using a circuit as shown in Figure 3, dip a pair of electrodes into a 1 cm depth of sodium chloride crystals. What happens?

Now slowly add water.

● What happens?
● Explain your observations.

SUMMARY QUESTIONS

1 Copy and complete using the words below:

   attraction   conduct   high   lattice   molten   move
   oppositely   solution

   Ionic compounds have ...... melting points and boiling points because of the strong electrostatic forces of...... between ...... charged ions in the giant .... Ionic compounds will ...... electricity when ...... or in ...... because the ions are able to ...... freely.

2 Why is sea water a better conductor of electricity than water from a freshwater lake?

KEY POINTS

1 It takes a lot of energy to break the bonds which hold a giant ionic lattice together. So ionic compounds have very high melting points – they are all solids at room temperature.

2 Ionic compounds will conduct electricity when we melt them or dissolve them in water because their ions can then move freely.

C2 2.2

Simple molecules

LEARNING OBJECTIVES

1 Which type of substances have low melting points and boiling points?
2 Why are some substances gases or liquids at room temperature? [Higher]
3 Why don't these substances conduct electricity?

When the atoms of non-metal elements react to form compounds, they share electrons in their outer shells. Then each atom gets a full outer shell of electrons. The bonds formed like this are called **covalent bonds**.

Water
H_2O

Figure 1 Covalent bonds hold the atoms found within molecules tightly together

a) How are covalent bonds formed?

Substances made up of covalently bonded molecules tend to have low melting points and boiling points.

Look at the graph in Figure 2.

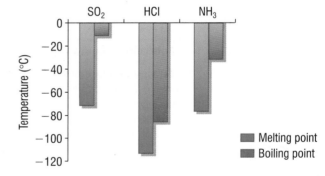

Figure 2 Substances made of simple molecules usually have low melting points and boiling points.

These low melting points and boiling points mean that many substances with simple molecules are liquids or gases at room temperature. Others are solids with quite low melting points, such as iodine and sulfur.

b) Do the compounds shown on the graph exist as solids, liquids or gases at 20°C?

c) You have a sample of ammonia (NH_3) at −120°C. Describe the changes that you would see as the temperature of the ammonia rises to 20°C (approximately room temperature).

Covalent bonds are very strong. So the atoms within each molecule are held very tightly together. However, each molecule tends to be quite separate from its neighbouring molecules. The attraction between the individual molecules in a covalent compound tends to be small. We say that there are weak *intermolecular forces* between molecules. Overcoming these forces does not take much energy.

d) How strong are the forces between the atoms in a covalent bond?
e) How strong are the forces between molecules in a covalent compound?

The covalent bonds between the hydrogen and oxygen atoms within a water molecule are strong. However, the forces of attraction between water molecules are relatively weak.

Look at the molecules in a sample of chlorine gas:

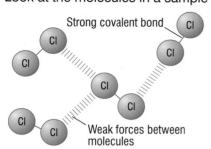

Strong covalent bond

Weak forces between molecules

Figure 3 Covalent bonds and the weak forces between molecules in chlorine gas. It is the weak intermolecular forces that are overcome when substances made of simple molecules melt or boil. The covalent bonds are **not** broken.

HIGHER

GET IT RIGHT!

Although the covalent bonds in molecules are strong, the forces between molecules are weak. [Higher]

Although a substance that is made up of simple molecules may be a liquid at room temperature, it will not conduct electricity.

Look at the demonstration below.

DEMONSTRATION

Conductivity

Figure 4 Compounds made of simple molecules do not conduct electricity

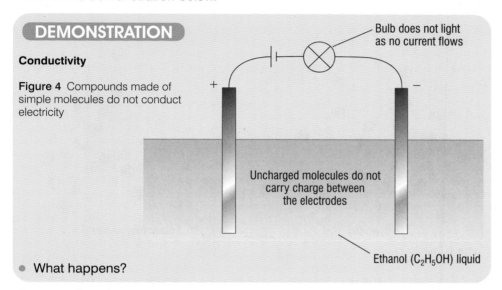

Bulb does not light as no current flows

Uncharged molecules do not carry charge between the electrodes

Ethanol (C_2H_5OH) liquid

● What happens?

Because there is no overall charge on the molecules in a compound like ethanol, the molecules cannot carry electrical charge. This makes it impossible for substances which are made up of simple molecules to conduct electricity.

f) Why don't molecular substances conduct electricity?

SUMMARY QUESTIONS

1 Copy and complete using the words below:

boiling   covalent   melting   molecules   strongly

Non-metals react to form ...... which are held together by ...... bonds. These hold the atoms together very .... The forces between molecules are relatively weak, so these substances have low ...... points and ...... points.

2 A compound called sulfur hexafluoride (SF_6) is used to stop sparks forming inside electrical switches designed to control large currents. Explain why the properties of this compound make it particularly useful in electrical switches.

3 The melting point of hydrogen chloride is $-115°C$ whereas sodium chloride melts at $801°C$. Explain why. [Higher]

KEY POINTS

1 Substances made up of simple molecules have low melting points and boiling points.

2 The forces between simple molecules are weak. These weak intermolecular forces explain their low melting points and boiling points. [Higher]

3 Simple molecules have no overall charge, so they cannot carry electrical charge. Therefore substances containing simple molecules do not conduct electricity.

C2 2.3 Giant covalent substances

While most non-metals react and form covalent bonds which join the atoms together in molecules, a few form very different structures. Instead of joining a small number of atoms together in individual molecules, the covalent bonds form large networks of covalent bonds. We call networks like this **giant covalent structures**. They are sometimes called macromolecules or giant molecular structures.

Substances such as diamond, graphite and silicon dioxide have giant covalent structures.

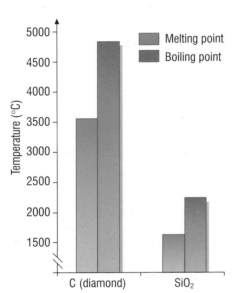

Figure 2 The large attractive forces in a giant lattice of covalently bonded atoms means that these compounds have high melting points and boiling points

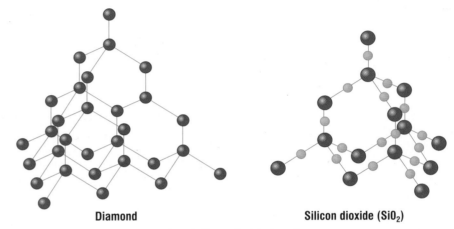

Diamond   **Silicon dioxide (SiO$_2$)**

Figure 1 The structures of diamond and silicon dioxide (sand)

All of the atoms in these giant lattices are held together by strong covalent bonds in both diamond and silicon dioxide. This gives these substances some very special properties. They are very hard, they have high melting points and boiling points and they are chemically very unreactive.

a) What do we call the structure of compounds which contain lots (millions) of atoms joined together by a network of covalent bonds?
b) What kind of physical properties do these substances have?

Figure 3 Hard, shiny and transparent – diamonds make beautiful jewellery

We don't always find carbon as diamonds – another form is graphite (well known as the 'lead' in a pencil). In graphite, carbon atoms are arranged in giant layers. There are only weak forces between the layers so they can slide over each other quite easily.

c) Why is graphite slippery?

HIGHER

Another important property of graphite comes from the fact that there are free electrons within its structure. These free electrons allow graphite to conduct electricity, which diamond – and most other covalent compounds – simply cannot do. We call the free electrons found in graphite **delocalised electrons**. They behave rather like the electrons in a metallic structure.

The carbon atoms in graphite's layers are arranged in hexagons. So each carbon atom bonds to three others. (See Figure 4.) This leaves one spare outer electron on each carbon atom. It is this electron that becomes delocalised along the layers of carbon atoms.

d) Why can graphite conduct electricity?

Fullerenes

Apart from diamond and graphite, there are other different molecules that carbon can produce. In these structures the carbon atoms join together to make large cages which can have all sorts of weird shapes. Chemists have made shapes looking like balls, onions, tubes, doughnuts, corkscrews and cones!

Chemists discovered carbon's ability to behave like this in 1985. We call the large carbon molecules containing these cage structures **fullerenes**. They are sure to become very important in nanoscience applications. (See pages 112 and 113.)

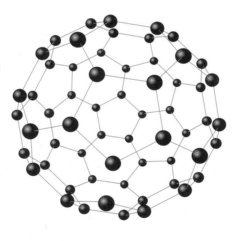

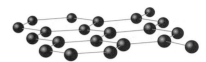

Figure 4 The giant structure of graphite. When you write with a pencil, some layers of carbon atoms slide off the 'lead' and are left on the paper.

Giant covalent structures are held together by covalent bonds throughout the structure.

Figure 5 The first fullerene to be discovered contained only 60 carbon atoms, but chemists can now make *giant fullerenes* which contain many thousands of carbon atoms. Scientists can now place other molecules inside these carbon cages. This has exciting possibilities, including the delivery of drugs to specific parts of the body.

KEY POINTS

1 Some covalently bonded substances contain giant structures.
2 These substances have high melting points and boiling points.
3 The giant structure of graphite contains layers of atoms that can slide over each other which make graphite slippery. The atoms in diamond have a different structure and cannot slide like this – so diamond is a very hard substance.
4 Graphite can conduct electricity because of the delocalised electrons along its layers. [Higher]

SUMMARY QUESTIONS

1 Copy and complete using the words below:

atoms   boiling   carbon   hard   high   layers   slide   soft

Giant covalent structures contain many …… joined by covalent bonds. They have …… melting points and …… points. Diamond is a very …… substance because the …… atoms in it are held strongly to each other. However, graphite is …… because there are …… of atoms which can …… over each other.

2 Graphite is sometimes used to reduce the friction between two surfaces that are rubbing together. How does it do this?

3 Explain in detail why graphite can conduct electricity but diamond cannot. [Higher]

C2 2.4   Giant metallic structures

LEARNING OBJECTIVES

1 Why can we bend and shape metals?
2 Why do metals conduct electricity and heat? [Higher]

We can hammer and bend metals into different shapes, and draw them out into wires. This is because the layers of atoms in a pure metal are able to slide easily over each other.

Force

Atoms are all the same size

Pure metal

Layers slide over each other easily in a pure metal

Metal cooking utensils are used all over the world, because metals are good conductors of heat. Wherever electricity is generated, metal wires carry the electricity to where it is needed. That's because metals are also good conductors of electricity.

a) Why can metals be bent and shaped when forces are applied?

The atoms in metals are held together in a giant structure by a sea of delocalised electrons. These electrons are a bit like 'glue', holding the atoms (or positively charged ions) together. (See page 98.)

However, unlike glue the electrons are able to move throughout the whole lattice. Because they can move and hold the metal ions together at the same time, the delocalised electrons enable the lattice to distort so that the metal atoms can move past one another.

b) How are metal atoms held together?

Metals conduct heat and electricity as a direct result of the ability of the delocalised electrons to flow through the giant metallic lattice.

c) Why do metals conduct electricity and heat?

HIGHER

Figure 1 Drawing copper out into wires depends on being able to make the layers of metal atoms slide easily over each other

Figure 2 Metals are essential in our lives – the delocalised electrons mean that they are good conductors of both heat and electricity

PRACTICAL

Making models of metals

Tube connected to gas tap

Fine-pointed tube

Plastic container with soap solution

A regular arrangement of bubble 'atoms'

A larger bubble 'atom' has a big effect on the arrangement around it

Areas of bubble 'atoms' meet like grain boundaries within a metal

We can make a model of the structure of a metal by blowing small bubbles on the surface of soap solution to represent atoms. Compressing or stretching the raft slightly leads to bubble 'atoms' being squashed together or pulled apart slightly. This shows how metals can return to their original shape after they have been bent slightly.

Compressing or stretching the bubble 'atoms' more leads to a permanent change in their position. This is what happens when we change the shape of a piece of metal permanently. In some areas a regular arrangement of bubble 'atoms' may be affected by a larger or smaller bubble. In others, areas of bubbles meet at different angles like the grain boundaries found in metals.

- Why are models useful in science?

SUMMARY QUESTIONS

1 Copy and complete using the words below:

delocalised   electricity   heat   shape   slide

The atoms in metals are held together by …… electrons. These also allow the atoms to …… over each other so that the metal's …… can be changed. They also allow the metal to conduct …… and …… .

[Higher]

2 Use your knowledge of metal structures to explain how adding larger metal atoms to a metallic lattice can make the metal harder.

3 How can metals be hard and easily bent at the same time?

4 Explain why metals are good conductors of heat and electricity. [Higher]

KEY POINTS

1 We can bend and shape metals because the layers of atoms (or ions) in a metal can slide over each other.

2 Delocalised electrons in metals allow them to conduct heat and electricity well. [Higher]

C2 2.5   Nanoscience and nanotechnology

The science of tiny things – what can we do?

Nanoscience – Nanoscience – Nanoscience – Nanoscience – Nanoscience – Nanoscience – Nanoscience – Nanoscience

Nanoscience

Nanoscience is a new and exciting area of science. 'Nano' is a prefix like 'milli' or 'mega'. While 'milli' means 'one-thousandth', 'nano' means 'one-thousand-millionth' – so nanoscience is the science of really tiny things.

What is nanoscience?

Our increasing understanding of science through the 20th century means that we now know that materials behave very differently at a very tiny scale. When we arrange atoms and molecules very carefully at this tiny scale, their properties can be truly remarkable.

Nanoscience at work

Glass can be coated with titanium oxide nanoparticles. Sunshine triggers a chemical reaction that breaks down dirt which then lands on the window. When it rains the water spreads evenly over the surface of the glass washing off the dirt.

Socks that are made from a fabric which contains silver nanoparticles never smell!

A type of lizard called a gecko can hang upside down from a sheet of glass. That's because the hairs on its feet are so tiny they can use the forces that hold molecules together. Scientists can make sticky tape lined with tiny nano-hairs that work in the same way.

Using nanoscience, health workers may soon be able to test a single drop of blood on a tiny piece of plastic no bigger than a ten pence piece. The tiny nanolab would replace individual tests for infectious diseases such as malaria and HIV/AIDS. On a larger scale these tests are both time-consuming and costly.

Nanoscience can do some pretty amazing things – these toy eyes are being moved using a tiny current from an electric battery

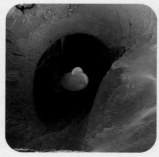

But some nanoscience is pure science fiction – tiny subs that travel through your blood to zap cancer cells with a laser; self-reproducing nanobots that escape and cover the Earth in 'grey goo' – only in airport novels!

The science of tiny things – what should we do?

STAR IN SCANDAL SHOCK
We Find Out What They Don't Want You To Know... And WE TELL YOU!

IT'S ALL GOING GREY GOO...!

Boffins working on nanorobots reckon that there's a real danger that one day they will learn to reproduce.

When that happens, if the tiny creatures escape from the lab they may devour everything in sight, covering the world in grey goo…

A leading specialist in nanotechnology has warned that any…

THE END OF THE LINE FOR DOCTORS?

R.I.P. G.Ps?!?

It could be the end of the line for your family doctor if nanotechnology carries on developing at this rate.

One day it may be possible to inject tiny robots into your blood. They'll work out what's wrong with you, send a message to a control centre outside your body and call for reinforcements to deal with what's wrong!

2010 WARRIORS

THE US Army is developing nanotech suits – thin uniforms which are flexible and tough enough to withstand bullets and blasts.

The uniforms would have GPS guidance systems and live satellite feeds of the battlefield piped directly into the soldier's brain. There is also a built-in air conditioning system to keep the body temperature normal. Inside the suit a full range of bio-sensors will send medical data back to a medical team.

Yesterday, a spokesman for the Pentag…

CUTTING EDGE ENVIRONMENTAL NEWS EVERY WEEK!

NANOTECHNOLOGY GIVES CLEAN WATER

One-sixth of the world's population has no access to clean, safe water, and two million children die each year from water-related diseases. But nanoscience may come to the rescue.

Nano-membranes are portable and easily-cleaned systems that purify, detoxify and desalinate water far better than ordinary filters. Not only that – they are cheap too!

ACTIVITY

Whenever we are faced with a possible development in science there are two possible questions – what **can** we do? and what **should** we do?

Look at the ideas on the previous page and the four headlines on this page. Ask yourself these two questions about **one** of the headlines – and present your answers to your group.

SUMMARY QUESTIONS

1 Match the sentence halves together:

a) Ionic compounds have ……	A …… conduct electricity when molten or in solution.
b) Ionic compounds ……	B …… held together by strong electrostatic forces.
c) The oppositely charged ions in an ionic compound are ……	C …… a giant lattice of ions.
d) Ionic compounds are made of ……	D …… high melting points.

2 A certain ionic compound melts at exactly 800°C. Suggest how this compound could be used in a device to activate a warning light and buzzer when the temperature in a chemical reactor rises above 800°C.

3 The table contains data about some different substances:

Substance	Melting point (°C)	Boiling point (°C)	Electrical conductor
nickel	1455	2730	good
carbon dioxide	–	−78	poor
aluminium oxide	2072	2980	solid – poor liquid – good
copper	1083	2567	good
sodium bromide	747	1390	solid – poor liquid – good
silicon dioxide	1610	2230	poor
hydrogen chloride	−115	−85	poor
graphite	3652	4827	good

a) Make a table with the following headings: Giant covalent, Giant ionic, Molecular, Giant metallic. Now write the name of each substance above in the correct column.

b) One of these substances behaves in a slightly different way than its structure suggests – why?

4 'Both graphite and metals can conduct electricity – but graphite is soft while metals are not.' Use your knowledge of the different structures of graphite and metals to explain this statement. [Higher]

EXAM-STYLE QUESTIONS

1 The table contains information about some substances. Complete the missing information (a) to (g).

Melting point (°C)	Boiling point (°C)	Electrical conductivity when solid	Electrical conductivity when molten	Solubility in water	Type of bonding	Type of structure
1660	3287	(a)	good	insoluble	metallic	giant
−101	−35	poor	(b)	soluble	covalent	(c)
712	1418	poor	good	soluble	(d)	giant
−25	144	(e)	poor	insoluble	(f)	small molecules
1410	2355	poor	poor	insoluble	covalent	(g)

(7)

2 Quartz is a very hard mineral that is used as an abrasive. It is insoluble in water. It is a form of silica, SiO_2. It can form large, attractive crystals that are transparent and can be used for jewellery. It melts at 1610°C. It does not conduct electricity when solid or when molten. It is used in the form of sand in the building and glass-making industries.

(a) Give **three** pieces of evidence from the passage that tell you that quartz has a giant structure. (3)

(b) What type of bonding is in quartz? Explain your answer. (2)

3 Copper can be used to make electrical wires, water pipes, and cooking pans.

(a) Suggest **three** reasons why copper is used to make cooking pans. (3)

(b) Which **two** properties of copper depend on the ability of delocalised electrons to flow through the metal? (2)

(c) Explain what happens to the atoms in the metal when a piece of copper is pulled into a wire. (2)
[Higher]

4 Nanotechnology promises to revolutionise our world. Nanoparticles and new devices are being rapidly developed but production is still on a very small scale. The properties of nanoparticles that make them useful can cause problems if they are made in large quantities. These include explosions because of spontaneous combustion on contact with air.

(a) What are nanoparticles? (2)

(b) Suggest **two** reasons why nanotechnology is being developed rapidly. (2)

(c) Why are nanoparticles more likely to catch fire when exposed to air compared with normal materials? (2)

5 Piezoceramics are smart materials that can be made to vibrate by passing an electric current through them. They can be made small enough to work inside mobile phones.

(a) Suggest a possible economic advantage of piezoceramics. (1)

(b) Suggest an environmental advantage of piezoceramics. (1)

Some smart materials can only be seen at higher temperatures. They can be used in the manufacture of clothing.

(c) Suggest how this feature could be useful. (1)

6 A molecule of pentane can be represented as shown:

$$H - \overset{\overset{\displaystyle H}{|}}{\underset{\underset{\displaystyle H}{|}}{C}} - \overset{\overset{\displaystyle H}{|}}{\underset{\underset{\displaystyle H}{|}}{C}} - \overset{\overset{\displaystyle H}{|}}{\underset{\underset{\displaystyle H}{|}}{C}} - \overset{\overset{\displaystyle H}{|}}{\underset{\underset{\displaystyle H}{|}}{C}} - \overset{\overset{\displaystyle H}{|}}{\underset{\underset{\displaystyle H}{|}}{C}} - H$$

(a) What do the letters C and H represent? (1)

(b) What do the lines between each C and H represent? (2)

(c) Explain why liquid pentane does not conduct electricity. (2)

(d) Pentane boils at 36°C. Explain what happens to the molecules of pentane when liquid pentane boils and becomes a gas. (2)

[Higher]

HOW SCIENCE WORKS QUESTIONS

A circuit was set up to test the conductivity of different solutions.

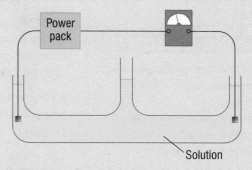

Two acids were tested to see how good they were at conducting electricity.
The results were set out in a graph:

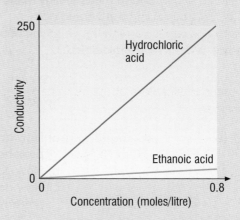

a) Describe the pattern shown by the graph for the hydrochloric acid. (1)

b) Could the relationship between the concentration of the hydrochloric acid and the conductivity be described as directly proportional? Explain your answer. (2)

c) i) What evidence is there, on the graph, that a solution of ethanoic acid does conduct electricity? (1)

ii) What evidence is there that it does not conduct electricity as well as the hydrochloric acid conducts? (1)

d) What conclusion can you make about the conductivity of acids in general? (1)

e) A range of different acids were then tested. Their conductivity was measured at 0.4 moles/dm³. How would this data be presented? (1)

f) Does this evidence prove that acids separate into positive and negative ions? Explain your answer. (1)

Mass numbers

LEARNING OBJECTIVES

1 What are the relative masses of protons, neutrons and electrons?
2 What is an atom's mass number?
3 What are isotopes?

As we saw earlier on, an atom consists of a nucleus containing positively charged protons, together with neutrons which have no charge. The negatively charged electrons are arranged in energy levels (shells) around the nucleus.

Every atom has the same number of electrons orbiting its nucleus as it has protons in its nucleus. The number of protons that an atom has is its **atomic number**.

The mass of a proton and a neutron are the same. Another way of putting this is to say that the *relative mass* of a neutron compared with a proton is 1. Electrons are far, far smaller than protons and neutrons – their mass is negligible. Because of this, the mass of an atom is concentrated in its nucleus. You can ignore the tiny mass of the electrons when it comes to thinking about the mass of an atom!

Type of sub-atomic particle	Relative mass
proton	1
neutron	1
electron	negligible (very small)

a) How does the number of electrons in an atom compare to the number of protons?
b) How does the mass of a proton compare to the mass of a neutron?
c) How does the mass of an electron compare to the mass of a neutron or proton?

Mass number

Almost all of the mass of an atom is found in the nucleus, because the mass of the electrons is so tiny. We call the total number of protons and neutrons in an atom its **mass number**.

When we want to show the atomic number and mass number of an atom we do it like this:

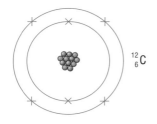

● Proton — Number of protons gives atomic number

● Neutron — Number of protons plus number of neutrons gives mass number

Figure 1 Chemists use the atomic number and the mass number of an element in many ways

$$\text{Mass number} \quad {}^{12}_{6}\text{C} \text{ (carbon)} \qquad {}^{23}_{11}\text{Na} \text{ (sodium)}$$
Atomic number

We can work out the number of neutrons in the nucleus of an atom by subtracting its atomic number from its mass number. The difference is the number of neutrons:

mass number − atomic number = number of neutrons

For the two examples here, carbon has 6 protons and a mass number of 12, so the number of neutrons is $(12 - 6) = 6$.

Sodium, on the other hand, has an atomic number of 11 but the mass number is 23, so $(23 - 11) = 12$. In this sodium atom there are 11 protons and 12 neutrons.

d) How do we calculate the number of neutrons in an atom?

Isotopes

Atoms of the same element always have the same number of protons, but they do not always have the same number of neutrons.

We give the name **isotopes** to atoms of the same element which have different numbers of neutrons.

For example, carbon has two common isotopes, $^{12}_{6}C$ (carbon-12) and $^{14}_{6}C$ (carbon-14). The carbon-12 isotope has 6 protons and 6 neutrons in the nucleus. The carbon-14 isotope has 6 protons and 8 neutrons.

Sometimes the extra neutrons in the nucleus make it unstable so that it is radioactive. However, not all isotopes are radioactive – they are simply atoms of the same substance with a different mass.

e) What are isotopes?

Different isotopes of the same element have different *physical* properties. For example, they have a different mass and they may be radioactive. However, they always have the same *chemical* properties.

For example, hydrogen has three isotopes: hydrogen, deuterium and tritium. (See Figure 2.) They each have a different mass and tritium is radioactive but they can all react with oxygen to make water.

f) Which isotope of hydrogen is heaviest?

$^{1}_{1}H$ Hydrogen

$^{2}_{1}H$ Deuterium

$^{3}_{1}H$ Tritium

Figure 2 The isotopes of hydrogen – they have similar chemical properties but different physical properties

SUMMARY QUESTIONS

1 Copy and complete using the words below:

electrons   isotopes   mass   one

The relative mass of a neutron compared to a proton is .... Compared to protons and neutrons ...... have almost no mass. The total number of protons and neutrons in an atom is called its ...... number. Atoms of an element which have different numbers of neutrons are called ....

2 State how many protons there would be in the nucleus of each of the following elements:

a) $^{7}_{3}Li$,   b) $^{15}_{7}N$,   c) $^{22}_{10}Ne$,   d) $^{33}_{16}S$,   e) $^{79}_{35}Br$.

3 State how many neutrons each atom in question 2 has.

4 a) How do the physical properties of isotopes of the same element vary?
  b) Why do isotopes of the same element have identical chemical properties?

KEY POINTS

1 The relative mass of protons and neutrons is 1.
2 The mass number of an atom tells you the total number of protons and neutrons in its nucleus.
3 Isotopes are atoms of the same element with different numbers of neutrons.

C2 3.2   Masses of atoms and moles

LEARNING OBJECTIVES

1 How can we compare the mass of atoms? [Higher]
2 How can we calculate the mass of compounds from the elements they are made from?

Chemical equations show you how many atoms of the reactants we need to make the products. But when we actually carry out a chemical reaction we need to know what amounts to use in grams or cm^3. You might think that a chemical equation would also tell you this.

For example, does the equation:

$$Mg + 2HCl \rightarrow MgCl_2 + H_2$$

mean that we need twice as many grams of hydrochloric acid as magnesium to make magnesium chloride?

Unfortunately it isn't that simple. The equation tells us that we need twice as many hydrogen and chlorine atoms as magnesium atoms – but this doesn't mean that the mass of hydrochloric acid will be twice the mass of magnesium. This is because atoms of different elements have different masses.

To turn equations into something that we can actually use in the lab or factory we need to know a bit more about the mass of atoms.

a) Why don't chemical equations tell us how much of each reactant to use in a chemical reaction?

Relative atomic masses

The mass of a single atom is so tiny that it would be impossible to use it in calculations. To make the whole thing manageable we use a much simpler way of thinking about the masses of atoms. Instead of working with the **real** masses of atoms we just focus on the **relative** masses of atoms of different elements. We call these **relative atomic masses (A_r)**.

We use an atom of carbon ($^{12}_6C$) as a standard atom. We give this a 'mass' of 12 units, because it has 6 protons and 6 neutrons. We then compare all of the masses of the atoms of all the other elements to this standard carbon atom.

The mass of an atom found by comparing it with the $^{12}_6C$ atom is called its relative atomic mass (A_r).

The relative atomic mass of an element is usually the same as, or very similar to, the mass number of that element. The A_r takes into account any isotopes of the element. The relative atomic mass is the average mass of the isotopes of the element in the proportions in which they are usually found (compared with the standard carbon atom).

When atoms change into ions they either lose or gain electrons. However, for all practical purposes the mass of electrons isn't worth bothering about. So the 'relative ionic mass' of an ion is exactly the same as the relative atomic mass of that element.

b) What do we call the mass of an atom compared with the mass of an atom of carbon-12?

Figure 1 The A_r of carbon is 12. Compared with this, the A_r of helium is 4 and the A_r of magnesium is 24

Relative atomic mass	Relative ionic mass
Na 23	Na$^+$ 23
O 16	O^{2-} 16
Mg 24	Mg^{2+} 24

Relative formula masses

We can use the A_r of the various elements to work out the **relative formula mass (M_r)** of chemical compounds. This is true whether the compounds are made up of molecules or collections of ions. A simple example is a substance like sodium chloride. We know that the A_r of sodium is 23 and the A_r of chlorine is 35.5. So the relative formula mass of sodium chloride (NaCl) is:

$$23 + 35.5 = 58.5$$
$$A_r \text{ Na} \quad A_r \text{ Cl} \quad M_r \text{ NaCl}$$

Another example is water. Water is made up of hydrogen and oxygen. The A_r of hydrogen is 1, and the A_r of oxygen is 16. Water has the formula H_2O, containing two hydrogen atoms for every one oxygen, so the M_r is:

$$(1 \times 2) + 16 = 18$$
$$A_r \text{ H} \times 2 \quad A_r \text{ O} \quad M_r \text{ H}_2\text{O}$$

c) What is the relative formula mass of hydrogen sulfide, H_2S?
   (A_r values: H = 1, S = 32)

Moles

Saying or writing 'relative atomic mass in grams' or 'relative formula mass in grams' is rather clumsy. So chemists have a shorthand word for it – **mole**.

They say that the relative atomic mass in grams of carbon (i.e. 12 g of carbon) is a mole of carbon atoms. One mole is simply the relative atomic mass or relative formula mass of any substance expressed in grams. A mole of any substance always contains the same number of particles.

Figure 2 We know how many actual atoms or molecules a mole contains, thanks to an Italian count born in the 18th century, Amedeo Avogadro. He worked out that a mole of any element or compound contains 6.02×10^{23} atoms, ions or molecules. That's 602 000 000 000 000 000 000 000! This is called **Avogadro's number**.

We can use the same approach with relatively complicated molecules like sulfuric acid, H_2SO_4. Hydrogen has a A_r of 1, the A_r of sulfur is 32 and the A_r of oxygen 16. This means that the M_r of sulfuric acid is:

$$(1 \times 2) + 32 + (16 \times 4) =$$
$$2 + 32 + 64 = 98$$

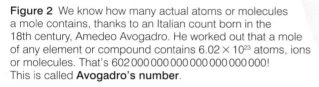

GET IT RIGHT!

You don't have to remember Avogadro's number! But practise calculating the mass of one mole of different substances from relative atomic masses that you are given.

SUMMARY QUESTIONS

1 Copy and complete using the words below:

   atomic   carbon-12   elements   formula   number

   We measure the masses of atoms by comparing them to the mass of one atom of .... The relative ...... mass of an element is usually almost the same as its mass .... We calculate the relative ...... mass of a compound from the relative atomic masses of the ...... in it.

2 The equation for the reaction of magnesium and fluorine is:

   $$Mg + F_2 \rightarrow MgF_2$$

   a) How many moles of fluorine molecules react with one mole of magnesium atoms?
   b) What is the relative formula mass of MgF_2? (A_r values: Mg = 24, F = 19)

3 The relative atomic mass of oxygen is 16, and that of magnesium is 24. How many times heavier is a magnesium atom than an oxygen atom?

KEY POINTS

1 We compare the masses of atoms by measuring them relative to atoms of carbon-12. [Higher]
2 We work out the relative formula mass of a compound from the relative atomic masses of the elements in it.
3 One mole of any substance always contains the same number of particles.

C2 3.3   Percentages and formulae

Figure 1 A tiny difference in the amount of iron in the ore might not seem very much, but when millions of tonnes of iron ore are extracted and processed each year, it all adds up!

To calculate the percentage of an element in a compound:

- Write down the formula of the compound.
- Using the relative atomic masses from your data sheet work out the relative formula mass of the compound. Write down the mass of each element making up the compound as you work it out.
- Write the mass of the element you are investigating as a fraction of the total M_r.
- Find the percentage by multiplying your fraction by 100.

We can use the formula mass of a compound to calculate the percentage mass of each element in it. Calculations like this are not just done in GCSE chemistry books! In life outside the school laboratory, geologists and mining companies base their decisions about whether to exploit mineral finds on calculations like these.

Working out the amount of an element in a compound

We can use the relative atomic mass (A_r) of elements and the relative formula mass (M_r) of compounds to help us work out the percentage of an element in a compound.

Worked example (1)

What percentage mass of white magnesium oxide is actually magnesium, and how much is oxygen?

Solution

The first thing we need is the formula of magnesium oxide, MgO.
The A_r of magnesium is 24, while the A_r of oxygen is 16.

Adding these together gives us a M_r of 40 i.e. $(24 + 16)$.

So from 40 g of magnesium oxide, 24 g is actually magnesium:

$$\frac{\text{mass of magnesium}}{\text{total mass of compound}} = \frac{24}{40}$$

so the percentage of magnesium in the compound is:

$$\frac{24}{40} \times 100\% = 60\%$$

Worked example (2)

A white powder is found at the scene of a crime. It could be strychnine, a deadly poison with the formula $C_{21}H_{22}N_2O_2$ – but is it?!

When a chemist analyses the powder, 83% of its mass is carbon. What is the percentage mass of carbon in strychnine, and is this the same?

Solution

The formula mass (M_r) of strychnine is:

$$(12 \times 21) + (1 \times 22) + (14 \times 2) + (16 \times 2) = 252 + 22 + 28 + 32 = 334$$

The percentage mass of carbon in strychnine is therefore:

$$\frac{252}{334} \times 100 = 75.4\%$$

This is **not** the same as the percentage mass of carbon in the white powder – so the white powder is not strychnine.

a) What is the percentage mass of hydrogen in methane, CH_4?
   (A_r values: C = 12, H = 1)

Working out the formula of a compound from its percentage composition

We can also do this backwards! If we know the percentage composition of a compound we can work out the ratio of the numbers of atoms in the compound. We call this its **empirical formula**. It tells us the simplest whole number ratio of elements in a compound.

This is sometimes the same as the actual number of atoms in one molecule (which we call the **molecular formula**) – but not always. For example, the empirical formula of water is H_2O, which is also its molecular formula. However, hydrogen peroxide has the empirical formula HO, but its molecular formula is H_2O_2.

Figure 2 Chemical analysis of substances found at the scene of a crime may help to bring a murderer to justice – or free an innocent suspect

Worked example

If 9 g of aluminium react with 35.5 g of chlorine, what is the empirical formula of the compound formed?

Solution

We can work out the ratio of the number of atoms by dividing the mass of each element by its relative atomic mass:

$$\text{For aluminium: } \frac{9}{27}\,\text{g} = \tfrac{1}{3} \text{ mole of aluminium atoms}$$

$$\text{For chlorine: } \frac{35.5}{35.5}\,\text{g} = 1 \text{ mole of chlorine atoms}$$

So this tells us that one mole of chlorine atoms combines with $\tfrac{1}{3}$ mole of aluminium atoms.

This means that the simplest whole number ratio is 3 (Cl) : 1 (Al). In other words 1 aluminium atom combines with 3 chlorine atoms. So the empirical formula is $AlCl_3$.

b) A compound contains 16 g of sulfur and 24 g of oxygen. What is its empirical formula? (A_r values: S = 32, O = 16)

Given the percentage composition and asked to find the empirical formula, just assume you have 100 g of the compound. Then do a calculation as shown above to find the simplest ratio of elements.

GET IT RIGHT!

Make sure that you can do these calculations from formula to percentage mass and the other way round.

How to work out the formula from reacting masses:

- Begin with the number of grams of the elements that combine.
- Change the number of grams to the moles of atoms by dividing the number of grams by the A_r. This tells you how many moles of the different elements combine.
- Use this to tell you the simplest ratio of atoms of the different elements combined in the compound.
- This gives you the empirical formula of the compound.

SUMMARY QUESTIONS

1 Copy and complete using the words below:

> **compound   dividing   hundred   relative formula mass**

The percentage of an element in a …… is calculated by …… the mass of the element in the compound by the …… …… …… of the compound and then multiplying the result by one …… .

2 Ammonium nitrate (NH_4NO_3) is used as a fertiliser. What is the percentage mass of nitrogen in it? (A_r values: H = 1, N = 14, O = 16)

3 22.55% of the mass of a sample of phosphorus chloride is phosphorus. What is the formula of phosphorus chloride? (A_r values: P = 31, Cl = 35.5)
[Higher]

KEY POINT

1 The relative atomic masses of the elements in a compound can be used to work out its percentage composition.
2 We can calculate empirical formulae given the masses or percentage composition of elements present. [Higher]

C2 3.4   Equations and calculations

HIGHER

LEARNING OBJECTIVES

1 What do chemical equations tell us about chemical reactions?
2 How do we use equations to calculate masses of reactants and products?

Chemical equations can be very useful when we want to know how much of each substance is involved in a chemical reaction. But to do this, we must be sure that the equation is balanced.

To see how we do this, think about what happens when hydrogen molecules (H_2) react with oxygen molecules (O_2), making water molecules (H_2O):

$$H_2 + O_2 \rightarrow H_2O \text{ (not balanced)}$$

This equation shows the reactants and the product – but it is not balanced. There are 2 oxygen atoms on the left-hand side and only 1 oxygen atom on the right-hand side. To balance the equation there need to be 2 water molecules on the right-hand side:

$$H_2 + O_2 \rightarrow 2H_2O \text{ (still not balanced)}$$

This balances the number of oxygen atoms on each side of the equation – but now there are 4 hydrogen atoms on the right-hand side and only 2 on the left-hand side. So there need to be 2 hydrogen molecules on the left-hand side:

$$2H_2 + O_2 \rightarrow 2H_2O \text{ (balanced!)}$$

This balanced equation tells us that '2 hydrogen molecules react with one oxygen molecule to make 2 water molecules'. But remember that 1 mole of any substance always contains the same number of particles. So our balanced equation also tells us that '2 moles of hydrogen molecules react with one mole of oxygen molecules to make two moles of water molecules'.

a) What must we do to a chemical equation before we use it to work out how much of each chemical is needed or made?
b) '$2H_2$' has two meanings – what are they?

2 hydrogen molecules	1 oxygen molecule	2 water molecules
$2H_2$	$+$ O_2 $\longrightarrow$	$2H_2O$
2 moles of hydrogen molecules	1 mole of oxygen molecules	2 moles of water molecules

This is really useful, because we can use it to work out what mass of hydrogen and oxygen we need, and how much water is made.

To do this, we need to know that the A_r for hydrogen is 1 and the A_r for oxygen is 16:

A_r of hydrogen = 1 ...... so mass of 1 mole of H_2 = $2 \times 1 = 2\,g$
A_r of oxygen = 16 ...... so mass of 1 mole of O_2 = $2 \times 16 = 32\,g$
M_r of water = $(16 + 2) = 18$ ...... so mass of 1 mole of water = $18\,g$

Our balanced equation tells us that 2 moles of hydrogen react with one mole of oxygen to give 2 moles of water. So turning this into masses we get:

2 moles of hydrogen = $2 \times 2\,g = 4\,g$
1 mole of oxygen   = $1 \times 32\,g = 32\,g$
2 moles of water   = $2 \times 18\,g = 36\,g$

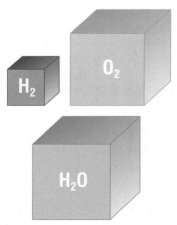

Figure 1 When 4 g of hydrogen react with 32 g of oxygen we get 36 g of water

Calculations

These kind of calculations are important when we want to know how much of two chemicals to react together. For example, a chemical called sodium hydroxide reacts with chlorine gas to make bleach.

Here is the equation for the reaction:

$$2\,NaOH + Cl_2 \rightarrow NaOCl + NaCl + H_2O$$

sodium   chlorine   bleach   salt   water
hydroxide

This reaction happens when chlorine gas is bubbled through a solution of sodium hydroxide dissolved in water.

If we have a solution containing 100 g of sodium hydroxide, how much chlorine gas should we pass through the solution to make bleach? Too much, and some chlorine will be wasted, too little and not all of the sodium hydroxide will react.

	So mass of 1 mole of	
	NaOH	**Cl_2**
A_r of hydrogen = 1		
A_r of oxygen = 16		
A_r of sodium = 23	= 23 + 16 + 1 = 40	= 35.5 × 2 = 71
A_r of chlorine = 35.5		

The table shows that 1 mole of sodium hydroxide has a mass of 40 g.

So 100 g of sodium hydroxide is $\dfrac{100}{40}$ = 2.5 moles.

The chemical equation for the reaction tells us that for every two moles of sodium hydroxide we need one mole of chlorine.

So we need $\dfrac{2.5}{2}$ = 1.25 moles of chlorine.

The table shows that 1 mole of chlorine has a mass of 71 g.

So we will need 1.25 × 71 = **88.75 g** of chlorine to react with 100 g of sodium hydroxide.

Figure 2 Bleach is used in some swimming pools to control and kill harmful bacteria. Getting the quantities right involves some careful calculation!

SUMMARY QUESTIONS

1 Copy and complete using the words below:

balanced   equations   mole   mass   product

Chemical ...... can tell us about the amount of substances in a reaction if they are .... To work out the mass of each substance in a reaction we need to know the mass of 1 ...... of it. We can then work out the ...... of each reactant needed, and the mass of ...... that will be produced.

2 Hydrogen peroxide, H_2O_2, decomposes to form water and oxygen gas. Write a balanced equation for this reaction.

3 Calcium reacts with oxygen like this:

$$2\,Ca + O_2 \rightarrow 2\,CaO$$

What mass of oxygen will react exactly with 60 g of calcium?
(A_r values: O = 16, Ca = 40)

KEY POINTS

1 Chemical equations tell us the number of moles of substances in the chemical reaction.

2 We can use chemical equations to calculate the masses of reactants and products in a chemical reaction from the masses of one mole of each of the substances involved in the reaction.

C2 3.5   Making as much as we want

LEARNING OBJECTIVES

1 What do we mean by the yield of a chemical reaction and what factors affect it?

2 How do we calculate the yield of a chemical reaction? [Higher]

3 What is atom economy and why is it important?

4 How do we calculate atom economy? [Higher]

Many of the substances that we use every day have to be made from other chemicals, using complex chemical reactions. Food colourings, flavourings and preservatives, the ink in your pen or computer printer, the artificial fibres in your clothes – all of these are made using chemical reactions.

One simple kind of reaction for making a new substance is when we make a new chemical from two others, like this:

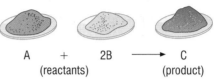

$$A \quad + \quad 2B \quad \longrightarrow \quad C$$
$$\text{(reactants)} \qquad\qquad \text{(product)}$$

If we need 1000 kg of C it seems quite simple for us to work out how much A and B we need to make it. As we saw earlier in this chapter, all we need to know is the relative formula masses of A, B and C.

a) How many moles of B are needed to react with each mole of A in this reaction?

b) How many moles of C will this make?

If we carry out our reaction, it is very unlikely that we will get as much of C as we think. This is because our calculations assumed that *all* of A and B would be turned into C. We call the amount of product that a chemical reaction produces its **yield**.

Calculating percentage yield

Rather than talking about the yield of a chemical reaction in grams, kilograms or tonnes it is much more useful to talk about its **percentage yield**. This compares the amount of product that the reaction *really* produces with the maximum amount that it could *possibly* produce:

$$\text{percentage yield} = \frac{\text{amount of product produced}}{\text{maximum amount of product possible}} \times 100\%$$

Worked example

Using known masses of A and B, it was calculated that the chemical reaction above could produce 2.5 g of product, C. When the reaction is carried out, only 1.5 g of C is produced.

What is the percentage yield of this reaction?

Solution

$$\text{Percentage yield} = \frac{\text{amount of product produced}}{\text{maximum amount of product possible}} \times 100\%$$

$$= \frac{1.5}{2.5} \times 100\%$$

$$= 60\%$$

The percentage yield is **60%**.

---

c) How is percentage yield calculated?

Very few chemical reactions have a yield of 100% because:

- The reaction may be reversible (so as products form they react to form the reactants again).
- Some reactants may react to give unexpected products.
- Some of the product may be left behind in the apparatus.
- The reactants may not be completely pure.
- Some chemical reactions produce more than one product, and it may be difficult to separate the product that we want from the reaction mixture.

Atom economy

Chemical companies use chemical reactions to make products which they sell. So it is very important to use chemical reactions that produce as much product as possible. In other words, it is better for them to use chemical reactions with high yields.

Making as much product as possible means making less waste. It means that as much product as possible is being made from the reactants. This is good news for the company's finances, and good news for the environment too.

The amount of the starting materials that end up as useful products is called the **atom economy**. So the aim is to achieve maximum atom economy.

We can calculate percentage atom economy using this equation:

$$\text{percentage atom economy} = \frac{\text{relative formula mass of useful product}}{} \times 100$$

Worked example

Ethanol (C_2H_5OH) can be converted into ethene (C_2H_4) which can be used to make poly(ethene).

Solution

$$C_2H_5OH \longrightarrow C_2H_4 \quad + \quad H_2O$$

M_r values: $\quad (12 \times 2) + (1 \times 4) \quad (1 \times 2) + (16 \times 1)$
$$= 28 \qquad\qquad = 18$$

$$\text{percentage atom economy} = \frac{28}{(28 + 18)} \times 100 = 61\%$$

To conserve the Earth's resources, as well as reduce pollution and waste, industry tries to maximise both atom economy and percentage yield.

HIGHER

Figure 1 When you make and sell large quantities of chemicals, it's important to know the yield of the reactions you are using

KEY POINTS

1 The yield of a chemical reaction describes how much product is made.
2 The percentage yield of a chemical reaction tells us how much product is made compared with the maximum amount that could be made (100%). [Higher]
3 Factors affecting the yield of a chemical reaction include product being left behind in the apparatus and difficulty separating the products from the reaction mixture.
4 It is important to maximise atom economy to conserve resources and reduce pollution.

SUMMARY QUESTIONS

1 Copy and complete using the words below:

   high   maximum   percentage   product   waste   yield

   The amount of …… made in a chemical reaction is called its …… . The …… yield tells us the amount of product that is made compared to the …… amount that could be made. Reactions with …… yields are important because they make less …… .

2 A reaction produces a product which has a relative formula mass of 80. The total of the relative formula masses of all the products is 120. What is the percentage atom economy of this reaction? [Higher]

3 A reaction that could produce 200 g of product produces only 140 g. What is its percentage yield? [Higher]

4 If the percentage yield for a reaction is 100%, 60 g of reactant A would make 80 g of product C. How much of reactant A is needed to make 80 g of product C if the percentage yield of the reaction is only 75%? [Higher]

C2 3.6 Reversible reactions

LEARNING OBJECTIVES

1 What is a reversible reaction?
2 How can we change the amount of product in a reversible reaction? [Higher]

In all of the chemical reactions that we have looked at so far the reactants have reacted together to form products. We show this by using an arrow pointing *from* the reactants *to* the products, like this:

$$A + B \rightarrow C + D$$

But in some chemical reactions the products can react together to produce the original reactants again. We call this a **reversible reaction**.

Because a reversible reaction can go in both directions we use two arrows in the equation, one going in the forwards direction and one backwards instead of the usual single arrow:

$$A + B \rightleftharpoons C + D \quad (\rightleftharpoons \text{ is equilibrium sign})$$

a) What does a single arrow in a chemical equation mean?
b) What does a double arrow in a chemical equation mean?

HIGHER

So what happens when we start with just reactants in a reversible reaction?

1) A+B ⟶ (Reactants only at start of reaction)

2) A+B ⇄ C+D (Rate of ⟶ much greater than ⟵ at first)

3) A+B ⇄ C+D (Rate of ⟵ increases as C+D build up. Rate of ⟶ slows down as reactants get used up)

4) A+B ⇄ C+D (Eventually the rates of ⟶ and ⟵ are the same)

In a system that is **closed**, no reactants or products can get in or out. In a closed system, as more and more products are made in a reversible reaction the rate at which these get converted back into reactants increases. As the rate of the backward (reverse) reaction increases, the rate of the forward reaction decreases until both reactions are going at the same rate.

When this happens the reactants are making products at the same rate as the products are making reactants again – so overall there is no change in the amount of products and reactants. We say that the reaction is at the point of **equilibrium**. At equilibrium the rate of the forward reaction equals the rate of the reverse reaction.

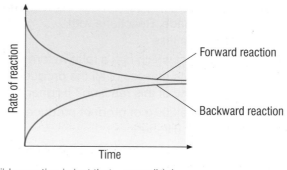

Figure 1 A reversible reaction is just that – reversible!

c) How does the rate of the backward reaction compare to the rate of the forward reaction at equilibrium?

One example of a reversible reaction is the reaction between iodine monochloride (ICl) and chlorine gas. Iodine monochloride is a brown liquid, while chlorine is a green gas. We can react these substances together to make yellow crystals of iodine trichloride (ICl₃).

When there is plenty of chlorine gas the forward reaction makes iodine trichloride crystals which are quite stable. But if we lower the concentration of chlorine gas the backward (reverse) reaction turns iodine trichloride back to iodine monochloride and chlorine.

Figure 2 The situation at equilibrium is just like running up an escalator which is going down – if you run *up* as fast as the escalator goes *down*, you will get *nowhere*!

> **DID YOU KNOW?**
>
> Many of the chemical reactions that take place in your body are reversible. The rate of the reaction in each direction is controlled by special chemicals called **enzymes**.

With plenty of chlorine gas

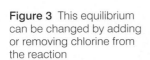

Iodine monochloride		Chlorine		Iodine trichloride
ICl	$+$	Cl_2	$\rightleftharpoons$	ICl_3

Figure 3 This equilibrium can be changed by adding or removing chlorine from the reaction

Remove chlorine gas

We can change the relative proportions of the reactants and products in a reaction mixture by changing the reaction conditions. This is very important, because if we want to collect the products of a reaction we need as much product as possible in the reacting mixture.

SUMMARY QUESTIONS

1 Copy and complete using the words below:

   **amount   conditions   equilibrium   forward   products
   rate   reactants   reverse   reversible**

   In some chemical reactions the …… can react to form the reactants again. We call this a …… reaction. At …… in a closed system, the …… of the …… reaction is the same as the rate of the …… reaction. If we change the reaction ……, this can affect the …… of the …… and products in the mixture.   [Higher]

2 What does the ⇌ sign mean in a chemical equation?

3 In general how can we change the amount of product made in an equilibrium reaction? [Higher]

KEY POINTS

1 In a reversible reaction the products of the reaction can react to make the original reactants.

2 In a closed system the rate of the forward and backward (reverse) reactions are equal at equilibrium. [Higher]

3 Changing the reaction conditions can change the amounts of products and reactants in a reaction mixture. [Higher]

C2 3.7

Making ammonia – the Haber process

LEARNING OBJECTIVES

1 Why is ammonia important?
2 How do we make ammonia?
3 How can we make ammonia without wasting raw materials?

We need plants – for food, and as a way of providing the oxygen that we breathe. Plants need nitrogen to grow, and although this gas makes up about 80% of the air around us, plants cannot use it because it is very unreactive.

Instead, plants absorb soluble nitrates from the soil through their roots. When we harvest plants these nitrates are lost – so we need to replace them. Nowadays we usually do this by adding nitrate fertilisers to the soil. We make these fertilisers using a process invented nearly 100 years ago by a young German chemist called Fritz Haber.

a) Why can't plants use the nitrogen from the air?
b) Where do plants get their nitrogen from?

Figure 1 Plants are surrounded by nitrogen in the air. They cannot use this nitrogen, and rely on soluble nitrates in the soil instead. We supply these by spreading fertiliser on the soil.

The Haber process

The Haber process provides us with a way of turning the nitrogen in the air into ammonia. We can use ammonia in many different ways. One of the most important of these is to make fertilisers.

The raw materials for making ammonia are:

● nitrogen from the air, and
● hydrogen which we get from natural gas (containing mainly methane, CH_4).

The nitrogen and hydrogen are purified and then passed over an iron catalyst at high temperatures (about 450°C) and pressures (about 200 atmospheres). The product of this chemical reaction is ammonia.

c) What are the two raw materials needed to make ammonia?

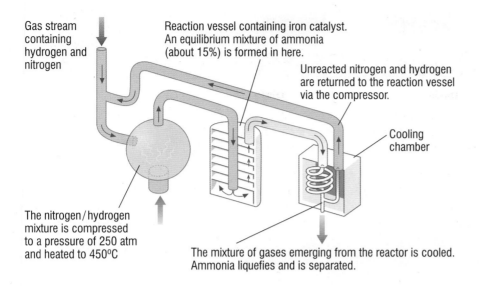

Figure 2 The Haber process

The reaction used in the Haber process is reversible, which means that the ammonia breaks down again into hydrogen and nitrogen. To reduce this, we have to remove the ammonia by cooling and liquefying it as soon as it is formed. We can then recycle any hydrogen and nitrogen that is left so that it has a chance to react again.

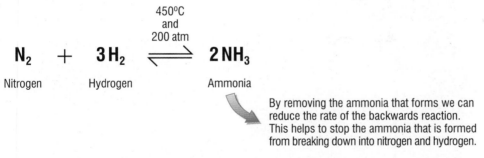

We carry out the Haber process in conditions that have been carefully chosen to give a reasonable yield of ammonia as quickly as possible. (See pages 152–3.)

d) How is ammonia removed from the reaction mixture?
e) How do we make sure the reactants are not wasted?

SUMMARY QUESTIONS

1 Copy and complete using the words below:

**air   fertilisers   gas   450   hydrogen   iron   liquefying
nitrogen   removed   200**

Ammonia is an important chemical used for making .... The raw materials are ...... from the ...... and ...... from natural .... These are reacted at about ...... °C and ...... atmospheres pressure using an ...... catalyst. Ammonia is ...... from the reaction mixture before it can break down into the reactants again by ...... the gas.

2 Draw a flow diagram to show how the Haber process is used to make ammonia.

KEY POINTS

1 Ammonia is an important chemical for making other chemicals, including fertilisers.
2 Ammonia is made from nitrogen and hydrogen in the Haber process.
3 We carry out the Haber process under conditions which are chosen to give a reasonable yield of ammonia as quickly as possible.
4 Any unused nitrogen and hydrogen are recycled in the Haber process.

C2 3.8   Aspects of the Haber process

Using reversible reactions – 'green' chemistry

- Using relative atomic masses we can work out the relative formula mass of compounds so that we know the mass of 1 mole

- Balanced chemical equations show us the number of moles of reactants and products in reactions

- We can make more products from a reversible reaction by removing them as they are formed

- The yield of a chemical reaction tells us how much product a reaction will REALLY give us compared with what it could POSSIBLY give us

- We use chemical equations to work out what mass of each reactant we need to make as much product as we want

- Some chemical reactions go both ways – they are REVERSIBLE

- Processes with a high percentage atom economy are more profitable and are better for sustainable development

- By carefully choosing chemical reactions and the conditions, we can make as much product from a chemical reaction as possible – with as little waste as possible

ACTIVITY

Look at the ideas on this page. Use them to design a poster about 'Crafty Chemists', showing how chemistry helps us to use chemical reactions which make as much of what we want as efficiently as possible.

Fritz Haber – a good life or a bad one?

Der Newswen

Donnerstag 14. Oktober 1920

Fritz Haber - German Patriot

Early on in the First World War both sides became bogged down in trench warfare. Fritz Haber focused on what he could do to bring about German victory. He thought that poison gas would penetrate the strongest defences, allowing Germany to win the war.

Poison gases were already available as unwanted by-products of chemical processes. Haber experimented with these gases to find those suitable to use on the battlefield. He focused on chlorine gas.

The Germans used chlorine for the first time on 22nd April 1915, against French and Algerian troops in Belgium. They released 200 tonnes of gas which rolled into the allied lines. The allied soldiers choked

in agony, and slowly died. The gas cloud tinted everything a sickly green. Those who could escape the cloud fled in panic.

The soldier Wilfrid Owen wrote:

GAS! Gas! Quick, boys! – An ecstasy of fumbling,
Fitting the clumsy helmets just in time;
But someone still was yelling out and stumbling
And floundering like a man in fire or lime.
Dim, through the misty panes and thick green light
As under a green sea, I saw him drowning.
In all my dreams, before my helpless sight,
He plunges at me, guttering, choking, drowning.

19th November 1920 1d   Palestine becomes British mandate - page 4

Tragedy of Clara Haber

Clara Haber had graduated as the first woman from the University of Breslau in Germany in 1900. At this time many professors were still against female students. She married Fritz Haber in 1901. Clara could not continue her research work because she was a woman. Instead, she contributed to her husband's work, although her support was never mentioned. Because of her support Haber was promoted very quickly.

Clara was deeply opposed to warfare, and especially to the use of science in war. She called Haber's work a 'perversion of science'. Unable to stop him, Clara committed suicide in May 1915. Her death was never annouced in the newspapers.

League of Nations holds first meeting in Geneva, Switzerland

ACTIVITY

A new laboratory has been set up to develop a new chemical to be used as a weapon.

Either: As a brilliant young chemist you have been invited to go and work in this laboratory. Write a letter or e-mail to a friend explaining why you are planning to accept this invitation.

Or: A friend has been invited to go and work in this laboratory. Write a letter or e-mail to this friend explaining why you think they should not go and work in this laboratory.

SUMMARY QUESTIONS

1 Match up the parts of the sentences:

a) Neutrons have a relative mass of ……	A …… negligible mass compared to protons and neutrons.
b) Electrons have ……	B …… 1 compared to protons.
c) Protons have a relative mass of ……	C …… found in its nucleus.
d) Nearly all of an atom's mass is ……	D …… 1 compared to neutrons.

2 Calculate the mass of 1 mole of each of the following compounds:

a) CO_2

b) B_2H_6

c) $CaCO_3$

d) K_2O

e) $KMnO_7$

(A_r values: C = 12, O = 16, B = 11, H = 1, Ca = 40, K = 39, Mn = 55)

3 How many moles of

a) Ag atoms are there in 54 g of silver,

b) P atoms are there in 3.1 g of phosphorus,

c) Fe atoms are there in 0.56 g of iron?

(A_r values: Ag = 108, P = 31, Fe = 56)

4 When aluminium reacts with bromine, 1.35 g of aluminium reacts with 12.0 g of bromine. What is the empirical formula of aluminium bromide?

(A_r values: Al = 27, Br = 80) [Higher]

5 In a lime kiln, calcium carbonate is decomposed to calcium oxide:

$CaCO_3 \rightarrow CaO + CO_2$

Calculate the percentage atom economy for the process (assuming 100% conversion).

(A_r values: Ca = 40, O = 16, C = 12) [Higher]

6 a) What is a reversible reaction?

b) How does a reversible reaction differ from an 'ordinary' reaction?

c) State the conditions chosen for the Haber process to convert nitrogen and hydrogen into ammonia.

EXAM-STYLE QUESTIONS

1 Hydrogen has three isotopes, $_1^1H$, $_1^2H$, and $_1^3H$.

(a) What are isotopes? (2)

(b) How many protons, neutrons and electrons are there in an atom of $_1^3H$? (3)

(c) Heavy water contains atoms of the isotope $_1^2H$ instead of $_1^1H$. It has the formula $_1^2H_2O$. What is the mass of one mole of heavy water? (2)

2 Tablets taken by people with iron deficiency anaemia contain 0.200 g of anhydrous iron(II) sulfate, $FeSO_4$.

(a) Calculate the relative formula mass of iron(II) sulfate, $FeSO_4$. (2)

(b) Calculate the percentage of iron in iron(II) sulfate. (2)

(c) Calculate the mass of iron in each tablet. (2)

3 The equation for the main reaction to make ammonia is:

$$N_2 + 3H_2 \rightleftharpoons 2NH_3$$

(a) What does the symbol $\rightleftharpoons$ tell you about this reaction? (1)

(b) The flow diagram shows the main stages in making ammonia.

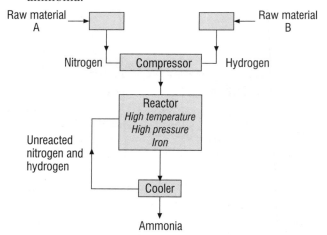

(i) Name the two raw materials **A** and **B**. (2)

(ii) What is the purpose of the iron in the reactor? (1)

(iii) Why do the nitrogen and hydrogen not react completely. (1)

(iv) How is wastage of unreacted nitrogen and hydrogen prevented? (1)

4 The equation for the reaction of calcium carbonate with hydrochloric acid is:

$$CaCO_3 + 2HCl \rightarrow CaCl_2 + CO_2 + H_2O$$

(a) How many moles of hydrochloric acid react with one mole of calcium carbonate? (1)

(b) How many moles of calcium chloride are produced from one mole of calcium carbonate? (1)

(c) What is the mass of calcium chloride that can be made from one mole of calcium carbonate? (2)

(d) What is the mass of one mole of calcium carbonate? (2)

(e) A student reacted 10 g of calcium carbonate with hydrochloric acid and collected 7.4 g of calcium chloride. What was the percentage yield? (2)
[Higher]

5 Chromium can be obtained from chromium oxide, Cr_2O_3, by reduction with aluminium or carbon. For the first reaction, chromium is mixed with aluminium and ignited in a crucible. The reaction using carbon is done at high temperatures in a low-pressure furnace. The equations for the reactions are:

$$Cr_2O_3 + 2Al \rightarrow 2Cr + Al_2O_3$$
$$2Cr_2O_3 + 3C \rightarrow 4Cr + 3CO_2$$

(a) Calculate the maximum mass of chromium that can be obtained from one mole of chromium oxide. (2)

(b) Calculate the percentage atom economy for both reactions to show which reaction has the better atom economy. (4)

(c) Suggest one advantage and one disadvantage of using carbon to manufacture chromium. (2)
[Higher]

6 Ibuprofen is used as a pain killer throughout the world. You might know it as Nurofen or Ibuleve. The traditional way to manufacture ibuprofen involved a lot of chemical reactions and produced a lot of waste. The atom economy was just 32%.
Recently it became possible for any pharmaceutical (drug) company to make ibuprofen. As there was a lot of money to be made, the race was on to find the most economic way to make it. This meant cutting down waste. The new method involves catalysts, some of which can be completely recovered and do not go out as waste. The atom economy is increased to 77%, partly because only the active form of ibuprofen is made. This also means that lower doses are needed and they take a shorter time to kill any pain.

Evaluate the two methods of manufacture in terms of the social, economic and environmental issues involved.
[Higher] (6)

HOW SCIENCE WORKS QUESTIONS

A class of students were given the task of finding out how much hydrogen would be produced by different amounts of calcium reacting with water. The hydrogen was collected in an upturned measuring cylinder. The apparatus was set up as is shown.

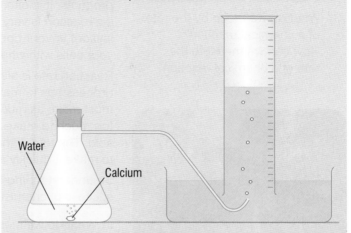

Different amounts of calcium were weighed. Each piece was put separately into the flask and the bung put on as quickly as possible. The reaction was left to finish and the volume of hydrogen measured.

The results of the different groups are in the table below.

Mass of Ca (g)	Volume of hydrogen (cm³)				
	A	B	C	D	E
0.05	25	26	27	18	26
0.10	55	53	55	55	52
0.15	85	86	81	89	84
0.20	115	117	109	116	113
0.25	145	146	148	141	140

a) Produce a table to show the mean for all of the groups for each mass of calcium used. (5)

b) Why is the mean often a more useful set of results than any one group? (1)

c) What is the range of volumes when 0.25 grams of calcium are used? (1)

d) What is the sensitivity of the balance used to weigh out the calcium? (1)

e) How could you determine which group had the most accurate results? (1)

f) Look at the method described. Is there any possibility of a systematic error? If so, say how this error could arise. (1)

C2 4.1   How fast?

LEARNING OBJECTIVES

1 What do we mean by the rate of a chemical reaction?
2 How can we measure the rate of a chemical reaction?

Figure 1 All living things depend on very precise control of the millions of chemical reactions happening inside their cells

The rate of a chemical reaction tells us how fast the reactants are turned into products. It is often very important for us to know about this. In a science class, if a reaction is very slow you won't get your results before the end of the lesson! In your body, chemical reactions must take place at rates which supply your cells with what they need exactly when they need them.

Reaction rate is also very important in the chemical industry. Any industrial process has to make money by producing useful products. This means we must make as much of the product we want as cheaply as possible. If it costs too much to make a chemical, it will be hard to make much profit when it is sold. The rate of the reaction used to make our chemical must be fast enough to make it quickly and safely.

So understanding and controlling reaction rates is always necessary for successful chemistry – whether in a cell or a chemical factory!

a) What do we mean by the **rate** of a chemical reaction?
b) Why is understanding the rate of chemical reactions so important?

How can we measure the rate of chemical reactions?

Chemical reactions happen at all sorts of different rates. Some are astonishingly fast – think of a firework exploding! Others are very slow, like rusting – the reaction between iron and oxygen in damp conditions.

There are two ways we can measure the rate of a chemical reaction. We can measure how quickly the reactants are used up as they react to make products. Or we can measure the rate at which the products of the reaction are made.

There are three main ways we can make these kinds of measurements.

GET IT RIGHT!

The steeper the line on a graph, the faster the reaction rate.

PRACTICAL

Measuring the mass of a reaction mixture

We can measure the rate at which the **mass** of the reaction mixture changes if a gas is given off.

As the reaction takes place the mass of the reaction mixture will decrease. We can measure and record this at time intervals very easily.

Some balances can be attached to a computer to monitor the loss in mass continuously.

● Why is the cotton wool placed in the neck of the conical flask?
● How would the line on the graph differ if you plot 'Loss in mass' on the vertical axis?

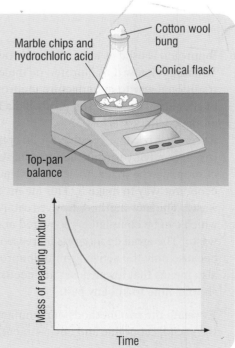

Measuring the volume of gas given off

If a gas is produced in a reaction, we can measure the rate of reaction. We do this by collecting the gas and measuring its volume at time intervals.

● What are the sources of error when measuring the volume of gas?

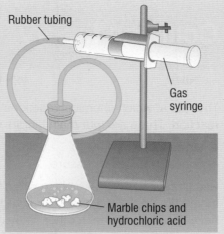
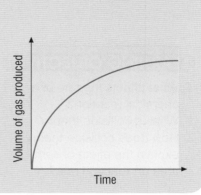

Rubber tubing

Gas syringe

Marble chips and hydrochloric acid

Volume of gas produced

Time

PRACTICAL

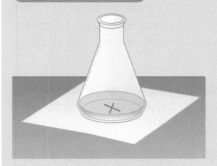

Measuring the light transmitted through a solution

Some reactions make an insoluble solid (precipitate) which makes the solution go cloudy. We can measure the rate at which the solid appears.

If the reaction is set up in a flask under which we put on a piece of paper marked with a cross, we can record the time taken for the cross to disappear. The shorter the time, the faster the reaction rate.

Or we can use a light meter connected to a data logger to measure the amount of light that can get through the solution, as the graph shows.

● What are the advantages of using a light meter rather than using the 'disappearing cross' method?

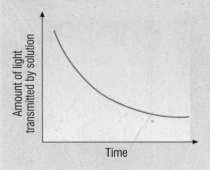

Amount of light transmitted by solution

Time

We can summarise these methods of working out the rate of a reaction using this equation:

$$\text{Rate of reaction} = \frac{\text{amount of reactant used or amount of product formed}}{\text{time}}$$

SUMMARY QUESTIONS

1 Copy and complete using the words below:

  explosion   products   rate   reactants   rusting

  Measuring the rate at which ...... are used up or ...... are made are two ways of measuring the ...... of a chemical reaction. An example of a reaction that happens quickly is an .... A reaction that happens slowly is ....

2 Sketch graphs to show the results of the two main ways in which we can measure the rate of a chemical reaction. (See the first sentence in question 1 above.)

3 If we measure the time taken for a solution to become cloudy (see above) how is the time taken for the cross on the paper to disappear related to the rate of the chemical reaction?

KEY POINTS

1 Knowing and controlling the rate of chemical reactions is important in living cells, in the laboratory and in industry.

2 We can measure the rate of a chemical reaction by following the rate at which reactants are used up. Alternatively, we can measure the rate at which products are made.

C2 4.2   Collision theory

Figure 1 There is no doubt that the chemicals in these fireworks have reacted – but how do we explain what happens in a chemical reaction?

Figure 2 Cooking – an excellent example of controlling reaction rates!

Figure 3 When a solid reacts, the size of its pieces make a big difference to the rate of the reaction – the smaller the pieces, the faster the reaction

The rate at which chemical reactions happen is very different, depending on the reaction. There are four main factors which affect the rate of chemical reactions:

- temperature,
- concentration or pressure,
- surface area,
- presence of a catalyst.

Reactions can only take place when the particles (atoms, ions or molecules) that make up the reactants come together. But the reacting particles don't just have to bump into each other. They need to collide with enough energy too, otherwise they will not react. This is known as **collision theory**.

The smallest amount of energy that particles must have before they will react is known as the **activation energy**. So anything which increases the chance of reacting particles bumping into each other, or which increases the energy that they have when they collide will make it more likely that reactions will happen. If we increase the chance of individual particles reacting, we will also increase the rate of reaction.

a) What must happen before two particles can stand a chance of reacting?
b) Particles must have a certain amount of energy before they will react – what is this energy called?

In everyday life we control the rates of chemical reactions often without any idea what we are doing and why! For example, cooking cakes in ovens or spraying a mixture of fuel and air into our car engines. But in chemistry we need to know exactly how to control the rate of chemical reactions and why our method works.

Surface area and reaction rate

If we want to light a fire we don't pile large logs together and try to set them alight. We use small pieces of kindling to begin with. Doing this increases the surface area of the logs, so there is more wood that can react with the air.

When a solid reactant reacts with a solution, the size of the pieces of the solid material make a big difference to the rate of the reaction. The inside of a large piece of solid is not in contact with the solution it is reacting with, so it can't react. It has to wait for the outside to react first.

In smaller lumps, or in a powder, each tiny piece is surrounded by solution. This means that reactions can take place much more easily.

c) How does the surface area of a solid affect its rate of reaction?

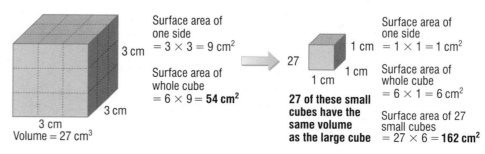

Surface area of one side
$= 3 \times 3 = 9 \text{ cm}^2$

Surface area of whole cube
$= 6 \times 9 = \textbf{54 cm}^2$

3 cm
3 cm
3 cm
Volume = 27 cm³

27

1 cm
1 cm
1 cm

27 of these small cubes have the same volume as the large cube

Surface area of one side
$= 1 \times 1 = 1 \text{ cm}^2$

Surface area of whole cube
$= 6 \times 1 = 6 \text{ cm}^2$

Surface area of 27 small cubes
$= 27 \times 6 = \textbf{162 cm}^2$

PRACTICAL

Which burns faster – ribbon or powder?

Make sure you have a heatproof mat under the Bunsen burner and you must wear goggles. Try lighting a 2 cm length of magnesium ribbon and time how long it takes to burn. Take a small spatula tip of magnesium powder and sprinkle it into the Bunsen flame.

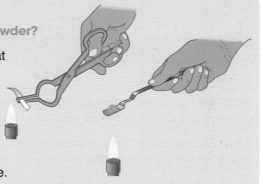

● What safety precautions should you take in this experiment?

PRACTICAL

Investigating surface area

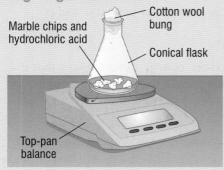

Marble chips and hydrochloric acid

Cotton wool bung

Conical flask

Top-pan balance

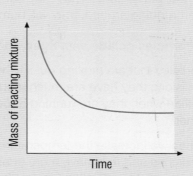

You can investigate the effect of changing surface area by measuring the mass lost against time for different sizes of marble chips. You need at least two different sizes of marble chips. These should be washed in dilute acid, rinsed with water and dried before they are used (to remove any powder on the surface).

● What variables should you control to make this a fair test?

A data logger would help to plot graphs of the results.

GET IT RIGHT!

Particles collide all the time, but only some collisions lead to reactions.
Increasing the number of collisions and the energy of collisions produces faster rates.
Larger surface area does not result in collisions with more energy but does increase the frequency of collisions.

SUMMARY QUESTIONS

1 Match the sentence fragments:

a) For two particles to react ...... _D_	A ...... only if they have enough energy.
b) Two particles will react ...... _A_	B ...... is called the activation energy.
c) The energy required for particles to react ...... _B_	C ...... increases the rate at which it will react.
d) Increasing the surface area of a solid ...... _C_	D ...... they must first collide.

2 Draw a diagram to explain why it is easier to light a fire using small pieces of kindling rather than big logs.

3 Why do you digest your food more quickly if you chew it well before you swallow it?

KEY POINTS

1 The minimum amount of energy that particles must have in order to react is called the activation energy.

2 The rate of a chemical reaction increases if the surface area of any solid reactants is increased.

C2 4.3   The effect of temperature

LEARNING OBJECTIVES

1 How does changing temperature affect the rate of reactions?

Figure 1 Moving faster means it's more likely that you'll bump into someone else – and the bump will be harder too!

When we increase the temperature of a reaction it always increases the rate of the reaction. Collision theory tells us why this happens – there are two reasons.

Both of these reasons are related to the fact that when we heat up a mixture of reactants the particles in the mixture move more quickly.

1 Particles collide more often

When we heat up a substance, energy is transferred to the particles that make up the substance. This means that they move faster. And when particles move faster they have more collisions. Imagine a lot of people walking around in the school playground. They may bump into each other occasionally – but if they start running around, they will bump into each other even more often!

2 Particles collide with more energy

Particles that are moving quickly have more energy, which means that the collisions they have are much more energetic. It's just like two people who collide when they are running about as opposed to just walking into each other!

When we increase the temperature of a reaction, the particles have more collisions and they have more energy. This speeds up the reaction in two ways – the particles will collide more often and they have more energy when they do collide.

Both of these changes increase the chance that two molecules will react. Around room temperature, if we increase the temperature of the reaction by 10°C the rate of the reaction will roughly double.

a) Why does increasing the temperature increase the rate of a reaction?
b) How much does a 10°C rise in temperature increase reaction rate at room temperature?

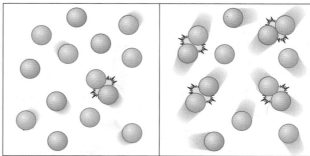

Cold – slow movement, few collisions, little energy

Hot – fast movement, more collisions, more energy

Figure 2 More collisions with more energy – both of these increase the rate of a chemical reaction as the temperature increases

This change in reaction rate is why we use fridges and freezers – because reducing the temperature slows down the rate of a chemical reaction. When food goes bad it is because of chemical reactions. Reducing the temperature slows down these reactions, so the food goes off much less quickly.

PRACTICAL

The effect of temperature on rate of reaction

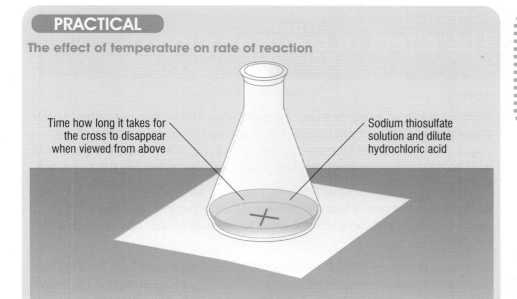

Time how long it takes for the cross to disappear when viewed from above

Sodium thiosulfate solution and dilute hydrochloric acid

NEXT TIME YOU...

. . . turn the heat up when you're cooking a meal, remember that you're increasing the rate at which chemical reactions are happening!

When we react sodium thiosulfate solution and hydrochloric acid it produces sulfur. This makes the solution go cloudy. We can record the length of time it takes for the solution to go cloudy at different temperatures.

- Which variables do you have to control to make this a fair test?
- Why is it difficult to get accurate timings by eye in this investigation?
- How can you improve the reliability of the data you collect?

The results of an investigation like this can be plotted on a graph:

The graph shows how the time for the solution to go cloudy changes with temperature.

c) What happens to the time it takes the solution to go cloudy as the temperature increases?

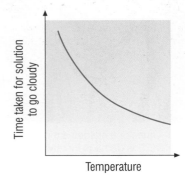

Temperature

SUMMARY QUESTIONS

1 Copy and complete using the words below:

**chemical   collide   decreases   doubles   energy   off
quickly   rate   reducing   rise**

When we increase the temperature of a reaction, we increase its .... This makes the particles move more ...... so they ...... more often and they have more .... At room temperature, a temperature ...... of about 10°C roughly ...... the reaction rate. This explains why we use fridges and freezers – because ...... the temperature ...... the rate of the ...... reactions which make food go ....

2 Water in a pressure cooker boils at a much higher temperature than water in a saucepan because it is under pressure. Why does food take longer to cook in a saucepan than it does in a pressure cooker?

3 Use your knowledge of the effect of temperature on chemical reactions to explain why cold-blooded animals like reptiles or insects may move very slowly in cold weather.

KEY POINTS

1 Reactions happen more quickly as the temperature increases.
2 A 10°C increase in temperature at room temperature roughly doubles the rate of a reaction.
3 The rate of a chemical reaction increases with temperature because the particles collide more often and they have more energy.

C2 4.4

The effect of concentration

LEARNING OBJECTIVES

1 How does changing the concentration of reactants affect the rate of reactions?
2 How does changing the pressure of reacting gases affect the rate of reactions?

Figure 1 Limestone statues are damaged by acid rain. This damage increases as the concentration of the acids in rainwater increases.

Some of our most beautiful buildings are made of limestone or marble. These buildings have stood for centuries, but in the last 50 years or so they have begun crumbling away increasingly fast. This is because limestone and marble both contain calcium carbonate. This reacts with acids, leaving the stone soft and crumbly.

We think that the rate of this reaction has speeded up because the concentration of sulfuric and nitric acids found in rainwater has been steadily increasing.

Increasing the concentration of reactants in a solution, increases reaction rate because there are more particles of the reactants moving around in the same volume. The more 'crowded' together the reactant particles are, the more likely it is that they will bump into each other and a reaction will take place.

Increasing the pressure of a reaction involving gases has the same effect. It squashes the gas particles more closely together. This increases the chance that they will collide and react and so speeds up the rate of the reaction.

a) Why does increasing concentration or pressure increase reaction rate?

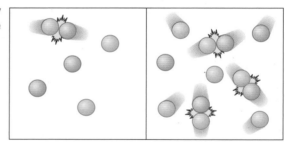

Low concentration/ low pressure

High concentration/ high pressure

Figure 2 Increasing concentration and pressure both mean that particles are closer together. This increases the number of collisions between particles, so the reaction rate increases.

The concentration of a solution tells us how many particles of solute we have dissolved in a certain volume of the solution. Concentration is measured in moles per cubic decimetre, which is shortened to mol/dm^3. Solutions with the same concentration always contain the same number of particles of solute in the same volume.

b) What unit do we use to measure the concentration of solute in a solution?

We never talk about the concentration of a gas – but the number of particles in a certain volume of gas depends on its temperature and its pressure. At the same temperature and pressure, equal volumes of gases all contain the same number of particles.

0.5 dm³   1.0 dm³   2.0 dm³

2.0 mol/dm³ 1.0 mol/dm³ 0.5 mol/dm³

Figure 3 These different volumes of solution all contain the same amount of solute – but at different concentrations

c) Two identical containers of gas are at the same temperature and pressure. What can we say about the number of particles in the two containers?

PRACTICAL

Investigating the effect of concentration on rate of reaction

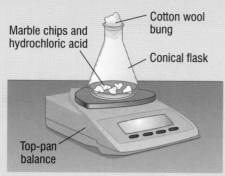

Cotton wool bung

Marble chips and hydrochloric acid

Conical flask

Top-pan balance

We can investigate the effect of changing concentration by reacting marble chips with different concentrations of hydrochloric acid, which produces carbon dioxide gas:

$$CaCO_3 + 2HCl \rightarrow CaCl_2 + CO_2 + H_2O$$

We can measure the rate of reaction by plotting the mass of the reaction mixture as carbon dioxide gas is given off in the reaction.

● How do you make this a fair test?
● What conclusion can you draw from your results?

If we plot the results of an investigation like the one above on a graph they look like this:

The graph shows how the rate at which the mass of the reaction mixture decreases changes with concentration.

d) Which line on the graph shows the fastest reaction? How could you tell?

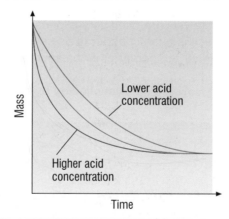

Mass

Lower acid concentration

Higher acid concentration

Time

SUMMARY QUESTIONS

1 Copy and complete using the words below:

> **collisions   concentration   faster   gases   increases**
> **number   pressure   rate   volume**

The ...... of a chemical reaction is affected by the ...... of reactants in solution and by ...... if the reactants are .... Both of these tell us the ...... of particles that there are in a certain ...... of the reaction mixture. Increasing this ...... the number of ...... that particles make with each other, making reactions happen ....

2 Acidic cleaners are designed to remove limescale when they are used neat. They do not work so well when they are diluted. Using your knowledge of collision theory, explain why this is.

3 How are the 'concentration of a solution' and the 'pressure of a gas' similar? [Higher]

KEY POINTS

1 Increasing the concentration of reactants increases the frequency of collisions between particles, increasing the rate of reaction.
2 Increasing the pressure of reacting gases results in particles colliding more often, increasing the rate of reaction.

C2 4.5   The effect of catalysts

Figure 1 Catalysts are all around us, in the natural world and in industry. Our planet would be very different without them.

Sometimes we need to change the rate of a reaction but this is impossible using any of the ways we have looked at so far. Or sometimes a reaction might be possible only if we use very high temperatures or pressures – which can be very expensive. However we can speed chemical reactions up another way – by using a special substance called a **catalyst**.

a) Apart from using a catalyst, what other ways are there of speeding up a chemical reaction?

A catalyst is a substance which increases the rate of a chemical reaction but it is not affected chemically itself at the end of the reaction. It is not used up in the reaction, so it can be used over and over again to speed up the conversion of reactants to products.

We need to use different catalysts with different reactions. Many of the catalysts we use in industry are transition metals or their compounds. For example, iron is used in the Haber process, while platinum is used in the production of nitric acid.

Catalysts are often very expensive because they are made of precious metals. But it is often cheaper to use a catalyst than to pay for all the energy needed for higher temperatures or pressures in a reaction.

b) How is a catalyst affected by a chemical reaction?

Figure 2 The transition metals platinum and palladium are used in the catalytic converters in cars

Some catalysts work by providing a surface for the reacting particles to come together. They lower the activation energy needed for the particles to react. This means that more of the collisions between particles result in a reaction taking place. We normally use catalysts in the form of powders, pellets or fine gauzes. This gives the biggest possible surface area for them to work.

c) Why is a catalyst divided up into pellets more effective than a whole lump of the catalyst?

PRACTICAL

Investigating catalysis

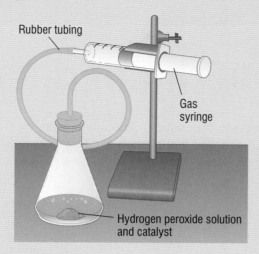

Rubber tubing

Gas
syringe

Hydrogen peroxide solution
and catalyst

We can investigate the effect of different catalysts on the rate that hydrogen peroxide solution decomposes:

$$2H_2O_2 \rightarrow 2H_2O + O_2$$

The reaction produces oxygen. We can collect this in a gas syringe using the apparatus shown above.

We can investigate the effect of many different substances on the rate of this reaction. Examples include manganese(IV) oxide and potassium iodide.

- State the independent variable in this investigation. (See page 276.)

A simple table of the time taken to produce a certain volume of oxygen can then tell us which catalyst makes the reaction go fastest.

- What type of graph would you use to show the results of your investigation? Why? (See page 280.)

Apart from speeding up a chemical reaction, the most important thing about a catalyst is that it does not get used up in the chemical reaction. We can use a tiny amount of catalyst to speed up a chemical reaction over and over again.

SUMMARY QUESTIONS

1 Copy and complete using the words below:

    activation   energy   increases   more   react

A catalyst ...... the rate of a chemical reaction. It does this by reducing the ...... energy needed for the reaction. This means that ...... particles have enough ...... to ....

2 Solid catalysts used in chemical plants are often shaped as tiny beads or cylinders with holes through them. Why are they made in this shape?

3 Why is the number of moles of catalyst needed to speed up a chemical reaction very small compared to the number of moles of reactants?

KEY POINTS

1 A catalyst speeds up the rate of a chemical reaction.

2 A catalyst is not used up during a chemical reaction.

C2 4.6 · Catalysts in action

Cleaning the car with chemical catalysts

Cars are a major source of pollution, although they are much cleaner now than they used to be. One reason that petrol-fuelled cars are much cleaner is down to catalysts . . .

Fuel travels to the engine. Here it is mixed with air and passes into the cylinders. At just the right point the petrol and air mixture is made to explode by a tiny electric spark. This explosion provides the force that pushes the piston downwards to make the car move. The explosion makes carbon dioxide and water as the hydrocarbon reacts with oxygen in the air. But carbon monoxide and nitrogen oxides are made too. Carbon monoxide is toxic and nitrogen oxides contribute towards acid rain.

Petrol, a fuel made of hydrocarbons, goes into the tank. Lead compounds used to be added to the petrol to improve the performance of the engine. Lead is no longer added to petrol as it is poisonous.

The exhaust gases from the engine pass out through the exhaust pipe and through a catalytic converter. Here the gases pass over a metal catalyst. This removes the oxygen from the nitrogen oxides and reacts it with the carbon monoxide. The result is carbon dioxide and nitrogen.

The catalyst used may be platinum, palladium or rhodium, or a combination of these transition metals. The catalyst is arranged so that it has a very large surface area. Catalysts can be 'poisoned' by lead in petrol – so it is very important to use 'unleaded' petrol in a car that is fitted with a catalytic converter.

ACTIVITY

The diagram shows some of the chemistry that goes to make cars much 'cleaner' than they used to be.

Write a short article for the motoring section of a local newspaper describing why a modern car causes much less pollution than a car built thirty years ago. Remember that the readers may not have much scientific knowledge, so any chemistry will need to be explained using simple language.

Remember to think of a catchy title for your article!

ENZYMES – CLEVER CATALYSTS THAT ARE GETTING EVERYWHERE

ENZYMES MAKE CLOTHES CLEANER AND CLASSIER!

For years we've been used to enzymes helping to get our clothes clean. Biological washing powders contain tiny molecules that help to literally 'break apart' dirt molecules such as proteins at low temperatures. But why stop there? Why not make washing powders that help to repair clothes and make them like new? Searching the surface of fabric for any tears or breaks in the fibres, enzymes could join these back together, while other enzymes might look for frayed or 'furry' bits of fabric and could makes these smooth again. And not only that . . . . . .

ENZYMES TO THE RESCUE

Everyone knows how upsetting it is to cut yourself. And it can be a pain to have to wear a sticking plaster until your body has repaired your skin. But enzymes may be the answer to this. By choosing the right enzyme mixture we may one day be able to mend cuts and other damage to our skin simply by painting a liquid onto our skin. But until then . . . . . .

SAY 'AAAHH' FOR THE ENZYME!

Those lengthy waits for the results of a blood test to come back could soon be a thing of the past. By combining biological molecules like enzymes with electronics, scientists reckon that they can make tiny measuring probes that will enable doctors to get an instant readout of the level of chemicals in your blood. These sensors are so tiny that it is possible to take more than a dozen measurements at the same time, doing away with the need for lots of tests.

SCIENTISTS MAKE ENZYMES MAKE COMPUTER

Scientists announced today that they are close to making a biological computer made of enzymes and DNA. The tiny device could change the face of computing in the future, which up until now has been based on electronic devices made from silicon. The idea of using DNA in computers first took off in 1994, when a scientist in California used it to solve a maths problem. Computers made from DNA would be so tiny that a trillion of them could fit in a single drop of water.

ACTIVITY

There is more than a grain of truth in all of these ideas about enzymes. Use some or all of these news reports to produce a short piece for the 'and finally' slot in a TV news broadcast. Remember to use your knowledge of catalysts to explain why enzymes are important in all of these developments.

SUMMARY QUESTIONS

1 Select from A, B and C to show how the rate of each reaction, a) to d), could be measured.

a) Gas evolved from reaction mixture   A Measure mass

b) Mass of reaction mixture changes   B Measure light transmitted

c) Precipitate produced   C Measure volume

d) Colour of solution changes

2 A student carried out a reaction in which she dropped a piece of magnesium ribbon in sulfuric acid with a concentration of 1 mol/dm³.

a) Suggest **one** way in which the student could measure the rate of this reaction.

b) Suggest **three** ways in which the student could increase the rate of this reaction.

c) Explain how each of these methods changes the rate of the reaction.

3 The following results show what happened when two students investigated the reaction of some marble chips with acid.

Time (seconds)	Investigation 1 Volume of gas produced (cm³)	Investigation 2 Volume of gas produced (cm³)
0	0	0
30	5	10
60	10	20
90	15	30
120	20	40
150	25	50
180	28	57
210	30	59
240	30	60

a) Plot a graph of these results with time on the *x*-axis.

b) After 30 seconds, how does the rate of the reaction in investigation 2 compare with the rate of reaction in investigation 1?

c) How does the final volume of gas produced in investigation 2 compare with the final volume of gas produced in investigation 1?

d) Suggest how the reaction in investigation 2 differs from the reaction in investigation 1. Explain your answer.

EXAM-STYLE QUESTIONS

1 Marble chips (calcium carbonate) react with hydrochloric acid as shown in the equation.

$$CaCO_3(s) + 2HCl(aq) \rightarrow CaCl_2(aq) + H_2O(l) + CO_2(g)$$

Some students investigated the effect of the size of marble chips on the rate of this reaction. They did the reactions in a conical flask, which they put onto a balance connected to a computer to record their results. They used three different sizes of marble chips and kept all of the other conditions the same. The graphs show the total mass of the flask and reaction mixture plotted against time for the three experiments.

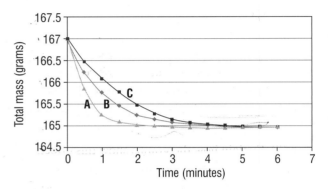

(a) Which curve, **A**, **B** or **C**, shows the results for the fastest reaction? (1)

(b) Which curve, **A**, **B** or **C**, shows the results for the largest marble chips? (1)

(c) Explain, using collision theory, why changing the size of marble chips changes the rate of reaction. (2)

(d) (i) Use curve **A** to describe how the rate of reaction changes from the start to the finish of the reaction.

(3)

(ii) Explain why the rate of reaction changes in this way. (2)

2 A student investigated the reaction between magnesium ribbon and hydrochloric acid.

$$Mg(s) + 2HCl(aq) \rightarrow MgCl_2(aq) + H_2(g)$$

The student reacted 20 cm³ of two different concentrations of hydrochloric acid with 0.050 g of magnesium. All other conditions were kept the same. The student's results are shown in the table on the next page.

Concentration of acid (moles per dm³)	Time (minutes)	0	1	2	3	4	5	6	7	8	9	10
1.0	Volume of gas (cm³)	0	15	24	31	37	41	44	46	47	48	48
2.0	Volume of gas (cm³)	0	30	39	45	47	48	48	48	48	48	48

(a) Name the dependent variable. (1)

(b) Suggest a control variable. (1)

(c) Suggest how the student might have controlled this variable. (1)

(d) Plot these results on the same axes, with time on the horizontal axis and volume of gas on the vertical axis. Draw a smooth line for each concentration. Label each line with the concentration of acid. (4)

(e) (i) What is the effect of doubling the concentration on the rate of reaction? (1)

(ii) Explain how the graphs show this effect. (2)

(iii) Explain this effect in terms of particles and collision theory. (2)

(f) Explain why the total volume of hydrogen is the same for both reactions. (2)

(g) Draw a labelled diagram of the apparatus you would use to do this experiment. (3)

3 Hydrogen peroxide solution is colourless and decomposes very slowly at 20°C.

$$2H_2O_2(aq) \rightarrow 2H_2O(l) + O_2(g)$$

Manganese(IV) oxide, a black powder, is a catalyst for the reaction.

(a) Explain what the word catalyst means. (2)

(b) What would you **see** if manganese(IV) oxide was added to hydrogen peroxide solution? (1)

(c) Describe briefly one way that you could show that manganese(IV) oxide was acting as a catalyst. (2)

(d) Explain, using particle and collision theory, how a solid catalyst works. (2)

(e) Hydrogen peroxide solution stored at 10°C decomposes at half the rate compared to when it is stored at 20°C. Explain, in terms of particles, why the rate of the reaction changes in this way. (3)

HOW SCIENCE WORKS QUESTIONS

This student's account of an investigation into the effect of temperature on the rate of a reaction was found on the Internet.

I investigated the effect of temperature on the rate of a reaction. The reaction was between sodium thiosulfate and hydrochloric acid. I set up my apparatus as in this diagram.

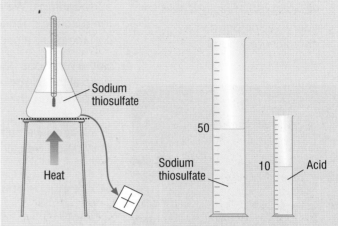

The cross was put under the flask. I heated the sodium thiosulfate to the temperature I wanted and then added the hydrochloric acid to the flask. I immediately started the watch and timed how long it took for the cross to disappear.

My results are below.

Temperature of the sodium thiosulfate	Time taken for the cross to disappear
15	110
30	40
45	21

My conclusion is that the reaction goes faster the higher the temperature.

a) Suggest a suitable prediction for this investigation. (1)

b) Describe one safety feature that is not mentioned in the method. (1)

c) Suggest some ways in which this method could be improved. For each suggestion, say why it is an improvement. (10)

d) Suggest how the table of results could be improved. (1)

e) Despite all of the problems with this investigation, is the conclusion appropriate? Explain your answer. (1)

C2 5.1 Exothermic and endothermic reactions

Figure 1 When a fuel burns in oxygen, energy is transferred to the surroundings. We usually don't need a thermometer to know that there is a temperature change!

Whenever chemical reactions take place, energy is involved. That's because energy is always transferred as chemical bonds are broken and formed.

Some reactions transfer energy *from* the reacting chemicals *to* the surroundings. We call these **exothermic** reactions. The energy transferred from the reacting chemicals often heats up the surroundings. This means that we can measure a rise in temperature as the reaction happens.

Some reactions transfer energy *from* the surroundings *to* the reacting chemicals. We call these **endothermic** reactions. Because they take in energy from their surroundings, these reactions cause a drop in temperature as they happen.

a) What do we call a chemical reaction that gives out heat?
b) What do we call a chemical reaction that absorbs heat from its surroundings?

Exothermic reactions

Fuels burning are an obvious example of exothermic reactions, but there are others which we often meet in the chemistry lab.

Neutralisation reactions between acids and alkalis are exothermic. We can easily measure the rise in temperature using simple apparatus (see opposite).

Similarly, heat is released when we add water to white anhydrous copper(II) sulfate (anhydrous means 'without water'). This reaction makes blue hydrated copper(II) sulfate crystals. The reaction gives out heat – it is an exothermic reaction.

Respiration is a very special kind of burning. It involves reacting sugar with oxygen inside the cells of every living thing. This makes the energy needed for all the reactions of life, and also makes water and carbon dioxide as waste products. Respiration is another exothermic reaction.

c) Give two examples of exothermic reactions.

Figure 2 All warm-blooded animals rely on exothermic reactions to keep their body temperatures steady

Endothermic reactions

Endothermic reactions are much less common than exothermic ones.

When we dissolve some ionic compounds like potassium chloride or ammonium nitrate in water the temperature of the solution drops.

Thermal decomposition reactions are also endothermic. An example is the decomposition of calcium carbonate to form calcium oxide and carbon dioxide. This reaction only takes place if we keep heating the calcium carbonate strongly. It takes in a great deal of energy from the surroundings.

The most important endothermic reaction of all is **photosynthesis**. This is the reaction in which plants turn carbon dioxide and water into sugar and oxygen, using energy from the Sun.

Figure 3 When we eat sherbet we can feel an endothermic reaction! Sherbet dissolving in the water in your mouth takes in energy – giving a slight cooling effect.

d) Name two endothermic reactions.

PRACTICAL

Investigating energy changes

The thermometer is used to measure the temperature change which takes place during the reaction.

Chemicals are mixed in the cup. The insulation reduces the rate at which energy can enter or leave the contents of the cup.

Styrofoam cup

We can use very simple apparatus to investigate the energy changes in reactions. Often we don't need to use anything more complicated than a Styrofoam drinks cup and a thermometer.

● State two ways in which you could make the data you collect more reliable.

GET IT RIGHT!

Remember that exothermic reactions involve energy EXiting (leaving) the reacting chemicals so the surroundings get hotter. In endothermic reactions energy moves INTO (sounds like 'endo'!) the reacting chemicals, so the surroundings get colder.

SUMMARY QUESTIONS

1 Copy and complete using the words below:

> **broken   endothermic   exothermic   made   neutralisation
> photosynthesis   respiration   thermal decomposition**

Chemical reactions involve energy changes as bonds are ...... and .... When a chemical reaction releases energy we say that it is an ...... reaction. Two important examples of this kind of reaction are ...... and .... When a chemical reaction takes in energy we say that it is an ...... reaction. Two important examples of this kind of reaction are ...... and ....

2 Potassium chloride dissolving in water is an endothermic process. What might you expect to observe when potassium chloride dissolves in water?

KEY POINTS

1 Energy may be transferred to or from the reacting substances in a chemical reaction.
2 A reaction where energy is transferred from the reacting substances is called an exothermic reaction.
3 A reaction where energy is transferred to the reacting substances is called an endothermic reaction.

C2 5.2   Energy and reversible reactions

LEARNING OBJECTIVES

1 How is energy involved in reversible reactions?
2 What happens to reactions at equilibrium when we change the temperature? [Higher]

Energy changes are involved in reversible reactions too. We can understand energy changes in a reversible reaction if we think carefully about the reaction itself.

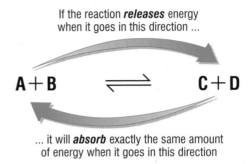

If the reaction **releases** energy when it goes in this direction ...

A + B ⇌ C + D

... it will **absorb** exactly the same amount of energy when it goes in this direction

Figure 1 A reversible reaction

Figure 1 shows a reversible reaction where A and B react to form C and D. The products of this reaction (C and D) can then react to form A and B again.

If the reaction between A and B is exothermic, energy will be released when the reaction happens and C and D are formed. If C and D then react to make A and B again, the reaction must be endothermic. What's more, it must absorb exactly the same amount of energy as it released when C and D were formed from A and B.

If this didn't happen it would be possible for us to 'make' energy just by continuously reacting A and B to make C and D, then going back again and so on. We know that we never get 'something for nothing' like this in science. So the amount of energy released when we go in one direction in a reversible reaction must be exactly the same as the energy absorbed when we go in the opposite direction.

a) How does the energy change for a reversible reaction in one direction compare to the energy change for the reaction in the opposite direction?

We can see how this works if we look at what happens when we heat blue copper sulfate crystals. The crystals contain water as part of the lattice formed when they crystallise. We say that the copper sulfate is **hydrated**. Heating the copper sulfate drives off the water from the crystals, producing white **anhydrous** ('without water') copper sulfate. This is an endothermic reaction.

$$\underset{\substack{\text{hydrated}\\\text{copper sulfate}}}{\overset{\text{blue crystals}}{CuSO_4.5H_2O}} \rightleftharpoons \underset{\substack{\text{anhydrous}\\\text{copper sulfate}}}{\overset{\text{white powder}}{CuSO_4}} + 5H_2O$$

When we add water to anhydrous copper sulfate we form hydrated copper sulfate. The colour change in the reaction is a useful test for water. The reaction in this direction is exothermic. In fact, so much energy may be produced that we may see steam rising as water boils.

PRACTICAL

Energy changes in a reversible reaction

Try these reactions yourself. Gently heat a few copper sulfate crystals in a test tube. Observe the changes. When the crystals are completely white allow the tube to cool to room temperature (takes several minutes). Add two or three drops of water from a dropper and observe the changes. Carefully feel the bottom of the test tube.

- Explain the changes you have observed.

You can repeat this with the same solid, as it is a reversible reaction or try with other hydrated crystals, like cobalt chloride. Some are not so colourful but the changes are similar.

b) What can anhydrous copper sulfate be used to test for?

Energy and equilibrium

HIGHER

We have a closed system when nothing is added or taken away from the reaction mixture. In a closed system the relative amounts of the reactants and products in a reversible reaction depend on the temperature.

The ability to change the balance of reactants and products is very important when we look at industrial processes. By changing the temperature we can get more of the products and less of the reactants. Look at the table:

If a reaction is exothermic ……	If a reaction is endothermic ……
… an increase in temperature decreases the yield of the reaction, so the amount of products formed is lower.	… an increase in temperature increases the yield of the reaction, so the amount of products formed is larger.
… a decrease in temperature increases the yield of the reaction, so the amount of products formed is larger.	… a decrease in temperature decreases the yield of the reaction, so the amount of products formed is lower.

SUMMARY QUESTIONS

1 Copy and complete using the words below:

   decreasing   endothermic   exothermic   increasing   reversible

   If a reversible reaction is …… in one direction it will be …… in the opposite direction. If a …… reaction is exothermic in the forward direction, …… the temperature will increase the amount of products formed. If it is endothermic in the forward direction, …… the temperature will increase the amount of products formed.   [Higher]

2 Blue cobalt chloride crystals turn pink when they become damp. The formula for the two forms can be written as $CoCl_2.2H_2O$ and $CoCl_2.6H_2O$.

   a) How many moles of water will combine with 1 mole of $CoCl_2.2H_2O$?
   b) Write a balanced equation for the reaction, which is reversible.
   c) You have some *pink* cobalt chloride crystals. Suggest how you could turn these into *blue* cobalt chloride crystals.

KEY POINTS

1 In reversible reactions, one reaction is exothermic and the other is endothermic.

2 In any reversible reaction, the amount of energy released when the reaction goes in one direction is exactly equal to the energy absorbed when the reaction goes in the opposite direction.

3 We can change the amount of products formed at equilibrium by changing the temperature at which we carry out a reversible reaction. [Higher]

C2 5.3 More about the Haber process

LEARNING OBJECTIVES

1 Why do we use a temperature of 450°C for the Haber process?
2 Why do we use a pressure of about 200 atmospheres for the Haber process?

We saw on the previous page that the temperature at which we carry out a reversible reaction can affect the amount of the products formed at equilibrium. But if the reaction we are carrying out involves gases, pressure can be very important too.

Many reversible reactions which involve gases have more moles of gas on one side of the equation than on the other. By changing the pressure at which we carry out the reaction we can change the amount of products that we produce. Look at the table below:

If a reaction produces a larger volume of gases	If a reaction produces a smaller volume of gases ......
... an increase in pressure decreases the yield of the reaction, so the amount of products formed is lower.	... an increase in pressure increases the yield of the reaction, so the amount of products formed is larger.
... a decrease in pressure increases the yield of the reaction, so the amount of products formed is larger.	... a decrease in pressure decreases the yield of the reaction, so the amount of products formed is lower.

To see how this is useful we can look at the Haber process which we met earlier.

a) Look at the table above. How does increasing the pressure affect the amount of products formed in a reaction which produces a larger volume of gas?

The economics of the Haber process

The Haber process involves the reversible reaction between nitrogen and hydrogen to make ammonia:

$$N_2 + 3H_2 \rightleftharpoons 2NH_3 \ (\rightleftharpoons \text{ is the equilibrium symbol})$$

Energy is released during this reaction, so it is exothermic. As the chemical equation shows, there are 4 moles of gas ($N_2 + 3H_2$) on the left-hand side of the equation. But on the right-hand side there are only 2 moles of gas ($2NH_3$). This means that the volume of the reactants is much greater than the volume of the products. So an increase in pressure will tend to produce more ammonia.

b) How does the volume of the products in the Haber process compare to the volume of the reactants?

To get the maximum possible yield of ammonia in the Haber process, we need to make the pressure as high as possible. But high pressures need expensive reaction vessels and pipes which are strong enough to withstand the pressure. Otherwise there is always the danger that an explosion may happen.

In the Haber process we have to make a compromise between using very high pressures (which would produce a lot of ammonia) and the expense of building a chemical plant which can withstand those high pressures. This compromise means that we usually carry out the Haber process at between 200 and 350 atmospheres pressure.

Figure 1 It is expensive to build chemical plants that operate at high pressures

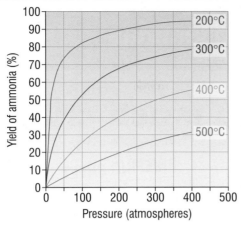

Figure 2 The conditions for the Haber process are a compromise between getting the maximum amount of product in the equilibrium mixture and getting the reaction to take place at a reasonable rate

The effect of temperature on the Haber process is more complicated than the effect of pressure. The forward reaction is exothermic. So if we carry it out at low temperature this would increase the amount of ammonia in the reaction mixture at equilibrium.

But at a low temperature, the rate of the reaction would be very slow. That's because the particles would collide less often and would have less energy. To make ammonia commercially we must get the reaction to go as fast as possible. We don't want to have to wait for the ammonia to be produced!

To do this we need another compromise. A reasonably high temperature is used to get the reaction going at a reasonable rate, even though this reduces the amount of ammonia in the equilibrium mixture.

We also use an iron catalyst to speed up the reaction. (Since this affects the rate of reaction in both directions, it does not affect the amount of ammonia in the equilibrium mixture.)

SUMMARY QUESTIONS

1 Copy and complete using the words below:

> **decreases   exothermic   fewer   increasing   left**
> **pressure   released**

The Haber process is …… so energy is …… during the reaction. This means that …… the temperature …… the amount of ammonia formed. Increasing the …… will increase the amount of ammonia formed, because there are …… moles of gas on the right-hand side of the equation than on the ……-hand side.

2 Look at Figure 2.

a) What is the approximate yield of ammonia at a temperature of 500°C and 400 atmospheres pressure?

b) What is the approximate yield of ammonia at a temperature of 500°C and 100 atmospheres pressure?

c) What is the approximate yield of ammonia at a temperature of 200°C and 400 atmospheres pressure?

d) What is the approximate yield of ammonia at a temperature of 200°C and 100 atmospheres pressure?

e) Why is the Haber process carried out at around 200 to 350 atmospheres and 450°C?

KEY POINTS

1 The Haber process uses a pressure of around 200 to 350 atmospheres to increase the amount of ammonia produced.

2 Although higher pressures would produce more ammonia, they would make the chemical plant too expensive to build.

3 A temperature of about 450°C is used for the reaction. Although lower temperatures would increase the amount of ammonia at equilibrium, the ammonia would be produced too slowly.

C2 5.4   Industrial dilemmas

How can we make as much chemical as possible . . .

ABC Laboratory Consultants

Haber House • Drudge Street • Anywhere • AD13 4FU

Dear Sirs

We are planning to build a factory to produce our new chemical, which has the secret formula AB. We are including some data sheets giving details of the reaction we shall be using to produce this chemical, and would like you to advise us about the best reaction conditions (temperature, pressure etc) to use to get as much AB as we can as cheaply as possible. We should like you to present your ideas in a short presentation to be held in your offices in two weeks' time.

Signed

BRIEFING SHEET 1

Project number: 45AB/L1670-J4550K
Specification: R MST3K 65 L7

Brief prepared by   J K Rolling
Checked by   L Skywalker   CHECKED

The equation for the reaction is:

$$A_2B_2 \rightleftharpoons 2AB$$

Both A_2B_2 and AB are gases. These are not their real formulae, which are secret. But the reaction does involve making two moles of product from one mole of reactants.

BRIEFING SHEET 2

Project number: 45AB/L1670-J4550K
Specification: R MST3K 65 L7   CHECKED

Brief prepared by   J K Rolling
Checked by   L Skywalker

The graph shows the amount of AB in the equilibrium mixture at different temperatures.

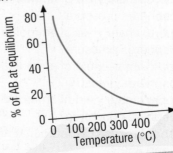

ACTIVITY

Working in teams, decide what you will advise Consolidated Chemicals to do about the conditions for the reaction. Prepare a presentation with your advice – the whole team should contribute to this. The following questions may help you:

- How does the amount of product change with temperature?
- How does the volume of the gases in the reaction change as AB is made from A_2B_2?
- What conditions may affect the reaction, and how?

... and what happens when the raw materials run out?!

NO MORE TINNED FOOD IN STOCK

Due to the world shortage of metals our suppliers have told us that there will be no more deliveries of tinned food. Until further notice.

'What do we do when our resources run low?'

The world population grows all the time. It grows in its demands for a better lifestyle as well. Why shouldn't everyone have access to cars, computers and the latest electrical goodies? Yet all this growth means greater use of our natural resources – chemicals, minerals, oil. Minerals and metals don't replace themselves as carefully managed living resources do. So either we will have to find alternative materials, or alternative sources of the minerals we have been using . . .

London today saw some of the worst rioting as people struggled to get their hands on the last deliveries to be made to the shops. The world shortage of minerals has really begun to bite now, with the supplies of raw materials like copper and zinc running low and prices going through the roof. As oil supplies dwindle too, the lights are going out all over London . . .

'SPACE IS THE ANSWER!!'

The **Bugle** says 'get into space to find more minerals!!' It must be obvious even to our dim-witted leaders that we need to go and explore. Just as explorers in the past found new lands and new riches, we must go into space to find minerals on other planets! We can then bring them back to Earth so that we can make the things we need!'

ACTIVITY

There are many technical problems that have to be solved to allow us to travel to other planets in the Solar System. But imagine that they could be overcome. Could we really travel to other worlds to find new resources and bring them back to Earth?

Work in teams. You have been asked to produce a report for a government department about the possibility of using the Moon and nearby planets as a source of minerals. You need to consider not only the practical aspects of this but also the economics and the politics too. For example, in 1969 American astronauts landed on the Moon. So does this mean that the USA owns the Moon? Who will decide who owns the minerals on Mars or on the Moon?

SUMMARY QUESTIONS

1 Select from A, B, C and/or D to describe correctly exothermic and endothermic reactions.

a) In an exothermic reaction ......

b) In an endothermic reaction ......

A ...... we may notice a decrease in temperature.

B ...... energy is released by the chemicals.

C ...... we may notice an increase in temperature.

D ...... energy is absorbed by the chemicals.

2 'When sherbet sweets dissolve in your mouth this is an endothermic process.' Devise an experiment to test your statement. Use words and diagrams to describe clearly what you would do.

3 Two chemicals are mixed and react endothermically. When the reaction has finished, the reaction mixture is allowed to stand until it has returned to its starting temperature.

a) Sketch a graph of temperature (y-axis) v time (x-axis) to show how the temperature of the reaction mixture changes.

b) Label the graph clearly and explain what is happening wherever you have shown the temperature changing.

4 A chemical reaction can make product Z from reactants X and Y. Under the reaction conditions, X, Y and Z are gases.

X, Y and Z react in the proportions $1:2:3$. The reaction is carried out at 250°C and 100 atmospheres. The reaction is reversible, and it is exothermic in the forward direction.

a) Write an equation for this (reversible) reaction.

b) How would increasing the pressure affect
   i) the amount of Z formed,
   ii) the rate at which Z is formed?

c) How would increasing the temperature affect
   i) the amount of Z formed,
   ii) the rate at which Z is formed?

d) A 10% yield of Z is obtained in 25 seconds under the reaction conditions. To get a 20% yield of Z under the same conditions takes 75 seconds. Explain why it makes more sense economically to set the reaction up to obtain a 10% yield rather than a 20% yield. [Higher]

EXAM-STYLE QUESTIONS

1 Match each of (a) to (g) with one of the following:

**endothermic reaction   exothermic reaction
no reaction**

(a) Burning petrol in a car engine.

(b) Respiration in living cells.

(c) Boiling water.

(d) Converting limestone into calcium oxide.

(e) Switching on an electric light bulb.

(f) Reducing lead oxide with carbon to produce lead.

(g) Carbon dioxide combining with water in cells of green plants.   (7)

2 When heated continuously, pink cobalt chloride crystals can be changed into blue crystals .

$$CoCl_2.6H_2O \rightleftharpoons CoCl_2.2H_2O + 4H_2O$$
pink   blue

(a) What does the symbol $\rightleftharpoons$ tell you about this reaction?   (1)

(b) How can you tell that the reaction to produce blue crystals is endothermic?   (1)

(c) (i) How could you change the blue crystals to pink crystals?   (1)

    (ii) What temperature change would you observe when this is done?   (1)

(d) Suggest how the colour changes of these crystals could be used.   (1)

3 The equation for the main reaction in the Haber process to make ammonia is:

$$N_2 + 3H_2 \rightleftharpoons 2NH_3$$

The table shows the percentage yield of the Haber process at different temperatures and pressures.

Pressure (atm)	Temp. (°C) 0	100	200	300	400	500
400	99	91	78	55	32	20
200	96	87	66	40	21	12
100	94	79	50	25	13	6
50	92	71	36	16	5	2

(a) Why does the yield of ammonia decrease with increased temperature?   (2)

(b) Why does the yield of ammonia increase with increased pressure?   (2)

(c) Why are conditions of 200 atm pressure and 450°C used in the industrial process? (3)

(d) Suggest a better way than a table to present this data. (1)

[Higher]

4 The reaction to produce poly(ethene) is exothermic.

$$n\ C_2H_4 \rightarrow \text{—}(CH_2\text{—}CH_2)_n\text{—}$$
ethene   poly(ethene)

The conditions used in two processes to make poly(ethene) are shown in the table.

Process	Temperature (°C)	Pressure (atm)	Catalyst
A	150–300	1 000–3000	no
B	40–80	1–50	yes

(a) What enables process **B** to be operated under less vigorous conditions? (1)

(b) Suggest one way to keep the energy used to a minimum in both processes. (1)

(c) Suggest **two** environmental advantages of using process **B** to make poly(ethene). (2)

5 A student had learned that the reaction between hydrochloric acid and sodium hydroxide solution was exothermic. She, therefore, predicted that when she added more acid to the alkali more heat would be produced. She used a burette to deliver exact amounts of hydrochloric acid to 20 cm³ of alkali in a flask. She used a thermometer to measure the temperature. Her results are in this table:

Volume of acid added (cm³)	Temperature recorded (°C)
0	17
10	21
20	24
30	21
40	21
50	20

(a) How should she have insulated the flask? (1)

(b) Explain why she should have taken the temperature of the acid before adding it to the sodium hydroxide solution. (2)

(c) Did she actually measure the heat produced by the reaction? Explain your answer. (1)

(d) How might she have used an indicator to increase the accuracy of her method? (1)

HOW SCIENCE WORKS QUESTIONS

Jack set up some apparatus to see the effect of temperature on the rate of a reaction between calcium carbonate and hydrochloric acid.

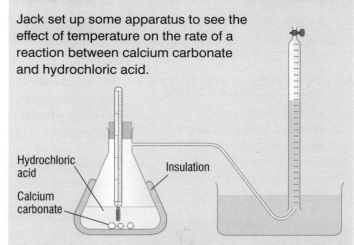

Jack was careful to ensure that the mass of the calcium carbonate, the concentration and the volume of the hydrochloric acid were kept the same for the start of each experiment. He also ensured that the temperature of the reactants was checked after the carbon dioxide had been collected. He timed how long it took, at each temperature, to fill the burette.

Here are his results:

Temperature of reactants (°C)	Average time taken (s)	Average temperature change (°C)
15	145	+1
20	105	+1
25	73	+3
30	51	+3
35	30	+4

a) Plot a graph of the temperature of the reactants against the average time taken. (3)

b) Describe the pattern that you think is shown by these results. (2)

c) List three variables that Jack controlled in this investigation. (3)

d) Name a variable that Jack could not control, but did take account of. (1)

e) What type of error was the changing temperature? Explain your answer. (1)

f) Was the sensitivity of the thermometer good enough? Explain your answer. (1)

g) Why is it not possible to judge the precision of Jack's results? (2)

h) Do you doubt the reliability of Jack's results? Explain your answer. (1)

Electrolysis – the basics

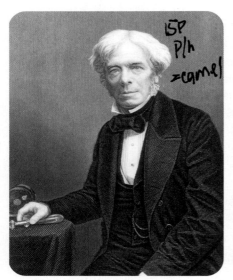

Figure 1 The first person to explain electrolysis was Michael Faraday, who worked on this and many other problems in science nearly 200 years ago. His work formed the basis of an understanding of electrolysis that we still use today.

The word electrolysis means 'splitting up using electricity'. In electrolysis we use an electric current to break down (or **decompose**) a substance made of ions into simpler substances. We call the substance broken down by electrolysis the **electrolyte**.

a) What is electrolysis?
b) What do we call the substance broken down by electrolysis?

We set up an electrical circuit for electrolysis that has two electrodes which dip into the electrolyte. The electrodes are conducting rods. One of these is connected to the positive terminal of a power supply, the other is connected to the negative terminal.

We normally make the electrodes out of an unreactive (or **inert**) substance like graphite or platinum. This is so they do not react with either the electrolyte or the products made during electrolysis. We use the name **anode** for positive electrode, while we call the negative electrode the **cathode**.

During electrolysis, positively charged ions move to the negative electrode (cathode) and negative ions move to the positive electrode (anode).

When the ions reach the electrodes they can lose their charge and be deposited as elements. Depending on the compound being electrolysed, gases may be given off or metals deposited at the electrodes.

DEMONSTRATION

The electrolysis of lead bromide

This demonstration needs a fume cupboard because bromine is toxic and corrosive.

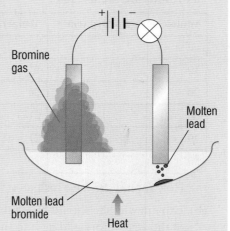

Bromine gas

Molten lead

Molten lead bromide

Heat

Figure 2 When we pass electricity through molten lead bromide it forms molten lead and brown bromine gas as the electrolyte is broken down by the electricity

● When does the bulb light up?

Figure 2 shows how electricity breaks down lead bromide into lead and bromine:

$$\text{lead bromide} \rightarrow \text{lead} + \text{bromine}$$
$$\text{PbBr}_2 \text{ (l)} \rightarrow \text{Pb (l)} + \text{Br}_2 \text{ (g)}$$

Lead bromide is an ionic substance which does not conduct electricity when it is solid. But when we melt it the ions can move freely towards the electrodes.

The positive lead ions move towards the cathode, while the negatively charged bromide ions move towards the anode. Notice how the state symbols in the equation tell us that the lead bromide and the lead are molten. The '(l)' stands for 'liquid', while bromine is given off as a gas, shown as '(g)'.

c) Which electrode do positive ions move towards during electrolysis?
d) Which electrode do negative ions move towards during electrolysis?

Many ionic substances have very high melting points. This can make electrolysis very difficult or even impossible. But some ionic substances dissolve in water, and when this happens the ions can move freely.

When we dissolve ionic substances in water to electrolyse them it is more difficult to predict what will be formed. This is because water also forms ions, and so the product at the anode and the cathode is not always exactly what we expect.

When we electrolyse a solution of copper bromide in water, copper ions move to the negative electrode (cathode) and the bromide ions move to the positive electrode (anode). Copper bromide is split into its two elements at the electrodes:

$$\text{copper bromide} \rightarrow \text{copper} + \text{bromine}$$
$$CuBr_2 \text{ (aq)} \quad \rightarrow Cu \text{ (s)} + Br_2 \text{ (aq)}$$

In this case the state symbols in the equation tell us that the copper bromide is dissolved in water, shown as '(aq)'. The elements that are produced are solid copper, shown as '(s)', and bromine which remains dissolved in the water – '(aq)'.

Covalent compounds cannot be split by electrolysis.

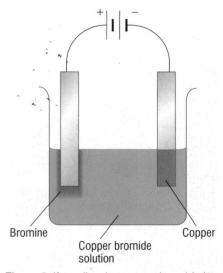

Bromine — Copper
Copper bromide solution

Figure 3 If we dissolve copper bromide in water we can decompose it by electrolysis. Copper metal is formed at the cathode, while brown bromine appears in solution around the anode.

SUMMARY QUESTIONS

1 Copy and complete using the words below:

> **anode**   **cathode**   **ions**   **molten**   **move**
> **negative**   **solution**

In electrolysis the ...... is the positive electrode while the ...... is the ...... electrode. For the current to flow, the ...... must be able to ...... between the electrodes. This can only happen if the substance is in ...... or if it is ....

2 Predict the products formed at each electrode when the following compounds are melted and then electrolysed:

a) copper iodide
b) potassium bromide
c) sodium fluoride.

3 Solid ionic substances do not conduct electricity. Using words and diagrams explain why they conduct electricity when molten or in solution.

KEY POINTS

1 Electrolysis involves splitting up a substance using electricity.
2 Ionic substances can be electrolysed when they are molten or in solution.
3 In electrolysis positive ions move to the negative electrode (cathode) and negative ions move to the positive electrode (anode).

C2 6.2

Changes at the electrodes

LEARNING OBJECTIVES

1 What happens during electrolysis?
2 How can we represent what happens in electrolysis? [Higher]
3 How does water affect the products of electrolysis?

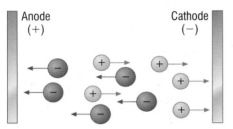

Figure 1 An ion always moves towards the oppositely charged electrode

During electrolysis ions move towards the electrodes. The direction they move in depends on their charge. As we saw on the previous page, positive ions move towards the negative electrode (the cathode). Negative ions move towards the positive electrode (the anode).

When ions reach an electrode, they either lose or gain electrons depending on their charge.

Negatively charged ions **lose** electrons to become neutral atoms. Positively charged ions form neutral atoms by **gaining** electrons.

a) How do negatively charged ions become neutral atoms in electrolysis?
b) How do positively charged ions become neutral atoms in electrolysis?

The easiest way to think about this is to look at an example:

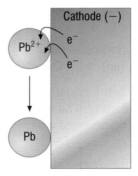

In the electrolysis of molten lead bromide, positively charged lead ions (Pb^{2+}) move towards the cathode (−). When they get there, each ion gains **two** electrons to become a neutral lead atom.

Gaining electrons is called **reduction** – we say that the lead ions are **reduced**. 'Reduction' is simply another way of saying 'gaining electrons'.

When molten lead bromide is electrolysed, negatively charged bromide ions (Br^-) move towards the anode (+). When they get there, each ion loses **one** electron to become a neutral bromine atom. Two bromine atoms then form a covalent bond to make a bromine molecule, Br_2.

Losing electrons is called **oxidation** – we say that the bromide ions are **oxidised**. 'Oxidation' is another way of saying 'losing electrons'.

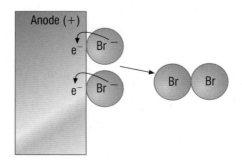

We represent what is happening at the electrodes using *half equations*. We call them this because what happens at one electrode is only half the story – we need to know what is happening at both electrodes to know what is happening in the whole reaction.

At the negative electrode:

$$Pb^{2+} + 2e^- \rightarrow Pb \qquad \text{(notice how an electron is written as 'e}^-\text{')}$$

At the positive electrode:

$$2Br^- \rightarrow Br_2 + 2e^-$$

Sometimes half equations are written showing the electrons being removed from negative ions, like this:

$$2Br^- - 2e^- \rightarrow Br_2$$

Neither method is more 'right' than the other – it just depends on how you want to write the half equation.

Because **RED**uction and **OX**idation take place at the same time in electrolysis (reduction at the cathode (−), oxidation at the anode (+)), it is sometimes called a **redox** reaction.

The effect of water

When we carry out electrolysis in water the situation is made more complicated by the fact that water contains ions. The rule for working out what will happen is to remember that if two elements can be produced at an electrode, the less reactive element will usually be formed.

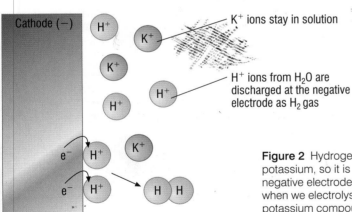

Cathode (−)

K⁺ ions stay in solution

H⁺ ions from H_2O are discharged at the negative electrode as H_2 gas

Figure 2 Hydrogen is less reactive than potassium, so it is produced at the negative electrode rather than potassium when we electrolyse a solution of a potassium compound

KEY POINTS

1 In electrolysis, the ions move towards the oppositely charged electrodes.
2 At the electrodes, negative ions are oxidised while positive ions are reduced.
3 Reactions where reduction and oxidation happen are called redox reactions.
4 When electrolysis happens in water, the less reactive element is usually produced at an electrode.

SUMMARY QUESTIONS

1 Copy and complete using the words below:

| anode (+) | cathode (−) | electrodes | gain | less | lose |
| ions | oxidised | reduced | | | |

During electrolysis ...... move towards the .... At the ...... positively charged ions are ...... and ...... electrons. At the ...... negatively charged ions are ...... and ...... electrons. When electrolysis is carried out in water, the ...... reactive element is usually produced.

2 Copy and complete the following half-equations where necessary:

a) $Cl^- \rightarrow Cl_2 + e^-$ c) $Ca^{2+} + e^- \rightarrow Ca$ e) $Na^+ + e^- \rightarrow Na$

b) $O^{2-} \rightarrow O_2 + e^-$ d) $Al^{3+} + e^- \rightarrow Al$ f) $H^+ + e^- \rightarrow H_2$ [Higher]

C2 6.3

Electrolysing brine

LEARNING OBJECTIVES

1 What is produced when we electrolyse brine?
2 How do we use these products?

PRACTICAL

Electrolysing brine in the lab

Turn off the electricity once the tubes are nearly full of gas to avoid inhaling chlorine gas (toxic).

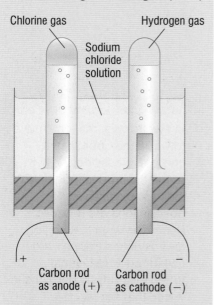

- How can you positively test for the gases collected?

The electrolysis of brine (sodium chloride solution) is an enormously important industrial process. When we pass an electric current through brine we get three products. Chlorine gas is produced at the positive electrode, hydrogen gas is made at the negative electrode, and a solution of sodium hydroxide is also formed:

$$\text{sodium chloride solution} \xrightarrow{\text{electrolysis}} \text{hydrogen} + \text{chlorine} + \text{sodium hydroxide solution}$$

a) What are the three products made when we electrolyse brine?

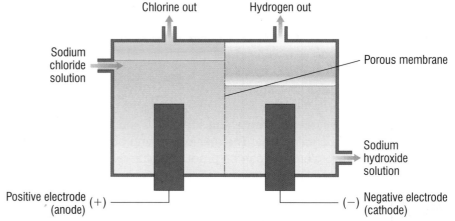

Figure 1 Brine can be electrolysed in a cell in which the two electrodes are separated by a porous membrane. This is called a **diaphragm cell**.

The half equations for what happens in the electrolysis of brine are:

At the positive electrode, $\quad 2Cl^- (aq) \rightarrow Cl_2 (g) + 2e^-$

At the negative electrode, $\quad 2H^+ (aq) + 2e^- \rightarrow H_2 (g)$

This leaves a solution containing Na^+ and OH^- ions, i.e. a solution of sodium hydroxide.

Using chlorine

Chlorine is a poisonous green gas which causes great damage to our bodies if it is inhaled in even tiny quantities. But it is also a tremendously useful chemical. The chlorine made when we electrolyse brine plays a vital role in public health. It is used to kill bacteria in drinking water and in swimming pools.

We can also react chlorine with the sodium hydroxide produced in the electrolysis of brine. This makes a solution called *bleach* (sodium chlorate(I)). Bleach is a strong oxidising agent which is very good at killing bacteria. We use it widely in homes, hospitals and industry to maintain good hygiene.

Chlorine is also an important part of many other disinfectants as well as the plastic (polymer) known as PVC.

b) What is chlorine used for?

Using hydrogen

The hydrogen that we make by electrolysing brine is particularly pure. This makes it very useful in the food industry. We make margarine by reacting hydrogen with vegetable oils under pressure and with a catalyst to turn the oil into a soft spreadable solid.

We can also react hydrogen with the chlorine made by the electrolysis of brine to make hydrogen chloride gas. We can then dissolve this gas in water to make hydrochloric acid. This very pure acid is used widely by the food and pharmaceutical industries.

c) What is hydrogen used for?

Using sodium hydroxide

The sodium hydroxide which is made when we electrolyse brine is used to make soap and paper. It is also used to control the pH in many industrial processes. The other major use of sodium hydroxide is to combine it with the chlorine produced to make bleach (see previous page).

d) What is sodium hydroxide used for?

Figure 2 Chlorine brings us clean, disease-free drinking water and helps to keep our homes, schools and hospitals free from disease

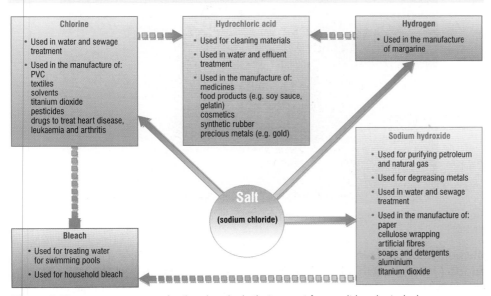

Figure 3 There are many uses for the chemicals that we get from salt by electrolysis

SUMMARY QUESTIONS

1 Copy and complete using the words below:

> **chlorine   hydrochloric   hydrogen   sodium chlorate(I)**
> **sodium hydroxide**

When we pass an electric current through brine we make ...... gas, ... gas and .... solution. These products are also used to make .... solution (bleach) and ...... acid.

2 a) Write a balanced chemical equation to show the production of chlorine, hydrogen and sodium hydroxide from salt solution by electrolysis. The equation is started off for you below:

$$NaCl + H_2O \rightarrow ?$$ [Higher]

b) We can also electrolyse *molten* sodium chloride. Compare the products formed with those from the electrolysis of sodium chloride solution. What are the differences?

KEY POINTS

1 When we electrolyse brine we get three products – chlorine gas, hydrogen gas and sodium hydroxide solution.

2 Chlorine is used to kill microbes in drinking water and swimming pools, and to make hydrochloric acid, disinfectants, bleach and plastics.

3 Hydrogen is used to make margarine and hydrochloric acid.

4 Sodium hydroxide is used to make bleach, paper and soap.

C2 6.4 Purifying copper

LEARNING OBJECTIVES

1 Why do we need to purify copper?
2 How do we use electrolysis to purify copper?

When we remove copper from its ore it is possible to get copper that is about 99% pure. The impurities include precious metals like gold, silver and platinum. These affect the conductivity of the copper, and must be removed before we can use the copper for electrical wires.

a) What impurities may be found in copper after it has been removed from its ore?
b) Why must these be removed?

Figure 1 A major use of copper is to make cables and wires for carrying electricity and electrical signals

We purify copper using electrolysis. A bar of impure copper is used as the anode (+), and a thin sheet of pure copper is the cathode (−). The electrolysis takes place in a solution containing copper ions (usually copper sulfate solution).

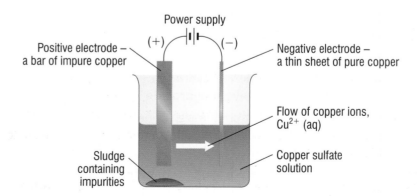

Power supply

Positive electrode – a bar of impure copper

(+)   (−)

Negative electrode – a thin sheet of pure copper

Flow of copper ions, Cu^{2+} (aq)

Sludge containing impurities

Copper sulfate solution

Figure 2 Copper is refined using electrolysis

At the positive electrode, copper atoms are oxidised. They form copper ions and go into the solution:

$$Cu \text{ (s)} \rightarrow Cu^{2+} \text{ (aq)} + 2e^-$$

[Higher]

At the negative electrode, copper ions are reduced. They form copper atoms which are deposited on the electrode:

$$Cu^{2+}\,(aq) + 2e^- \rightarrow Cu\,(s) \qquad\qquad \text{[Higher]}$$

c) Where are the copper atoms oxidised?

d) What is formed when copper atoms are oxidised?

Once we have purified the copper in the electrolytic cell, it is removed, melted and then formed into bars or ingots.

The sludge, containing precious metal impurities, is periodically removed from the electrolysis cell to collect the precious metals from it.

PRACTICAL

Comparing electrodes

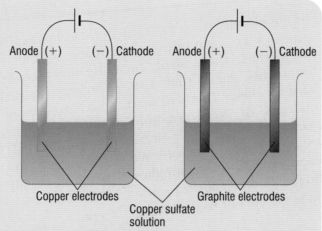

We can show the difference between the electrolysis of copper sulfate solution using copper electrodes and electrolysis using graphite electrodes.

- What happens at each electrode?

Here is a summary of the electrolysis of copper sulfate solution using different electrodes:

HIGHER

Using copper electrodes		Using graphite electrodes	
At anode (+)	At cathode (−)	At anode (+)	At cathode (−)
$Cu(s) \rightarrow Cu^{2+}(aq)$ $+ 2e^-$	$Cu^{2+}(aq) + 2e^-$ $\rightarrow Cu(s)$	$2H_2O(l) \rightarrow 4H^+(aq)$ $+ O_2(g) + 4e^-$	$Cu^{2+}(aq) + 2e^-$ $\rightarrow Cu(s)$

We can also show the half equation at the graphite anode (+) as:

$$4\,OH^-(aq) \rightarrow 2\,H_2O(l) + O_2(g) + 4e^-$$

SUMMARY QUESTIONS

1 Copy and complete using the words below:

**atoms   cathode (−)   copper   copper sulfate   deposited
electrolysis   electrons   impure   oxidised   reduced**

Copper is purified by ...... using electrodes made of .... An electric current is passed through a solution of .... The anode (+) is made of ...... copper. The copper atoms are ...... and go into the solution. At the ...... they gain ...... and are .... They form copper ...... and are ...... on the cathode (−).

2 What happens to the impurities that are removed from the copper when it is purified?

C2 6.5   To build or not to build?

Unemployment in Newtown may rise!

Two big local employers say that concerns over supplies of chemicals that they need for their factories mean that they may have to close. This will lead to hundreds of Newtown jobs being slashed.

A director of Allied Fats said 'We have been worried about supplies of hydrogen to our plant for some time since the cost of transporting this chemical is so high. We may have to close and relocate our business somewhere nearer to our present suppliers.'

Consolidated Paper are also worried about supplies of sodium hydroxide and chlorine to their paper mill in the town. Tracey Wiggins, the MP for Newtown, said 'This would be a tragedy for the town.'

Hope for new employment!

Following concerns about supplies of chemicals to two big local employers, we can exclusively reveal that a deal is being struck that would bring a manufacturer of these chemicals to Newtown.

BrineCo, one of the largest chemical companies in the country, is currently in talks with the council about building a big new plant to produce chemicals in a new factory near the town. BrineCo already manufacture chlorine and sodium hydroxide at other plants in the UK.

Local MP Tracey Wiggins said 'This would be a wonderful opportunity for workers and their families in Newtown and the surrounding area.'

QUESTIONS

Look at the two leaflets produced by BrineCo and by the local pressure group GREEN.

1 Make a list of the differences between the two maps on the leaflets.
2 How is BrineCo trying to persuade people that their factory is a good idea?
3 How is GREEN trying to persuade people that the factory is *not* a good idea?

ACTIVITY

Write an editorial for the local newspaper in which you examine both sides of the argument for bringing the BrineCo chemical factory to the town. The final part of your editorial should come down on one side or the other – but you must argue your point logically. You may also decide that the factory should go ahead, but on a different site. Can *you* persuade local people that *you* are the voice of reason?

BrineCo
working for you!

BrineCo produce chlorine and sodium hydroxide solution by passing electricity through brine (salt solution). This is called **electrolysis**.

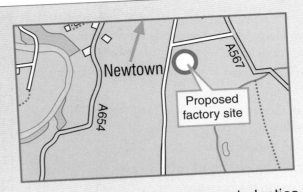

Proposed factory site

The chlorine that we make is used to make paper, chemicals and plastics, and for treating water to kill bacteria. Sodium hydroxide solution is sold to companies making paper, artificial fibres, soaps and detergents.

Our new factory can bring many benefits to Newtown. Consolidated Paper will be a major user of BrineCo's chemicals, and Allied Fats will buy the hydrogen produced by our factory.

This will give both companies a cheaper supply of raw materials than they have at present. *Think carefully about BrineCo's proposals – they mean a secure future for you and your children.*

KEEP NEWTOWN FREE FROM CHEMICALS!!!

GO GREEN
Keep Newtown clean!

*G*ive
*R*ights to
*E*veryone's
*E*nvironment in
*N*ewtown

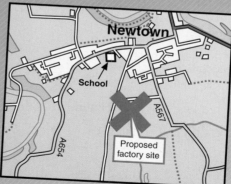

School

Proposed factory site

- Do you realise that chlorine gas was used as a weapon in World War I?!
- Do you want chlorine carried in tankers through our town?!
- What would a spill mean for YOUR children?
- Do we really know what these chemicals will do?
- BrineCo will make thousands of tonnes of these chemicals in our town EVERY DAY if this plan goes ahead!
- Are jobs worth the lives of our children?!

SUMMARY QUESTIONS

1 Select A or B to describe correctly what happens at the positive electrode and negative electrode in electrolysis for a) to f).

   a) Positive ions move towards this.   A Positive electrode

   b) Negative ions move towards this.   B Negative electrode

   c) Reduction happens here.

   d) Oxidation happens here.

   e) Connected to the negative terminal of the power supply.

   f) Connected to the positive terminal of the power supply.

2 Make a table to show which of the following ions would move towards the positive electrode and which towards the negative electrode during electrolysis. (You may need to use a copy of the periodic table to help you.)

   sodium, iodide, calcium, fluoride, zinc, oxide, aluminium, bromide

3 Water can be split into hydrogen and oxygen using electrolysis. The word equation for this reaction is:

   $$water \rightarrow hydrogen + oxygen$$

   a) Write a balanced equation for this reaction using the correct chemical symbols.

   b) Write half-equations to show what happens at the positive and negative electrodes.

   c) When some water is electrolysed it produces 2 moles of hydrogen. How much oxygen is produced?

   d) Where does the energy needed to split water into hydrogen and oxygen come from during electrolysis?

   [Higher]

4 Copy and complete the following half equations:

   a) $K^+ \rightarrow K$ b) $Ba^{2+} \rightarrow Ba$

   c) $I^- \rightarrow I_2$ d) $O^{2-} \rightarrow O_2$

   [Higher]

5 Electrolysis can be used to produce a thin layer of metal on the surface of a metal object. Using words and diagrams, describe how you would cover a small piece of steel with copper. Make sure that you write down the half equation that describes what happens at the surface of the steel.

   [Higher]

EXAM-STYLE QUESTIONS

1 The table shows the results of passing electricity through some substances. Carbon electrodes were used.

Substance	Product at negative electrode	Product at positive electrode
Molten lead bromide	lead	A
Molten B	magnesium	chlorine
Aqueous sodium sulfate solution	C	oxygen
Aqueous copper sulfate solution	D	E

   (a) Name **A, B, C, D** and **E**.   (5)

   (b) What is the name used for substances that conduct electricity and are decomposed by it?   (1)

   (c) Why must the substances be molten or in solution?   (1)

   (d) Explain why reduction takes place at the negative electrode.   (2)

2 The diagram shows a cell used for the electrolysis of brine. Brine is a solution of sodium chloride in water.

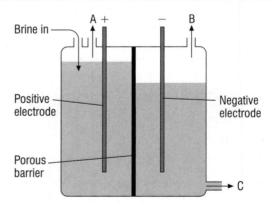

   (a) Name and give the formulae of the positive ions in brine.   (2)

   (b) Name and give the formulae of the negative ions in brine.   (2)

   (c) Name gases **A** and **B**.   (2)

   (d) Explain as fully as you can how gas B is produced.   (4)

   (e) Name the product in solution C.   (1)

3 Mild steel can be electroplated with tin in the laboratory. The diagram shows the apparatus used.

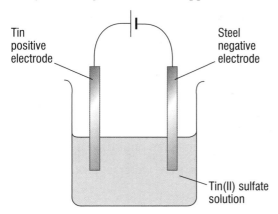

Tin positive electrode

Steel negative electrode

Tin(II) sulfate solution

(a) Explain what happens at the negative electrode to deposit tin on the steel. (3)

(b) What happens to tin at the positive electrode? (3)

(c) Why does the concentration of the tin(II) sulfate solution not change during the electrolysis? (2)

(d) Some food cans are made of mild steel coated with tin. Suggest **two** reasons why tin plated steel is chosen for this use. (2)

4 A student was interested in electrolysis. He knew that a current passes through a copper sulfate solution. With copper electrodes some of the copper would come away from one electrode and move to the other. He thought that there would be the same amount of copper leaving one electrode as attached to the other electrode. He set up his equipment and weighed each electrode several times over a 25 minute period. His results are in this table:

Loss in mass of positive electrode in 5 minutes (g)	Gain in mass of negative electrode in 5 minutes (g)	Time (mins)
0.027	0.021	5
0.022	0.027	10
0.061	0.030	15
0.001	0.025	20
0.025	0.027	25

(a) What evidence is there for an anomalous result? (1)

(b) What was the range for the results at the negative electrode? (1)

(c) What evidence is there to support the student's prediction? (1)

(d) Comment on the reliability of the results. (1)

HOW SCIENCE WORKS QUESTIONS

Hydrogen – the new petrol?

Hydrogen could be a very important fuel for personal transport. However, there are many practical problems to be solved.

Mikael came up with the idea of using the Sun's energy to produce hydrogen from sea water. The apparatus used was similar to what you might have seen in your school laboratory. However, he used a solar cell to produce a voltage to drive the electrolysis. Mikael left the electrolysis for the same time for each solution used.

The results are shown below.

Solution used	Volume of hydrogen (cm³)			mean
Sea water	33	27	45	

a) Calculate the mean volume of hydrogen produced. (1)

b) What do these results tell us about the precision of the method used? Explain your answer. (1)

c) What probably caused the variation in the student's results? (1)

d) Mikael's teacher dismissed the research saying, 'It could never come to anything that might produce large volumes of hydrogen.' Why do you think the teacher thought this? (1)

e) Mikael's dad thought it was a brilliant idea and a chance to make some money! He pictured a huge factory turning out millions of tonnes of hydrogen and millions of pounds of money! He quizzed Mikael about his results. He asked Mikael if he was telling the whole truth. Why was it important that Mikael was telling the whole truth about his investigation? (1)

f) What might be Mikael's next step towards becoming a millionaire? (1)

ACIDS, ALKALIS AND SALTS

C2 7.1

Acids and alkalis

LEARNING OBJECTIVES

1 Why are solutions acidic or alkaline?
2 How do we measure acidity?

Figure 1 Acids and bases are all around us, in many of the things we buy at the shops, in our schools and factories – and inside us too

Figure 2 Some common laboratory acids

Acids and bases are an important part of our understanding of chemistry. They play a vital part inside us and for all other living things too.

What are acids and bases?

When we dissolve a substance in water we make an **aqueous solution**. The solution may be acidic, alkaline or neutral, depending on the chemical we have dissolved. **Bases** are chemicals which can neutralise **acids**.

Alkalis are bases which dissolve in water. Pure water is **neutral**.

a) What is a base?
b) What is an alkali?

Acids include chemicals like citric acid, sulfuric acid and ethanoic acid. All acids taste very sour, although many acids are far too dangerous to put in your mouth. We use acids in many chemical reactions in the laboratory. Ethanoic acid (vinegar) and citric acid (the sour taste in citric fruit, fizzy drinks and squashes) are acids which we regularly eat.

One acid that we use in the laboratory is hydrochloric acid. This is formed when the gas hydrogen chloride (HCl) dissolves in water:

$$HCl \text{ (g)} \xrightarrow{\text{water}} H^+ \text{ (aq)} + Cl^- \text{ (aq)}$$

All acids form H^+ ions when we add them to water – it is hydrogen ions that make a solution acidic. Hydrogen chloride also forms chloride ions (Cl^-). The '(aq)' symbol shows that the ions are in an 'aqueous solution'. In other words, they are dissolved in water.

c) What ions do all acids form when we add them to water?

Bases are the opposite of acids in the way they react. Because alkalis are bases which dissolve in water they are the bases which we use most commonly. For example, sodium hydroxide solution is often found in our school laboratories. Sodium hydroxide solution is formed when we dissolve solid sodium hydroxide in water:

$$NaOH \text{ (s)} \xrightarrow{\text{water}} Na^+ \text{ (aq)} + OH^- \text{ (aq)}$$

All alkalis form hydroxide ions (OH^-) when we add them to water. It is hydroxide ions that make a solution alkaline.

d) What ions do all alkalis form when we add them to water?

Measuring acidity

Indicators are special chemicals which change colour when we add them to acids and alkalis. Litmus paper is one well-known indicator, but there are many more. These include some natural ones like the juice of red cabbage or beetroot.

We use the **pH scale** to show how acid or alkaline a solution is. The scale runs from 0 (most acidic) to 14 (most alkaline). **Universal indicator** is a very special indicator made from a number of dyes. It turns different colours at different values of pH. Anything in the middle of the pH scale (pH 7) is **neutral**, neither acid nor alkali.

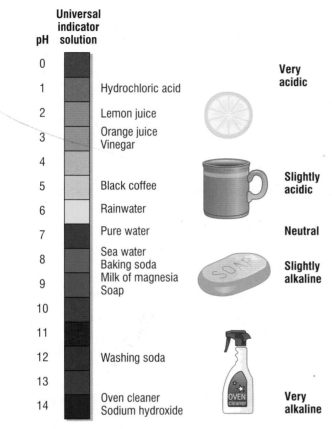

Figure 3 The pH scale tells us how acid or alkaline a solution is

A H⁺ ion is simply a hydrogen atom that has lost an electron – in other words a proton. So another way of describing an acid is to say that it is a 'proton donor'.

SUMMARY QUESTIONS

1 Copy and complete using the words below:

   alkaline   dissolve   greater   hydrogen   hydroxide   less   neutralise   pH   seven

   Acids form …… ions when we dissolve them in water. Bases react with acids and …… them. Alkalis are bases which …… in water. They form …… ions when they do this. The …… scale tells us how acidic or alkaline a solution is. If the pH is …… the solution is neutral, if it is …… than 7 the solution is acidic, and if it is …… than 7 the solution is …… .

2 How could you use paper containing universal indicator as a way of distinguishing between pure water, sodium hydroxide solution and citric acid solution?

KEY POINTS

1 Acids are substances which produce H⁺ ions when we add them to water.
2 Bases are substances that will neutralise acids.
3 An alkali is a soluble base. Alkalis produce OH⁻ ions when we add them to water.
4 We use the pH scale to show how acidic or alkaline a solution is.

C2 7.2   Making salts from metals or bases

Acids + metals

We can make salts by reacting acids with metals. This is only possible if the metal is above hydrogen in the reactivity series. If it is, then hydrogen gas is produced when the acid reacts with the metal, and a salt is also produced:

$$\text{acid} \quad + \quad \text{metal} \quad \rightarrow \quad \text{salt} \quad + \text{hydrogen}$$

$$2HCl\,(aq) \quad + \quad Mg\,(s) \quad \rightarrow \quad MgCl_2\,(aq) \quad + \quad H_2\,(g)$$

hydrochloric acid + magnesium → magnesium chloride + hydrogen
solution

a) What does the reaction between an acid and a metal produce?

Acid + insoluble base

When we react an acid with a base we produce a solution which contains a salt and water.

The general equation which describes all reactions of this type is:

$$\textbf{acid} + \textbf{base} \rightarrow \textbf{salt} + \textbf{water}$$

b) What two substances are formed when an acid and a base react?

The salt that we make depends on the metal or the base that we use in the reaction and the acid. So bases that contain sodium ions will always make sodium salts, while those that contain potassium ions will always make potassium salts.

In a similar way:

- the salts formed when we neutralise hydrochloric acid are always *chlorides*
- sulfuric acid always makes salts which are *sulfates*, and
- nitric acid always makes *nitrates*.

The oxide of a transition metal, such as iron(III) oxide, is an example of a base that we can use to make a salt in this way:

$$\text{acid} \quad + \quad \text{base} \quad \rightarrow \quad \text{salt} \quad + \quad \text{water}$$

$$6HCl\,(aq) \quad + \quad Fe_2O_3\,(s) \quad \rightarrow \quad 2FeCl_3\,(aq) \quad + 3H_2O\,(l)$$

hydrochloric acid + solid iron(III) oxide → iron(III) chloride + water
solution

c) Name the salt formed when dilute sulfuric acid reacts with zinc oxide.

DID YOU KNOW?

Chalk or limestone is added to lakes that are badly affected by acid rain to increase the pH of the water.

PRACTICAL

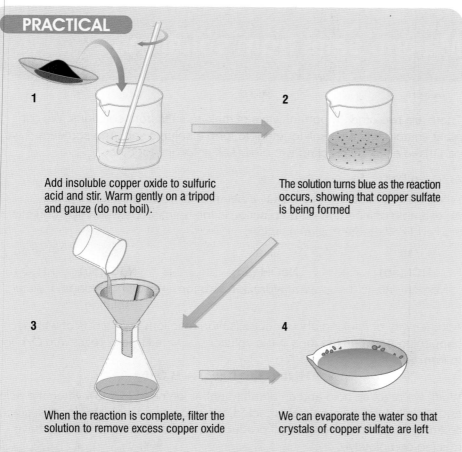

1 Add insoluble copper oxide to sulfuric acid and stir. Warm gently on a tripod and gauze (do not boil).

2 The solution turns blue as the reaction occurs, showing that copper sulfate is being formed

3 When the reaction is complete, filter the solution to remove excess copper oxide

4 We can evaporate the water so that crystals of copper sulfate are left

We can make copper sulfate crystals from copper oxide (an insoluble base) and sulfuric acid. The equation for the reaction is:

$$\text{acid} \quad + \quad \text{base} \quad \rightarrow \quad \text{salt} \quad + \text{water}$$

$$\text{H}_2\text{SO}_4\text{ (aq)} + \quad \text{CuO (s)} \quad \rightarrow \text{CuSO}_4\text{ (aq)} + \text{H}_2\text{O (l)}$$

sulfuric + solid copper(II) → copper sulfate + water
acid   oxide   solution

- What does the copper sulfate look like? Draw a diagram if necessary.

SUMMARY QUESTIONS

1 Copy and complete using the words below:

bases   hydrogen   metals   neutralisation   salt   water

The reaction between an acid and a base is called a …… reaction. When this happens, a …… is formed, together with …… . Salts can be made by reacting acids with ……, when …… gas is formed along with the salt. They can also be made by reacting acids with insoluble ……, when water is formed as well as the salt.

2 'Bicarbonate for bees and vinegar for vasps (wasps!!)' is one way of remembering what to do if you are stung by a bee or a wasp. What does this suggest about the pH of bee stings and wasp stings?

C2 7.3   Making salts from solutions

LEARNING OBJECTIVES

1 How can we make salts from an acid and an alkali?
2 How can we make insoluble salts?
3 How can we remove unwanted ions from solutions?

Figure 2 Ammonium nitrate is used as a fertiliser

Figure 3 Water treatment plants use chemical treatments to precipitate chemical compounds that can then be removed by filtering the solution

There are two other important ways of making salts from solutions. We can react an acid and an alkali together to form a soluble salt. And sometimes we can make a salt by reacting two other salt solutions together.

Acid + alkali

When an acid reacts with an alkali a neutralisation reaction takes place. An example of a neutralisation reaction is the reaction between hydrochloric acid and sodium hydroxide solution:

acid	+	alkali	→	salt	+ water
$HCl\ (aq)$	+	$NaOH\ (aq)$	→	$NaCl\ (aq)$	$+ H_2O\ (l)$

hydrochloric acid + sodium hydroxide solution → sodium chloride + water solution

Another way of thinking about neutralisation reactions is in terms of what is happening between the ions in the solutions, where H^+ ions react with OH^- ions to form water:

$$H^+\ (aq) + OH^-\ (aq) \rightarrow H_2O\ (l)$$

When we react an acid and an **alkali** together we need to know when the acid and the alkali have completely reacted. We can use an indicator for this, since a strong acid and a strong alkali produce a neutral solution when they have reacted completely.

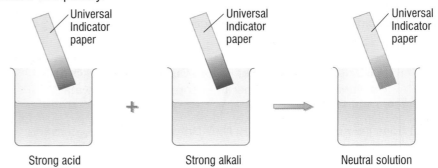

Strong acid   Strong alkali   Neutral solution

Figure 1 Universal indicator paper can show us when a strong acid and a strong alkali have reacted completely to form a salt because a neutral solution is formed

We can make ammonium salts by reacting an acid and alkali together. Ammonia reacts with water to form ammonium hydroxide (a weak alkali):

$$NH_3\ (aq) + H_2O\ (l) \rightleftharpoons NH_4OH\ (aq)$$

Ammonium hydroxide then reacts with an acid (for example, nitric acid):

acid	+	alkali	→	salt	+ water
$HNO_3\ (aq)$ +		$NH_4OH\ (aq)$	→	$NH_4NO_3\ (aq)$	$+ H_2O\ (l)$

nitric acid + ammonium hydroxide → ammonium nitrate + water solution   solution

Ammonium nitrate contains a large amount of nitrogen, and it is very soluble in water. This makes it ideal as a source of nitrogen to replace the nitrogen taken up from the soil by plants as they grow.

a) Write down a general equation for the reaction between an acid and an alkali.

Making insoluble salts

We can sometimes make salts by combining two solutions. When this makes an insoluble salt, we call the reaction a **precipitation** reaction because the insoluble solid that is formed is called a **precipitate**.

$$Pb(NO_3)_2 \text{ (aq)} + 2NaCl \text{ (aq)} \rightarrow PbCl_2 \text{ (s)} + 2NaNO_3 \text{ (aq)}$$

lead nitrate + sodium chloride → solid lead chloride + sodium nitrate
    solution   solution   (precipitate)   solution

The equation for the reaction shows how the lead chloride that forms is insoluble in water. It forms a solid precipitate that we can filter off from the solution.

b) What do we call a reaction that produces a precipitate?

PRACTICAL

Making an insoluble salt

Sodium chloride

Lead nitrate solution

1 We add sodium chloride solution to lead nitrate solution and stir

2 The precipitate of lead chloride that forms is filtered off from the solution

3 The precipitate is washed with distilled water and dried

We can make lead chloride crystals from lead nitrate solution and sodium chloride solution. The equation for the reaction is shown at the top of this page.

● What does the lead chloride look like?

Using precipitation

We use precipitation reactions to remove pollutants from the wastewater from factories and industrial parks before the effluent is discharged into rivers and the sea.

An important precipitation reaction is the removal of metal ions from water that has been used in industrial processes. By raising the pH of the water, we can make insoluble metal hydroxides precipitate out of the solution. This produces a sludge which we can easily remove from the solution.

The cleaned-up water can then be discharged safely into a river or into the sea.

SUMMARY QUESTIONS

1 Copy and complete using the words below:

acid   alkali   insoluble   metal   polluted   precipitation   solid   soluble   water

We can make salts by reacting an ...... with an .... This makes the salt and .... We can also make ...... salts by reacting two ...... salts together. We call this a ...... reaction because the salt is formed as a .... This type of reaction is also important when we want to remove ...... ions from ...... water.

2 Write word equations to show what is formed when:

a) nitric acid reacts with potassium hydroxide solution,
b) lead nitrate solution reacts with potassium bromide solution.

KEY POINTS

1 An indicator is needed when we produce a salt by reacting an alkali with an acid to make a soluble salt.
2 Insoluble salts can be made by reacting two solutions to produce a precipitate.
3 Precipitation is an important way of removing some substances from wastewater.

C2 7.4   It's all in the soil

The importance of rotation

No, nothing to do with rotating YOU! This is about not growing the same vegetables in the same place two years running. If you do this you are likely to find two problems.

First, pests and diseases which live on the particular vegetables will increase, and you will have real problems.

Second, growing the same crop in the same place year after year will lead to the soil becoming unbalanced, with the level of some nutrients becoming too low.

Getting the right amount of acid

When the soil in your garden is too acid or alkaline, nutrients present in the soil become locked-up or unavailable. Acidic soil has a 'pH' that is too low (less than 7) while alkaline soil has a 'pH' that is too high. In fact, a decrease of just one pH unit means that the soil is ten times more acidic!

Getting the pH right is the same as applying fertiliser since it 'unlocks' plant nutrients which are already present.

ACTIVITY

Although there is a lot of chemistry in gardening, it is not often that it is explained clearly (or correctly!). Your job is to write an article for a gardening newspaper or a leaflet for a local garden centre.

It should describe the chemistry behind getting the pH of the soil correct by testing it and then adding the necessary chemicals. You can even use simple chemical equations (especially word equations) if this helps you to explain things more clearly.

Testing your soil

You can find out the pH of your soil by testing it with a simple soil testing kit. This will tell you how acidic or alkaline your soil is.

Follow the instructions in the kit, which usually involves mixing a little soil with some water and testing it with some special paper. The colour that the paper turns will tell you if your soil has a 'pH' that is too low or too high.

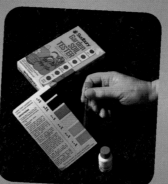

What to add . . . ?

If your soil has the wrong 'pH' you'll need to do something about it. Unless you live on chalky soil it's very unusual for the pH of soil to be too high. This is because adding fertiliser usually makes soil acidic. So the most common thing that you'll need to do every so often to keep your soil with a 'neutral pH' is to add lime.

Lime is made by heating limestone to decompose it. Lime reacts with acid in the soil, making it neutral. You can buy lime from your local garden centre.

Blue flag beaches

The idea of a way of showing clearly that a beach is clean was put forward in 1987, when 244 beaches from 10 countries were awarded a flag to show that the beach met certain standards. As far as water quality goes, these standards include:

- the cleanliness of the water must comply with the EU Bathing Water Directive,
- no industrial effluent or sewage discharges may affect the beach area,
- there must be local emergency plans to cope with pollution accidents.

In 2005 there were nearly 2500 blue flag beaches worldwide.

ACTIVITY

The town council of a seaside resort wishes to apply for a 'blue flag' for their beach. However, they have been told that they must get rid of a large amount of heavy metal pollution in the water discharged through the town's sewage system. The heavy metals come from a large factory near the town, which is a very important local employer.

Your job is to act as a consultant to the town council to advise them of the best way to go about cleaning up the effluent in order to be able to apply for a blue flag.

Write a report to the council explaining what they should do. You will need to explain the chemistry to them in simple terms (they should be able to understand simple word equations), and you will need to suggest who will pay for the treatment – whether this should be the local people (through their local taxes), the factory producing the pollution, or even the visitors to the town (through higher prices for their accommodation and other holiday costs).

Cleaning up industrial effluent

A lot of wastewater from industry contains salts of heavy (transition) metals dissolved in it. Before this can be discharged these must be removed. The simplest way of removing the metal ions is to raise the pH of the solution. The hydroxide ions in the alkaline solution then react with the metal ions, producing metal hydroxides. The hydroxides of most heavy metals are very insoluble. So these form a precipitate which can be removed from the wastewater before it is discharged into a river or into the sea.

SUMMARY QUESTIONS

1 Match the halves of the sentences together:

a)	A base that is soluble in water	A	...... a pH of exactly 7.
b)	Pure water is neutral with	B	...... form OH⁻ ions when they dissolve in water.
c)	Acids are substances that	C	...... is called an alkali.
d)	Alkalis are substances that	D	...... is acidic.
e)	Indicators are substances that	E	...... produce H⁺ ions when they dissolve in water.
f)	A solution with a pH less than 7	F	...... change colour when we add them to acids and alkalis.

2 The table shows the ions in substances in three pairs of beakers. Copy the table and draw lines between the ions that react in each beaker.

Beaker 1	Na^+ OH^-	H^+ Cl^-
Beaker 2	Cu^{2+} O^{2-}	H^+ H^+ SO_4^{2-}
Beaker 3	Pb^{2+} NO_3^- NO_3^-	Cu^{2+} Cl^- Cl^-

3 A student carried out an investigation in which she dropped a piece of magnesium ribbon into some acid. She measured the total amount of gas that had been produced every 10 seconds and plotted this on a graph. At the end of the reaction some magnesium ribbon remained that had not reacted.

a) What gas does this reaction produce?

b) Sketch a graph of volume of gas (y-axis) against time (x-axis) that this student could have obtained.

c) Sketch another line on the graph to show the results that might be obtained if the student repeated this investigation, using the same acid but diluted so that its concentration was half of that used in the first investigation.

4 Write chemical equations to describe the following chemical reactions. (Each reaction forms a salt.)

a) Potassium hydroxide (an alkali) and sulfuric acid.

b) Zinc oxide (an insoluble base) and nitric acid.

c) Calcium metal and hydrochloric acid.

d) Barium nitrate and sodium sulfate (this reaction produces an insoluble salt – **hint:** all sodium salts are soluble).

EXAM-STYLE QUESTIONS

1 Magnesium hydroxide, $Mg(OH)_2$, is used in many antacids for relieving acid indigestion.

(a) Magnesium hydroxide is slightly soluble in water.

(i) Give the formulae of the ions produced when it dissolves. (2)

(ii) Give a value for the pH of the solution it forms. (1)

(b) Write a word equation for the reaction of magnesium hydroxide with hydrochloric acid. (2)

(c) Write a balanced symbol equation for the reaction. (2)

(d) Suggest why sodium hydroxide would not be suitable for use as a cure for indigestion. (2)

2 Copper(II) sulfate crystals can be made from an insoluble base and sulfuric acid.

(a) Name the insoluble base that can be used to make copper(II) sulfate. (1)

(b) Describe how to make a solution of copper(II) sulfate from 25 cm³ of dilute sulfuric acid so that all of the acid is used. (3)

(c) Describe how you could make crystals of copper(II) sulfate from the solution. (3)

3 Salts are formed when acids react with alkalis.

(a) Complete the word equation:

acid + alkali → .... + ... (2)

(b) What type of reaction takes place when an acid reacts with an alkali? (1)

(c) (i) Name the acid and alkali used to make potassium nitrate. (2)

(ii) What would you use to show when the acid had completely reacted with the alkali? (1)

(iii) Write a balanced symbol equation for the reaction that takes place. (2)

4 The effluent from nickel plating works is treated with sodium carbonate to precipitate nickel ions from the solution. The precipitate is separated from the solution by settlement in a tank. Filtration is not usually used as the main method of removing the precipitate, but can be used to remove small amounts of solids from the effluent after settlement.

(a) Write a word equation for the reaction between nickel sulfate solution and sodium carbonate solution. (2)

(b) Name the precipitate that is formed. (1)

(c) How is most of the precipitate removed from the effluent? (1)

(d) Suggest one reason why filtration is not used to remove most of the precipitate. (1)

(e) Why is it necessary to remove metal ions like nickel from effluents? (1)

5 There are four main methods of making salts:

A Acid + metal
B Acid + insoluble base
C Acid + alkali
D Solution of salt A + solution of salt B

(a) A student wanted to make some sodium sulfate.
  (i) Which method would be the best one to use? (1)
  (ii) Explain why you chose this method. (3)
  (iii) Name the reagents you would use. (2)
  (iv) Write a word equation for the reaction. (1)

(b) Another student wanted to make some magnesium carbonate.
  (i) Which method would you use for this salt? (1)
  (ii) Explain why you chose this method. (2)
  (iii) Name the reagents you would use. (2)
  (iv) Write a word equation for the reaction. (1)

HOW SCIENCE WORKS QUESTIONS

Chemistry to help!

Modern living produces enormous quantities of wastewater. Most of this can be treated in sewage works by biological processes. Sometimes biology cannot solve all of the problems. Chemistry is needed.

Phosphates are one such problem. You might have seen patches of stinging nettles near to old farms. These are due to the high concentrations of phosphates produced in animal (and human!) waste. This is a real problem when you have farms producing beef. In parts of USA they rear cattle with very little land.

The waste would normally be put on the land. It would cost a lot of money to transport the waste back to the farms that produced the feed. The waste is therefore dumped. The problem is that the high concentration of the phosphates causes water pollution problems.

Removing the phosphates at the sewage works by adding iron(III) chloride is also expensive. The wastewater therefore is treated with struvite, a magnesium salt that precipitates the phosphates.

Use these notes and your experience to answer these questions.

a) What are the economic issues associated with the disposal of animal waste? (2)

b) What are the environmental issues associated with the disposal of animal waste? (2)

c) What are the ethical issues associated with the use of chemistry to solve the problems of pollution? (1)

d) Who should be making the decisions about using chemistry to solve these problems? Explain your answer. (1)

e) Struvite can become a problem by precipitating out and blocking water pipes.
What extra information would be useful to those using struvite? (1)

EXAMINATION-STYLE QUESTIONS

1 Match these substances with the descriptions (a) to (e):

diamond, hydrogen chloride, magnesium, neon, sodium chloride

See pages 104–11

(a) A compound made of small molecules.

(b) A gas at room temperature made of single atoms.

(c) A giant lattice of atoms that are covalently bonded.

(d) An ionic solid with a high melting point.

(e) A giant lattice that conducts electricity when it is solid. *(5 marks)*

2 (a) Draw a dot and cross diagram to show the electron arrangement of a lithium atom, atomic number 3. *(2 marks)*

See pages 90–3

(b) Draw a dot and cross diagram to show the electron arrangement of a fluorine atom, atomic number 9. *(2 marks)*

(c) Draw dot and cross diagrams to show the ions in lithium fluoride. *(3 marks)*

3 Complete the table that shows information about some atoms.

See pages 88–95, 116

Symbol	Atomic number	Mass number	Number of protons	Number of neutrons	Electron arrangement of atom	Formula of ion	Electron arrangement of ion
Al	13	27	(a)	14	(b)	Al^{3+}	$[2,8]^{3+}$
O	8	16	8	(c)	2,6	O^{2-}	(d)
K	19	(e)	19	20	2,8,8,1	(f)	$[2,8,8]^+$
Cl	17	35	17	(g)	2,8,7	Cl^-	(h)

(8 marks)

4 A student added 20 g of marble chips to 50 cm³ of dilute hydrochloric acid in a conical flask. The flask was put onto a balance. The table shows the mass of gas that was given off. Some marble chips were left in the flask at the end of the reaction.

See pages 137–9

Mass of gas given off (g)	0	0.14	0.27	0.38	0.47	0.51	0.57	0.59	0.60
Time (minutes)	0	1.0	2.0	3.0	4.0	5.0	6.0	7.0	8.0

(a) Plot a graph of the results. Put time on the horizontal axis and mass lost on the vertical axis. Draw a smooth line through the points, omitting any result that is anomalous. *(5 marks)*

(b) The rate of this reaction decreases with time. Explain how you can tell this from the graph. *(1 mark)*

The student decided to extend his work to see if temperature affected the rate at which the gas was produced.

(c) (i) Suggest one control variable he should use.

GET IT RIGHT!

It is important to express yourself clearly in answers that require explanations. In Question 4(b), you should make it clear that the gradient or slope of the graph shows the rate of reaction at that time. Also, if you are asked how collisions affect the rate of reaction, it is not enough to say there are more collisions. It is the frequency of collisions (the number of collisions per second) that the rate depends upon.

(ii) Describe how he would control that variable. *(2 marks)*

(d) Suggest a suitable range of temperatures he could use. *(1 mark)*

(e) Suggest a suitable interval between temperatures. *(1 mark)*

(f) Use the first set of data to suggest a suitable length of time to leave the reaction. *(1 mark)*

5 Complete the table that shows information about the electrolysis of different substances. Carbon electrodes were used.

See pages 160–1

Substance	Positive ions present	Negative ions present	Product at negative electrode	Product at positive electrode
Molten magnesium chloride	Mg^{2+}	Cl^-	magnesium	(a)
Aqueous solution of potassium chloride	K^+ H^+	(b)	hydrogen	chlorine
Dilute sulfuric acid	(c)	SO_4^{2-} OH^-	hydrogen	oxygen
Aqueous solution of copper(II) sulfate	Cu^{2+} H^+	SO_4^{2-} OH^-	(d)	(e)

(5 marks)

6 Ammonium sulfate $(NH_4)_2SO_4$, is an important fertiliser. It is made by reacting ammonia solution with sulfuric acid. The reaction can be represented by the equation:

See pages 170, 174

$$H_2SO_4(aq) + 2NH_4OH(aq) \rightarrow (NH_4)_2SO_4(aq) + 2H_2O(l)$$

(a) How can you tell from the equation that ammonium sulfate is soluble? *(1 mark)*

(b) (i) Which ions make the sulfuric acid solution acidic? *(1 mark)*

　　(ii) Which ions make the ammonia solution alkaline? *(1 mark)*

　　(iii) What name is used to describe the reaction between these ions? *(1 mark)*

(c) A student made 15.4 g of ammonium sulfate from 0.2 moles of sulfuric acid.

See pages 122–4

　　(i) What is the mass of one mole of ammonium sulfate? *(2 marks)*

　　(ii) What mass of ammonium sulfate can be made from 0.2 moles of sulfuric acid, according to the equation? *(1 mark)*

　　(iii) What was the percentage yield of ammonium sulfate obtained by the student? *(2 marks)*

[Higher]

GET IT RIGHT!

In calculations, always give your answer to an appropriate number of significant figures or decimal places (usually 2 or 3 significant figures or one or two decimal places).

P2 | Additional physics

Figure 1 Spot the units!

What you already know

Here is a quick reminder of previous work that you will find useful in this unit:

Electricity

- In an electric circuit, energy is transferred from a voltage supply to the other parts of the circuit.
- Current passes round an electric circuit if the circuit is complete.
- Insulators do not conduct electricity.

Force

- If the forces acting on an object are not balanced, they will change the motion of the object.
- Weight is caused by the force of gravity on a mass.
- Friction acts between two surfaces in contact with each other when they slide or try to slide past each other.

Energy

- Energy cannot be created or destroyed. It can only be transformed from one form to another form.
- Power is the rate of transfer of energy.

Radiation

- Radioactive substances decay because the nuclei of some atoms are unstable. An unstable nucleus emits α, β or γ radiation when it decays.
- X-rays and α, β and γ radiation ionise substances they pass through.

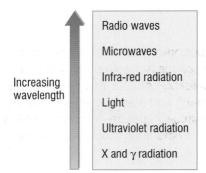

Figure 2 The electromagnetic spectrum

RECAP QUESTIONS

1 a) Sort the materials below into two lists – electrical conductors and insulators.

    air   brass   copper   plastic   wood

  b) A student replaces a battery in an electric torch but the torch still doesn't work. Suggest two possible reasons why it doesn't work.

2 a) List the forces acting on you at this moment, assuming you are sitting still.

  b) i) When you are sitting still, what can you say about the forces acting on you?

    ii) If the force your seat exerts on you suddenly decreased, what would happen to you?

3 a) Which has the longer wavelength, γ radiation or microwaves?

  b) Which electromagnetic waves can pass through the body?

4 a) i) What is an ion?

    ii) List four different types of ionising radiation.

  b) i) Which is most easily absorbed, α, β or γ radiation?

    ii) Where in the atom does α, β or γ radiation come from?

5 What are the units in the cartoon at the top of this page used to measure?

Making connections

Taking off!

To fly high, you need to take off first. The first powered flight was by the Wright brothers in 1903. Now planes can carry hundreds of people for thousands of miles in a few hours. We can send space probes far into space. Where will people have got to by the end of this century? Read on to find out where the physics in this module can take you.

Jets and rockets

The first jet engine was invented by a British engineer, Frank Whittle. He worked out how to create a jet of hot gases by burning aviation fuel. He used his scientific knowledge of materials, energy and forces to design and test the first jet engine.

On the launch pad

Space is only a few miles above your head but gravity stops you going there – unless you are in a rocket. A rocket is a jet engine with its own oxygen supply. Jet planes don't need to carry oxygen to burn aviation fuel in their engines because they use oxygen in the atmosphere. But a single-stage rocket can't get far enough into space to escape from the Earth. The Russian physicist, Konstanin Tsiolovsky predicted in 1895 that space rockets would need to be multistage.

Keeping in touch

Space travel would be impossible without electronic circuits for control and communications. A radio signal from a space probe is weaker than the light from a torch lamp on the Moon. The communication circuits in a space probe detect and process very weak signals. On-board cameras and sensors collect and send information back to Earth. Control circuits operate on-board rockets to change the path of a space probe. The electronic circuits in a space probe need to be totally reliable.

Interstellar travel

Voyager 2 was launched in 1975. Now it is on its way out of the Solar System after sending back amazing pictures of the outer planets and their moons. Space probes and satellites need power supplies that last for many years.

Space travel by astronauts far from the Sun would need powerful electricity generators powered by nuclear reactors. Nuclear submarines carry small nuclear reactors for their electricity. New types of nuclear reactors such as fusion reactors would be better. The probes and the reactors would probably need to be built on the Moon, using local materials.

ACTIVITY

Discuss:

What things do you think people will be able to do in the year 2099 that we can't do today? What breakthroughs in science will these rely on?

Chapters in this unit

Motion — Speeding up and slowing down — Work, energy and momentum — Static electricity — Current electricity — Mains electricity — Nuclear physics

P2 1.1   Distance–time graphs

Figure 1 Capturing the land speed record

Some motorways have marker posts every kilometre. If you are a passenger in a car on a motorway, you can use these posts to check the speed of the car. You need to time the car as it passes each post. The table below shows some measurements made on a car journey:

Distance (metres, m)	0	1000	2000	3000	4000	5000	6000
Time (seconds, s)	0	40	80	120	160	200	240

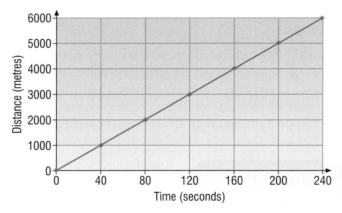

Figure 2 A distance–time graph

Look at the readings plotted on a graph of distance against time in Figure 2.

The graph shows that:

● the car took 40 s to go from each marker post to the next. So its speed was **constant**.
● the car went a distance of 25 metres every second (= 1000 metres ÷ 40 seconds). So its speed was 25 metres per second.

If the car had travelled faster, it would have gone further than 1000 metres every 40 seconds. So the line on the graph would have been **steeper**.

The slope on a distance–time graph represents speed.

a) What can you say about the steepness of the line if the car had travelled slower than 25 metres per second?

Speed

For an object moving at constant speed, we can calculate its speed using the equation:

$$\text{speed (metre/second, m/s)} = \frac{\text{distance travelled (metre, m)}}{\text{time taken (second, s)}}$$

The scientific unit of speed is the metre per second, usually written as metre/second or m/s.

Speed in action

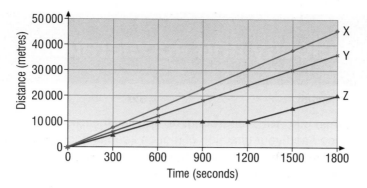

Figure 3 Comparing distance–time graphs

Long-distance vehicles are fitted with recorders that can check that their drivers don't drive for too long. The information from a recorder may be used to plot a distance–time graph.

Look at the distance–time graph above for three lorries, X , Y and Z, on the same motorway.

- X went fastest because it travelled furthest in the same time.
- Y travelled more slowly than X. From the graph, you can see it travelled 30 000 metres in 1500 seconds. So its speed was 20 m/s ($= 30\,000\,\text{m} \div 1500\,\text{s}$).

b) Calculate the speed of X.

- Z stopped for some of the time. Its speed was zero in this time.

c) How long did Z stop for?
d) Calculate the **average** speed of Z.

PRACTICAL

Be a distance recorder!

Take the measurements needed to plot distance–time graphs for a person:

- walking,
- running, and
- riding a bike.

Remember that you must always label the graph axes, which includes units.

- Compare the slopes of the lines and work out average speeds.

SUMMARY QUESTIONS

1 Choose the correct word from the list to complete a) to c) below.

distance   speed   time

a) The unit of ...... is the metre/second.
b) An object moving at steady ...... travels the same ...... every second.
c) The steeper the line on a distance–time graph of a moving object, the greater its ...... is.

2 A vehicle on a motorway travels 1800 m in 60 seconds. Calculate:

a) the speed of the vehicle in m/s.
b) how far it would travel at this speed in 300 seconds.

KEY POINTS

1 The steeper the line on a distance–time graph, the greater the speed it represents.
2 Speed (metre/second, m/s) =

$$\frac{\text{distance travelled (metre, m)}}{\text{time taken (second, s)}}$$

P2 1.2   Velocity and acceleration

LEARNING OBJECTIVES

1 What is the difference between speed and velocity?
2 What is acceleration and what are its units?
3 What is deceleration?

Figure 1 You experience plenty of changes in velocity on a corkscrew ride!

When you visit a fairground, do you like the rides that throw you round? Your speed and your direction of motion keep changing. We use the word **velocity** for speed in a given direction. An exciting ride would be one that changes your velocity often and unexpectedly!

Velocity is speed in a given direction.

● An object moving steadily round in a circle has a constant speed. Its direction of motion changes as it goes round so its velocity is not constant.

● Two moving objects can have the same speed but different velocities. For example, a car travelling north at 30 m/s on a motorway has the same speed as a car travelling south at 30 m/s. But their velocities are not the same because they are moving in opposite directions.

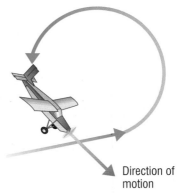

Direction of motion

Figure 2 Speed and velocity

a) How far apart are the two cars 10 seconds after they pass each other?

Acceleration

Figure 3 On a test circuit

A car maker claims their new car 'accelerates more quickly than any other new car'. A rival car maker is not pleased by this claim and issues a challenge. Each car in turn is tested on a straight track with a velocity recorder fitted.

The results are shown in the table:

Time from a standing start (seconds, s)	0	2	4	6	8	10
Velocity of car X (metre/second, m/s)	0	5	10	15	20	25
Velocity of car Y (metre/second, m/s)	0	6	12	18	18	18

Which car accelerates more? The results are plotted on the velocity–time graph in Figure 4. You can see the velocity of Y goes up from zero faster than the velocity of X does. So Y accelerates more in the first 6 seconds.

NEXT TIME YOU...

. . . go 'skateboarding', go round in a circle and think about how your velocity is changing.

Figure 4 Velocity–time graphs

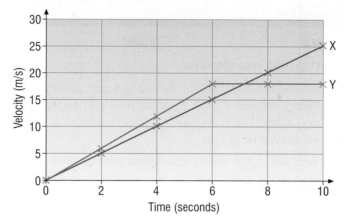

The acceleration of an object is its change of velocity per second. The unit of acceleration is the metre per second squared, abbreviated to m/s².

Any object with a changing velocity is accelerating. We can work out its acceleration using the equation:

$$\text{Acceleration (metre/second squared, m/s}^2) = \frac{\text{change in velocity (metre/second, m/s)}}{\text{time taken for the change (second, s)}}$$

Worked example

In Figure 4, the velocity of Y increases from zero to 18 m/s in 6 seconds. Calculate its acceleration.

Solution

Change of velocity = 18 m/s – 0 m/s = 18 m/s

Time taken = 6.0 s

$$\text{Acceleration} = \frac{\text{change in velocity (metre/second, m/s)}}{\text{time taken for the change (second, s)}} = \frac{18\,\text{m/s}}{6.0\,\text{s}} = 3.0\,\text{m/s}^2$$

b) Calculate the acceleration of X in Figure 4.

Deceleration

A car decelerates when the driver brakes. We use the term **deceleration** or *negative acceleration* for any situation where an object slows down.

SUMMARY QUESTIONS

1 Complete a) to c) using the words below:

> **acceleration   speed   velocity**

  a) An object moving steadily round in a circle has a constant ....

  b) If the velocity of an object increases by the same amount every second, its ...... is constant.

  c) Deceleration is when the ...... of an object decreases.

2 The velocity of a car increased from 8 m/s to 28 m/s in 8 s without change of direction. Calculate:

  a) its change of velocity,   b) its acceleration.

KEY POINTS

1 Velocity is speed in a given direction.

2 Acceleration is change of velocity per second.

3 A body travelling at a steady speed is accelerating if its direction is changing.

P2 1.3   More about velocity–time graphs

LEARNING OBJECTIVES

1 How can we tell from a velocity–time graph if an object is accelerating or decelerating?
2 What does the area under a velocity–time graph represent?

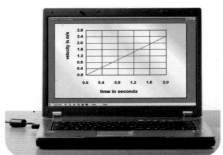

Figure 2 Measuring motion using a computer

Investigating acceleration

We can use a motion sensor linked to a computer to record how the velocity of an object changes. Figure 1 shows how we can do this, using a trolley as the moving object. The computer can also be used to display the measurements as a velocity–time graph.

Test A: If we let the trolley accelerate down the runway, its velocity increases with time. Look at the velocity–time graph from a test run in Figure 2.

Figure 1 A velocity–time graph on a computer

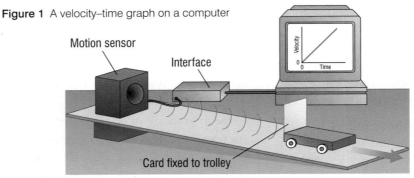

- The line goes up because the velocity increases with time. So it shows the trolley was accelerating as it ran down the runway.
- The line is straight which tells us that the increase in velocity was the same every second. In other words, the acceleration of the trolley was constant (or uniform).

Test B: If we make the runway steeper, the trolley accelerates faster. This would make the line on the graph in Figure 2 steeper than for test A. So the acceleration in test B is greater.

The slope on a graph is a measure of its steepness. The tests shows that:

the slope of the line on a velocity–time graph represents acceleration.

a) If you made the runway less steep than in test A, would the line on the graph be steeper or less steep than in A?

PRACTICAL

Investigating acceleration

Use a motion sensor and a computer to find out how the slope of a runway affects a trolley's acceleration.

- Name i) the independent variable, and ii) the dependent variable in this investigation. (See page 276.)
- What relationship do you find between the variables? (See page 280.)

Braking

Braking reduces the velocity of a vehicle. Look at the graph in Figure 3. It is the velocity–time graph for a vehicle that brakes to a standstill at a set of traffic lights. The velocity is constant until the driver applies the brakes.

***Using the slope of the line*:**

- The section of the graph for constant velocity is flat. The line's slope is zero so the acceleration in this section is zero.
- When the brakes are applied, the velocity decreases to zero and the vehicle decelerates. The slope of the line is negative in this section.

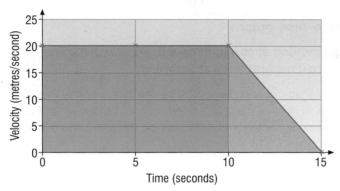

Figure 3 Braking

b) How would the slope of the line differ if the deceleration had taken longer?

Look at the graph in Figure 3 again.

Using the area under the line:

- Before the brakes are applied, the vehicle moves at a velocity of 20 m/s for 10 s. It therefore travels 200 m in this time (= 20 m/s × 10 s). This distance is represented on the graph by the area under the line from 0 s to 10 s. This is the shaded rectangle on the graph.
- When the vehicle decelerates in Figure 3, its velocity drops from 20 m/s to zero in 5 s. We can work out the distance travelled in this time from the area of the purple triangle in Figure 3. This area is $\frac{1}{2}$ × the height × the base of the triangle. So the vehicle must have travelled a distance of 50 m when it was decelerating.

The area under the line on a velocity–time graph represents distance travelled.

c) Would the total distance travelled be greater or smaller if the deceleration had taken longer?

P2 1.4   Using graphs

LEARNING OBJECTIVES

1 How can we calculate speed from a distance–time graph?
2 How can we calculate distance from a velocity–time graph?
3 How can we calculate acceleration from a velocity–time graph?

Using distance–time graphs

For an object moving at constant speed, we saw at the start of this chapter that the distance–time graph is a straight line.

The speed of the object is represented by the slope of the line. To find the slope, we need to draw a triangle under the line, as shown in Figure 1. The height of the triangle represents the distance travelled and the base represents the time taken. So

$$\text{the slope of the line} = \frac{\text{the height of the triangle}}{\text{the base of the triangle}}$$

and this represents the object's speed.

a) Find the speed of the object in the graph in Figure 1.

For a moving object with a changing speed, the distance–time graph is not a straight line. The graphs in Figure 2 show two examples.

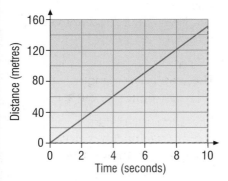

Figure 1 A distance–time graph for constant speed

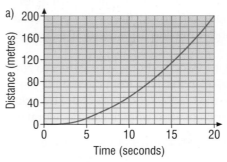
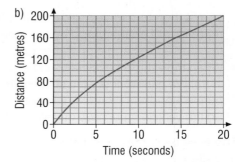

Figure 2 Distance–time graphs for changing speed

In Figure 2a, the slope of the graph increases gradually, so the object's speed must have increased gradually.

b) What can you say about the speed in Figure 2b?

Using velocity–time graphs

Look at the graph in Figure 3. It shows the velocity–time graph of an object X moving with a constant acceleration. Its velocity increases at a steady rate. So the graph shows a straight line which has a constant slope.

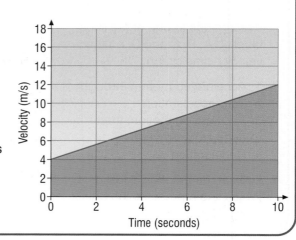

Figure 3 A velocity–time graph for constant acceleration

To find the acceleration from the graph, remember the slope of the line on a velocity–time graph represents the acceleration.

In Figure 3, the slope is given by the height divided by the base of the triangle under the graph.

The height of the triangle represents the change of velocity and the base of the triangle represents the time taken.

Therefore, the slope represents the acceleration, because:

$$\text{acceleration} = \frac{\text{change of velocity}}{\text{time taken}}$$

Worked example

Use the graph in Figure 3 to find the acceleration of object X.

Solution

The height of the triangle represents an increase of velocity of 8 m/s ($= 12\,\text{m/s} - 4\,\text{m/s}$).

The base of the triangle represents a time of 10 s.

Therefore, the acceleration $= \dfrac{\text{change of velocity}}{\text{time taken}} = \dfrac{8\,\text{m/s}}{10\,\text{s}} = 0.8\,\text{m/s}^2$

To find the distance travelled from the graph, remember the area under a velocity–time graph represents the distance travelled. The shape under the graph in Figure 3 is a triangle on top of a rectangle. So the distance travelled is represented by the area of the triangle plus the area of the rectangle under it.

Look at the worked example opposite:

Worked example

Use the graph in Figure 3 to calculate the distance moved by object X.

Solution

The area of the triangle $= \frac{1}{2} \times$ its height $\times$ its base.

Therefore, the distance represented by the area of triangle $= \frac{1}{2} \times 8\,\text{m/s} \times 10\,\text{s}$
$= 40\,\text{m}$

The area of the rectangle under the triangle $=$ its height $\times$ its base

Therefore, the distance represented by the area of the rectangle $= 4\,\text{m/s} \times 10\,\text{s}$
$= 40\,\text{m}$

So the distance travelled by X $= 40\,\text{m} + 40\,\text{m} = 80\,\text{m}$

SUMMARY QUESTIONS

1 The graph shows how the velocity of a cyclist on a straight road changes with time.

a) Describe the motion of the cyclist.
b) Use the graph to work out
   i) the initial acceleration of the cyclist,
   ii) the distance travelled by the cyclist in the first 40 s.

2 In a motor cycle test, the speed from rest was recorded at intervals.

Time (seconds, s)	0	5	10	15	20	25	30
Velocity (metre/second, m/s)	0	10	20	30	40	40	40

a) Plot a velocity–time graph of these results.
b) What was the initial acceleration?
c) How far did it move in:
   i) the first 20 seconds?
   ii) the next 10 s?

KEY POINTS

1 The slope on a distance–time graph represents speed.
2 The slope on a velocity–time graph represents acceleration.
3 The area under the line on a velocity–time graph represents the distance travelled.

The Big Fuel protest

In 2001, lorry drivers in Britain decided their fuel costs were too high so they blockaded fuel depots. They were angry at the government because most of the cost of the fuel is tax (which raises money for the government).

Garages ran out of petrol and drivers had to queue for hours to fill up. Car drivers were a lot more careful about using their precious fuel.

Car journeys in built-up areas use more fuel per kilometre than 'out of town' journeys at the same average speed. This is because cars slow down and speed up more often in built-up areas. More fuel is used by a car that keeps stopping and starting than one driven at constant speed.

On a motorway journey the faster the speed of a car, the more fuel it uses. Air resistance at high speed is much greater than at low speed, so more fuel is used.

QUESTION

The table shows some information about fuel usage by a petrol-engine car.

	Distance travelled per litre of fuel (km)	
	at 48 kilometres per hour (30 mph)	at 100 kilometres per hour (63 mph)
Driving in town	12	–
On the 'open road'	15	10

1 A driver on the 'open road' would use 6 litres of fuel to drive 60 kilometres at 100 km/h.
   a) How much fuel would the driver use to drive 60 km at 48 km/h:
      i) in town?   **ii)** on the open road?
   b) The driver pays 85 p per litre for petrol. How much would be saved on a motorway journey of 60 km by driving at 48 km/h instead of 100 km/h?

ACTIVITY

Discuss the issues below in a small group.

What are your views on the different ways that people might protest against the cost of fuel? Would you agree with the protesters? Think about the arguments that might be used by:

- An environmentalist
- A lorry driver
- An oil company
- A government official

Epic journeys

Journey 1: Christopher Columbus and his three ships left the Canary Islands on 8th September 1492. He reached the Bahama Islands on 12th October after a 5500 km journey across the Atlantic Ocean.

Journey 2: Neil Armstrong and Buzz Aldrin were the first astronauts to land on the Moon. They spent 22 hours on the Moon. The 380 000 km journey to the Moon took four days.

Journey 3: If a space rocket accelerated for a year at 2 m/s² (about the same as a car starting from rest), the rocket would reach a speed of 60 000 km/s – about a fifth of the speed of light.

QUESTION

2 Work out the speed, in kilometres per hour, of journeys 1 and 2.

Speed cameras

Speed cameras are very effective in stopping motorists speeding. A speeding motorist caught by a speed camera is fined and can lose his or her driving licence. In some areas, residents are supplied with 'mobile' speed cameras to catch speeding motorists. Some motorists think this is going too far. Lots of motorists say speed cameras are being used by councils to increase their income.

A report from one police force said that where speed cameras had been introduced:

- average speeds fell by 17%,
- deaths and serious injuries had fallen by 55%.

Another police force reported that, in their area, as a result of installing more speed cameras in 2003:

- there were no child deaths in road accidents for the first time since 1927,
- 420 fewer children were involved in road accidents compared with the previous year.

ACTIVITY

Discuss with your friends:

a) Do the bullet-pointed statements opposite prove the argument that speed cameras save lives.

b) In what sort of areas do you think speed cameras should be used?

ACTIVITY

Should more residents be supplied with mobile speed cameras? Write a letter to your local newspaper to argue your case.

ACTIVITY

Do you think congestion charges are a good solution to traffic problems in our cities? Discuss the issue with your friends and take a vote on the question.

Green travel

Travelling to and from school or work can take ages unless you live nearby. Everybody seems to want to travel at the same time. Traffic accidents and rail cancellations in the rush hour cause hours of chaos. Traffic fumes cause pollution and burning fuel produces greenhouse gases.

Green travel means changing the way we travel to improve the environment.

Here are some suggestions about a green travel plan for your school:

- School buses; use school buses instead of cars.
- Car sharing; encourage drivers to share their cars with other drivers.
- Flexitime; finish the school day at different times for each year group.
- Everybody should walk or cycle to school.

ACTIVITY

With the help of your friends, conduct a survey to find out

a) if people in your school and parents think a green travel plan is a good idea,

b) what they think of the suggestions above,

c) if they have any better suggestions.

Write a short report to tell your headteacher about your survey and your findings.

Was your sample large enough to draw any firm conclusions? Explain your answer.

Congestion charges

Travelling across London by road was quicker a hundred years ago than it is today – even though modern cars can travel ten times faster than the horse-drawn carriages that were used then. Congestion charges were introduced in London in 2003 to improve traffic flow. If motorists enter the congestion zone without paying the daily charge, they are likely to be fined heavily.

People in Edinburgh in 2004 voted against proposals for congestion charges. But many people in other cities want to introduce them. However, lots of people who need to travel into cities think they are unfair.

SUMMARY QUESTIONS

1 A train travels at a constant speed of 35 m/s. Calculate:

a) how far it travels in 20 s,

b) how long it takes to travel a distance of 1400 m.

2 The figure shows the distance–time graph for a car on a motorway.

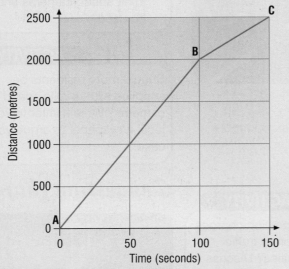

a) Which part of the journey was faster, A to B or B to C?

b) i) How far did the car travel from A to B and how long did it take?

ii) Calculate the speed of the car between A and B?

3 a) A car took 8 s to increase its velocity from 8 m/s to 28 m/s. Calculate

i) its change of velocity,

ii) its acceleration.

b) A vehicle travelling at a velocity of 24 m/s slowed down and stopped in 20 s. Calculate its deceleration.

4 The figure shows the velocity–time graph of a passenger jet before it took off.

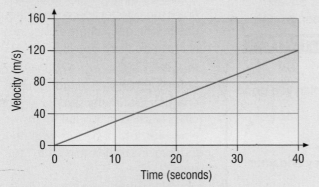

a) Calculate the acceleration of the jet.

b) Calculate the distance it travelled before it took off.

[Higher]

EXAM-STYLE QUESTIONS

1 The graph shows how far a marathon runner travels during a race.

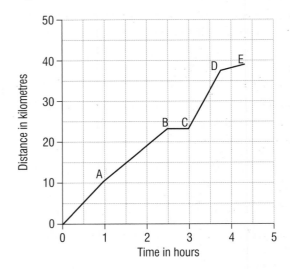

(a) What was the distance of the race? (1)

(b) How long did it take the runner to complete the race? (1)

(c) What distance did the runner travel during the first 2 hours of the race? (1)

(d) For how long did the runner rest during the race? (1)

(e) Ignoring the time for which the runner was resting, between which two points was the runner moving the slowest?

Give a reason for your answer (2)

2 The table gives values of distance and time for a cyclist travelling along a straight road.

Distance in metres	0	20	40	60	80	100
Time in seconds	0	2	4	6	8	10

(a) Draw a graph of distance against time. Two of the points have been plotted for you. (3)

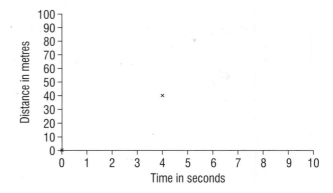

(b) Use your graph to find the distance travelled in 5 seconds. (1)

(c) Use your graph to find the time at which the distance is 30 metres. (1)

(d) Describe the motion of the cyclist. (1)

3 A van travels on a straight 'test-track' road. The graph shows how the speed of the van changes with time.

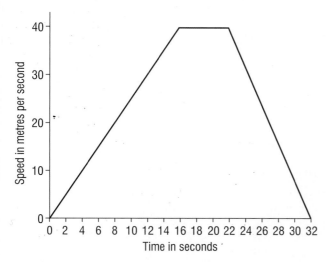

(a) (i) Name the independent variable shown on the graph. (1)

(ii) Would you describe this variable as categoric, discrete or continuous? (1)

(b) (i) A manufacturer of vans makes four different types of van. How should they display the data so that potential buyers can best compare the top speed of the vans carrying the same load? (1)

(ii) The data in (b) (i) is given for the same load each time. Would the load best be described as an independent, a dependent or a control variable? (1)

(c) Calculate the acceleration of the van during the first 16 seconds. Give a unit with your answer. (4)

(d) Calculate the distance travelled in metres between 22 and 32 seconds. (3)

[Higher]

Read the article below, then answer the questions that follow:

PARENTS DEMAND ROAD BUMPS

Parents protested yesterday at the speed of cars travelling through the Brooklands estate. They claimed that walking their young children to school was getting very dangerous. Mrs Nifty said that she often had to run across the road to miss the traffic. Mr Sloe claimed that the cars always travelled faster than the speed limit, and nothing was done about it. Mrs Divert said that it had got much worse since they put traffic calming measures, such as 'speed bumps', into the nearby Brands estate. The police sergeant attending the protest said that he understood their concerns and would investigate.

a) What do you think Mr Sloe's comments were based on? (1)

b) What evidence should have been gathered to show a link between the traffic calming measures in the Brands estate and the speed of traffic in the Brooklands estate? (1)

On hearing about the protests a science teacher decided to carry out an investigation with his students. He decided to investigate the speed of the traffic outside Brooklands School.

c) Describe a method for measuring the speed of passing cars which includes using a stopwatch. (2)

d) What time of day should this survey be carried out? Why? (2)

e) Suggest how many cars should be surveyed. (1)

f) Should the drivers know they are being surveyed? Explain your answer. (2)

P2 2.1   Forces between objects

LEARNING OBJECTIVES

1 When two objects interact, what can we say about the forces acting?
2 What is the unit of force?

Equal and opposite forces

Whenever two objects push or pull on each other, they exert equal and opposite forces on one another. The unit of force is the newton (abbreviated N).

- A boxer who punches an opponent with a force of 100 N experiences a reverse force of 100 N from his opponent.
- Two roller skaters pull on opposite ends of a rope. The skaters move towards each other. This is because they pull on each other with equal and opposite forces. Two newtonmeters could be used to show this.

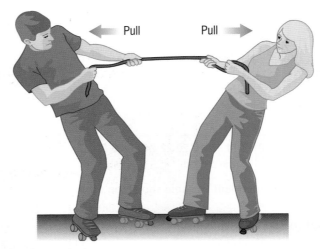

Figure 1 Equal and opposite forces

FOUL FACTS

Quicksand victims sink because they can't get enough support from the sand. The force of gravity on the victim (acting downwards) is greater than the upwards force of the sand on the victim. Sometimes the incoming tide drowns the victim!

PRACTICAL

Action and reaction

Test this with a friend if you can, using roller skates and two newtonmeters. Don't forget to wear protective head gear!

- What did you find out?
- Comment on the accuracy of your readings.

a) A hammer hits a nail with a downward force of 50 N. What is the size and direction of the force of the nail on the hammer?

In the mud

A car stuck in mud can be difficult to shift. A tractor can be very useful here. Figure 2 shows the idea. At any stage, the force of the rope on the car is equal and opposite to the force of the car on the rope.

To pull the car out of the mud, the force of the ground on the tractor needs to be greater than the force of the mud on the car. These two forces aren't necessarily equal to one another because the objects are not the same.

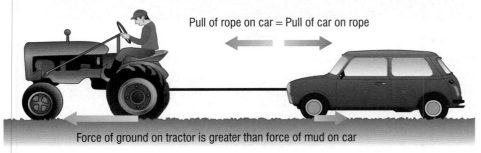

Pull of rope on car = Pull of car on rope

Force of ground on tractor is greater than force of mud on car

Figure 2 In the mud

b) A lorry tows a broken-down car. When the force of the lorry on the tow rope is 200 N, what is the force of the tow rope on the lorry?

Friction in action

The motive force on a car is the force that makes it move. This force is due to friction between the ground and the tyre of each drive wheel. Friction acts where the tyre is in contact with the ground.

Figure 3 Motive force

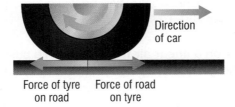

Direction of car

Force of tyre on road   Force of road on tyre

When the car moves forwards:

● the force of friction of the ground on the tyre is in the forward direction,
● the force of friction of the tyre on the ground is in the reverse direction.

The two forces are equal and opposite to one another.

c) What happens if there isn't enough friction between the tyre and the ground?

SUMMARY QUESTIONS

1 Complete the sentences below using words from the list.

downwards   equal   opposite   upwards

a) The force on a ladder resting against a wall is …… and …… to the force of the wall on the ladder.

b) A book is at rest on a table. The force of the book on the table is …… . The force of the table on the book is …… .

2 When a student is standing at rest on bathroom scales, the scales read 500 N.

a) What is the size and direction of the force of the student on the scales?

b) What is the size and direction of the force of the scales on the student?

KEY POINTS

1 When two objects interact, they always exert equal and opposite forces on each other.

2 The unit of force is the newton.

P2 2.2

Resultant force

1 What is a resultant force?
2 What happens if the resultant force on an object is zero?
3 What happens if the resultant force on an object is not zero?

Most objects around you are acted on by more than one force. We can work out the effect of the forces on an object by replacing them with a single force, the **resultant force**. This is a single force that has the same effect as all the forces acting on the object.

When the resultant force on an object is zero, the object:
- remains stationary if it was at rest, or
- continues to move at the same speed and in the same direction if it was already moving.

PRACTICAL

Investigating forces

Make and test a model hovercraft floating on a cushion of air from a balloon, and/or
Use a glider on an air track to investigate the relationship between force and acceleration.

- What relationship do you find between force and acceleration?
(See pages 280–1.)

1 **A glider on a linear air track** floats on a cushion of air. Provided the track is level, the glider moves at constant velocity (i.e. with no change of speed or direction) along the track because friction is absent. The resultant force on the glider is zero.

Figure 1 The linear air track

a) What happens to the glider if the air track blower is switched off, and why?

2 **When a heavy crate is pushed across a rough floor at constant volocity**, the resultant force on the crate is zero. The push force on the crate is equal in size but acts in the opposite direction to the force of friction of the floor on the crate.

b) What difference would it make if the floor were smooth?

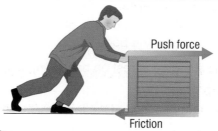

Figure 2 Overcoming friction

When the resultant force on an object is not zero, the movement of the object depends on the size and direction of the resultant force.

1 **When a jet plane is taking off,** the thrust force of its engines is greater than the force of air resistance on it. The resultant force on it is the difference between the thrust force and the force of air resistance on it. The resultant force is therefore non-zero. The greater the resultant force, the quicker the take-off is.

Figure 3 A passenger jet on take-off

Drag force

Engine force

c) What can you say about the thrust force and the force of air resistance when the plane is moving at constant velocity at constant height?

2 **When a car driver applies the brakes**, the braking force is the resultant force on the car. It acts in the opposite direction to that in which the car is moving, so it slows the car down.

d) What can you say about the resultant force if the brakes had been applied harder?

NEXT TIME YOU...

. . . are in a plane, think about the forces that are operating when you are taking off. What happens when a plane is taking off into a strong head wind?

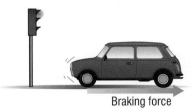

Braking force

Figure 4 Braking

KEY POINTS

	Object at the start	Resultant force	Effect on the object
1	at rest	zero	stays at rest
2	moving	zero	velocity stays the same
3	moving	non-zero in the same direction as the direction of motion of the object	accelerates
4	moving	non-zero in the opposite direction to the direction of motion of the object	decelerates

SUMMARY QUESTIONS

1 Complete the following sentences using words from the list.

greater than   less than   equal to

A car starts from rest and accelerates along a straight flat road.

a) The force of air resistance on it is …… the motive force of its engine.
b) The resultant force is …… zero.
c) The downward force of the car on the road is …… the support force of the road on the car.

2 A jet plane lands on a runway and stops.

a) What can you say about the direction of the resultant force on the plane as it lands?
b) What can you say about the resultant force on the plane when it has stopped?

GET IT RIGHT!

Remember that if a body is accelerating it can be speeding up, slowing down or changing direction. If a body is accelerating there must be a resultant force acting on it.

P2 2.3

Force and acceleration

LEARNING OBJECTIVES

1 How does the acceleration of an object depend on the size of the resultant force?
2 What effect does the mass of the object have on its acceleration?

PRACTICAL

Investigating force and acceleration

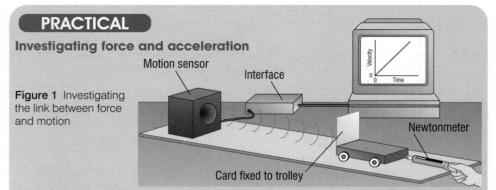

Figure 1 Investigating the link between force and motion

We can use the apparatus above to accelerate a trolley with a constant force.

Use the newtonmeter to pull the trolley along with a constant force.

You can double or treble the total moving mass by using double-deck and triple-deck trolleys.

A motion sensor and a computer record the velocity of the trolley as it accelerates.

● What are the advantages of using a data logger and computer in this investigation?

You can display the results as a velocity–time graph on the computer screen.

Figure 2 shows velocity–time graphs for different masses. You can work out the acceleration from the gradient of the line, as explained on page 191.

Look at some typical results in the table below:

Resultant force (newtons)	0.5	1.0	1.5	2.0	4.0	6.0
Mass (kilograms)	1.0	1.0	1.0	2.0	2.0	2.0
Acceleration (m/s²)	0.5	1.0	1.5	1.0	2.0	3.0
Mass × acceleration (kg m/s²)	0.5	1.0	1.5	2.0	4.0	6.0

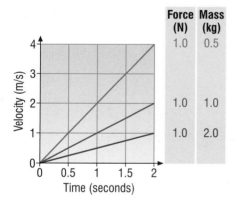

Force (N)	Mass (kg)
1.0	0.5
1.0	1.0
1.0	2.0

Figure 2 Velocity–time graph for different combinations of force and masses

The results show that the resultant force, the mass and the acceleration are linked by the equation

resultant force = mass × acceleration
(newtons, N)   (kilograms)   (metres/second²)

Worked example
Calculate the resultant force on an object of mass 6.0 kg when it has an acceleration of 3.0 m/s².

Solution
Resultant force = mass × acceleration = 6.0 kg × 3.0 m/s² = 18.0 N

---

a) Calculate the resultant force on a sprinter of mass 50 kg who accelerates at 8 m/s².

Maths notes

We can write the word equation on the previous page as:

Resultant force, $F = ma$,

where m = mass and a = acceleration.

Rearranging this equation gives $a = \dfrac{F}{m}$ or $m = \dfrac{F}{a}$

> **Worked example**
>
> Calculate the acceleration of an object of mass 5.0 kg acted on by a resultant force of 40 N.
>
> **Solution**
> Rearranging $F = ma$ gives $a = \dfrac{F}{m} = \dfrac{40\,\text{N}}{5.0\,\text{kg}} = 8.0\,\text{m/s}^2$

b) Calculate the acceleration of a car of mass 800 kg acted on by a resultant force of 3200 N.

Speeding up or slowing down

If the velocity of an object changes, it must be acted on by a resultant force. Its acceleration is always in the same direction as the resultant force.

- The velocity of the object increases if the resultant force is in the **same** direction as the velocity. We say its acceleration is positive because it is in the same direction as its velocity.
- The velocity of the object decreases (i.e. it decelerates) if the resultant force is **opposite** in direction. We say its acceleration is negative because it is opposite in direction to its velocity.

KEY POINTS

Resultant force $=$ mass $\times$ acceleration
(newtons, N) (kilograms) (metres/second²)

SUMMARY QUESTIONS

1 Complete a) to c) using the words below:

acceleration   resultant force   mass   velocity

a) A moving object decelerates when a …… acts on it in the opposite direction to its …… .

b) The greater the …… of an object, the less its acceleration when a …… acts on it.

c) The …… of a moving object increases when a …… acts on it in the same direction as it is moving in.

2 Copy and complete the following table:

	a)	b)	c)	d)	e)
Force (newtons, N)	?	200	840	?	5000
Mass (kilograms, kg)	20	?	70	0.40	?
Acceleration (metre/second squared, m/s²)	0.80	5.0	?	6.0	0.20

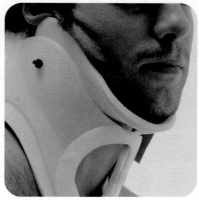

FOUL FACTS

If you're in a car that suddenly brakes, your neck pulls on your head and slows it down. The equal and opposite force of your head on your neck can injure your neck.

Figure 3 A 'whiplash' injury

GET IT RIGHT!

If an object is accelerating there must be a resultant force acting on it.

P2 2.4

On the road

Forces on the road

For any car travelling at constant velocity, the resultant force on it is zero. This is because the motive force of its engine is balanced by the resistive forces (i.e. friction and air resistance) on it.

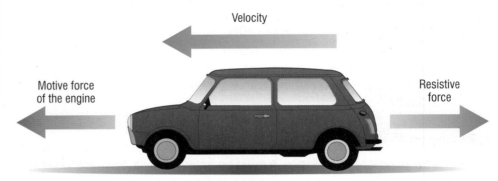

Figure 1 Constant velocity

A car driver uses the accelerator pedal (also called the gas pedal) to vary the motive force of the engine.

a) What do you think happens if the driver presses harder on the accelerator?

The braking force needed to stop a vehicle in a certain distance depends on:

- the velocity of the vehicle when the brakes are first applied
- the mass of the vehicle.

We can see this using the equation 'resultant force = mass × acceleration', in which the braking force is the resultant force.

1 The greater the velocity, the greater the deceleration needed to stop it in a certain distance. So the braking force must be greater than at low velocity.
2 The greater the mass, the greater the braking force needed for a given deceleration.

Stopping distances

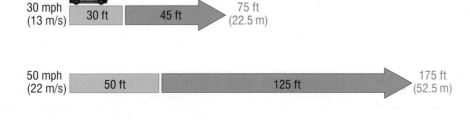

30 mph (13 m/s) | 30 ft | 45 ft | 75 ft (22.5 m)

50 mph (22 m/s) | 50 ft | 125 ft | 175 ft (52.5 m)

70 mph (31 m/s) | 70 ft | 245 ft | 315 ft (96 m)

Thinking distance   Braking distance

Figure 2 Stopping distances

Driving tests always ask about stopping distances. This is the shortest distance a vehicle can safely stop in, and is in two parts:

- **The thinking distance:** the distance travelled by the vehicle in the time it takes the driver to react (i.e. during the driver's reaction time).
- **The braking distance:** the distance travelled by the vehicle during the time the braking force acts.

> **The stopping distance = the thinking distance + the braking distance.**

Figure 2 shows the stopping distance for a vehicle on a dry flat road travelling at different speeds. Check for yourself that the stopping distance at 31 m/s (70 miles per hour) is 96 m.

b) What are the thinking distance, the braking distance and the stopping distance at 13 m/s (30 mph)?

Factors affecting stopping distances

1. **Tiredness, alcohol and drugs** all increase reaction times. So they increase the thinking distance (because thinking distance = speed × reaction time). Therefore, the stopping distance is greater.
2. **The faster a vehicle is travelling**, the further it travels before it stops. This is because the thinking distance and the braking distance both increase with increased speed.
3. **In adverse road conditions**, for example on wet or icy roads, drivers have to brake with less force to avoid skidding. Stopping distances are therefore greater in poor road conditions.
4. **Poorly maintained vehicles**, for example with worn brakes or tyres, take longer to stop because the brakes and tyres are less effective.

c) Why are stopping distances greater in poor visibility?

Figure 3 Stopping distances are further than you might think!

PRACTICAL

Reaction times

Use an electronic stopwatch to test your own reaction time under different conditions in an investigation. Ask a friend to start the stopwatch when you are looking at it with your finger on the stop button. The read-out from the watch will give your reaction time.

- How can you make your data as reliable as possible?
- What conclusions can you draw?

SUMMARY QUESTIONS

1. Each of the following factors affects the thinking distance or the braking distance of a vehicle. Which of these two distances is affected in each case below?

    a) The road surface condition affects the …… distance.

    b) The tiredness of a driver increases his or her .:.... distance.

    c) Poorly maintained brakes affects the …… distance.

2. a) Use the chart in Figure 2 to work out, in metres, the increase in i) the thinking distance, ii) the braking distance, iii) the stopping distance from 13 m/s (30 mph) to 22 m/s (50 mph). (1 foot = 0.30 m.)

    b) A driver has a reaction time of 0.8 s. Calculate her thinking distance at a speed of i) 15 m/s, ii) 30 m/s.

KEY POINTS

1. The **thinking distance** is the distance travelled by the vehicle in the time it takes the driver to react.
2. The **braking distance** is the distance the vehicle travels under the braking force.
3. The **stopping distance** = the **thinking distance** + the **braking distance**.

P2 2.5   Falling objects

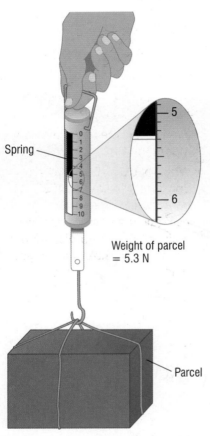

Spring

Weight of parcel = 5.3 N

Parcel

Figure 1 Using a newtonmeter to weigh an object

How to reduce your weight

Your weight is due to the gravitational force of attraction between you and the Earth. This force is very slightly weaker at the equator than at the poles. This is because the equator is slightly further from the centre of the Earth than the poles are.

So if you want to reduce your weight, go to the equator. However, your mass will be the same no matter where you are.

● The **weight** of an object is the force of gravity on it.
● The **mass** of an object is the quantity of matter in it.

We can measure the weight of an object using a newtonmeter.

The weight of an object:

● of mass 1 kg is 10 N,
● of mass 5 kg is 50 N

The force of gravity on a 1 kg object is the **gravitational field strength** at the place where the object is. The unit of gravitational field strength is the newton per kilogram (N/kg). The value of the Earth's gravitational field strength at its surface is about 10 N/kg.

If we know the mass of an object, we can calculate the force of gravity on it (i.e. its weight) using the equation

$$\underset{\text{(newtons, N)}}{\textbf{weight}} = \underset{\text{(kilograms, kg)}}{\textbf{mass}} \times \underset{\text{(newtons/kilogram, N/kg)}}{\textbf{gravitational field strength}}$$

> **Worked example**
> Calculate the weight in newtons of a person of mass 55 kg.
>
> **Solution**
> Weight = mass × gravitational field strength = 55 kg × 10 N/kg = 550 N

a) Calculate the weight of a steel bar of mass 20 kg.

The forces on falling objects

If we release an object above the ground, it falls because of its weight (i.e. the force of gravity on it).

If the object falls freely, no other forces act on it. So the resultant force on it is its weight. It accelerates downwards at a constant acceleration of 10 m/s², called the acceleration due to gravity. For example, if we release a 1 kg object above the ground,

● the force of gravity on it is 10 N, and
● its acceleration (= force/mass = 10 N/1 kg) = 10 m/s².

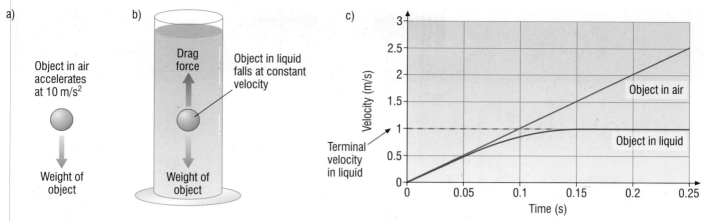

Figure 2 Falling objects. a) Falling in air, b) falling in a liquid, c) velocity–time graph for a) and b).

If the object falls in a fluid, the fluid drags on the object. The **drag force** increases with speed. At any instant, the resultant force on the object is its weight minus the drag force on it. When an object moves through the air (i.e. the fluid is air) the drag force is called air resistance.

- The acceleration of the object decreases as it falls. This is because the drag force increases as it speeds up. So the resultant force on it decreases.
- The object reaches a constant velocity when the drag force on it is equal and opposite to its weight. We call this velocity its **terminal velocity**. The resultant force is then zero, so its acceleration is zero.

b) Why does an object released in water eventually reach a constant velocity?

FOUL FACTS

If a parachute **fails** to open, the parachutist could reach a terminal velocity of more than 60 m/s (about 140 miles per hour). The drag force is then equal to his or her weight. The force of the impact on the ground would be equal to **many** times the weight, resulting in almost certain death.

SUMMARY QUESTIONS

1 Complete a) to c) using the words below:

   equal to   greater than   less than

   When an object is released in a fluid:

   a) the drag force on it is …… its weight before it reaches its terminal velocity.
   b) its acceleration is …… zero after it reaches its terminal velocity.
   c) the resultant force on it is initially …… its weight.

2 A parachutist of mass 70 kg supported by a parachute of mass 20 kg reaches a constant speed.

   a) Explain why the parachutist reaches a constant speed.
   b) Calculate:
      i) the total weight of the parachutist and the parachute,
      ii) the size and direction of the force of air resistance on the parachute when the parachutist falls at constant speed.

PRACTICAL

Investigating the motion of a parachutist

Release an object with and without a parachute.

Make suitable measurements to compare the two situations.

- Why does the object fall at constant speed when the parachute is open?
- Evaluate the reliability of the data you collected. How could you improve the quality of your data?

Figure 3 Using a parachute

KEY POINTS

1 The weight of an object is the force of gravity on it.
2 An object falling freely accelerates at about 10 m/s².
3 An object falling in a fluid reaches a terminal velocity.

P2 2.6   Speed limits

Speed kills!

At 35mph you are twice as likely to kill someone as you are at 30mph.

Kill your speed

- At 20 mph, the stopping distance is 12 metres.
- At 40 mph, the stopping distance is 36 metres.
- At 60 mph, the stopping distance is 72 metres.

ACTIVITY

A local radio station wants your help to make a 30-second road safety 'slot' aimed at car drivers. The idea is to repeat the slot every hour. With the help of your friends, decide what message to put across, then plan and record it. You could put the message across as a 'newsflash' or a catchy jingle.

GALILEO, THE FIRST SCIENTIST OF THE SCIENTIFIC AGE

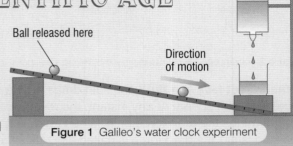

Figure 1 Galileo's water clock experiment

Galileo was one of the first scientists to test scientific ideas by doing experiments. He realised that if reliable observations don't support a theory, the theory has to be changed. He investigated accelerated motion by timing a ball as it rolled down a slope. He put marks down the slope at equal distances. He lived before the invention of mechanical clocks and watches. So he devised a 'water clock' to time the ball each time it passed a mark.

Figure 1 shows the arrangement. The clock was a dripping water vessel. He collected the water from when the ball was released to when it passed each mark. He used the mass of water collected as a measure of time. He repeated the test for each mark in turn. If possible, try this experiment yourself.

QUESTION

1 The table shows some results from Galileo's water clock experiment.

Mark	Start	1	2	3	4	5
Mass of water collected (grams)	0	28	39	48	56	63

a) What can you say about the time taken to pass from one mark to the next as the ball rolled down the slope?

b) Explain why the results show that the ball accelerated as it moved down the slope.

ACTIVITY

Sign Tests

Some road safety campaigners reckon there are too many road signs in some places. Drivers can't read them all as they approach them.

Look at these signs for a second and then write down from memory what the signs were. You and your friends could do a survey to see how the results from females and males compare.

2 Athletes are tested routinely to make sure they do not use drugs that boost performance.

a) Why are these tests important?

b) Why do athletes need to be careful about what they eat and drink in the days before a race?

c) Find out how scientific instruments help to fight the battle against drugs in sport.

d) Predict what the men's 100 m record will be in 2050.

SPEED RECORDS

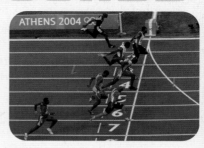

In athletics, the 100 m race is a dramatic event. Electronic timers are used to time it and cameras are used to record the finish in case there is a 'dead heat'. The world record for the time has become shorter and shorter over successive years.

● Jesse Owens	1936	10.2 s
● Jim Hines	1968	9.95 s
● Maurice Green	1999	9.79 s
● Tim Montgomery	2002	9.78 s
● Assafa Powell	2005	9.77 s

Anti-skid surfaces

Have you noticed that road surfaces near road junctions and traffic lights are often different from normal road surfaces?

● The surface is rougher than normal. This gives increased friction between the surface and a vehicle tyre. So it reduces the chance of skidding when a driver brakes.

● The surface is lighter in colour so it is marked out clearly from a normal road surface.

Skidding happens when the brakes are applied too harshly. The wheels lock and the tyres slide on the road as a result. Increased friction between the tyres and the road allows more force to be applied without skidding happening. So the stopping distance is reduced.

Discuss the following issues with your friends:

● Should drivers involved in accidents also be tested for tiredness and drugs?

● Would tiredness tests be reliable? Would drivers on medical drugs be caught unfairly?

● Should drivers be pulled over for 'on the spot' tests?

Campaigners in the village of Greystoke want the council to resurface the main road at the traffic lights in the village. A child was killed crossing the road at the traffic lights earlier in the year. The council estimates it would cost £45 000. They say they can't afford it. Campaigners have found some more data to support their case.

● There are about 50 000 road accidents each year in the UK.

● The cost of road accidents is over £3000 million per year.

● Anti-skid surfaces have cut accidents by about 5%.

a) Estimate how much each road accident costs.

b) Imagine you are one of the campaigners. Write a letter to your local newspaper to counter the council's response that they can't afford it.

SUMMARY QUESTIONS

1 A student is pushing a box across a rough floor. Friction acts between the box and the floor.

a) Complete the sentences below using words from the list.

in the same direction as
in the opposite direction to

i) The force of friction of the box on the floor is …… the force of friction of the floor on the box.

ii) The force of the student on the box is …… the force of friction of the box on the floor.

b) The student is pushing the box towards a door. Which direction, towards the door or away from the door, is

i) the force of the box on the student?

ii) the force of friction of the student on the floor?

2 a) The weight of an object of mass 100 kg on the Moon is 160 N.

i) Calculate the gravitational field strength on the Moon.

ii) Calculate the weight of the object on the Earth's surface.

The gravitational field strength near the Earth's surface is 10 N/kg.

b) Calculate the acceleration and the resultant force in each of the following situations.

i) A sprinter of mass 80 kg accelerates from rest to a speed of 9.6 m/s in 1.2 s.

ii) A train of mass 70 000 kg decelerates from a velocity of 16 m/s to a standstill in 40 s without change of direction.

3 The figure shows the velocity–time graphs for a metal object X dropped in air and a similar object Y dropped in a tank of water.

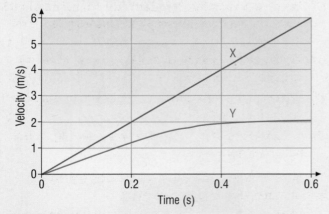

a) What does the graph for X tell you about its acceleration?

b) In terms of the forces acting on Y, explain why it reached a constant velocity.

EXAM-STYLE QUESTIONS

1

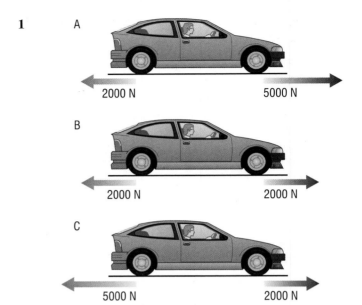

A car travels on a straight, level road.
The diagrams show the car at three stages, **A**, **B** and **C** of its journey. The arrows show the forward and backwards forces acting on the car.

(a) What is happening to the car at:

(i) Stage A?

(ii) Stage B?

(iii) Stage C? (3)

(b) The driver of the car sees some traffic lights ahead change to red. He applies the brakes. Between seeing the lights change and applying the brakes, there is a time delay called the reaction time.

(i) Suggest two things that would increase the reaction time of the driver.

(ii) Suggest two things that would increase the braking distance of the car. (4)

(c) The manufacturer of the car makes the same model but with three different engine sizes. The designers wanted to test which model had the highest top speed. They used light gates (sensors) and data loggers to take their measurements. Why didn't they use stopwatches to collect their data? (1)

2 The diagram shows a sky-diver. Two forces, **X** and **Y** act on the sky-diver.

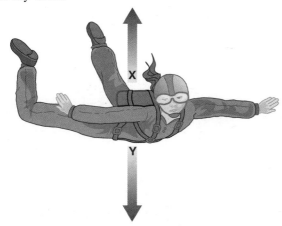

Force **Y** is the weight of the sky-diver.

(a) Write down the equation which links weight, gravitational field strength and mass. (1)

(b) What causes force **X**? (1)

(c) As the sky-diver falls, the size of force **X** increases. What happens to the size of force **Y**? (1)

(d) Describe the motion of the sky-diver when:

    (i) force **X** is smaller than force **Y**.

    (ii) force **X** is equal to force **Y**. (3)

3 The graph shows how the velocity of a parachutist changes with time during a parachute jump.

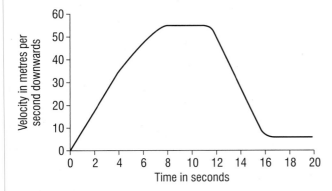

(a) Describe the motion of the parachutist during the first 4 seconds of the jump. (1)

(b) (i) What is the terminal velocity of the parachutist before her parachute opens? (1)

    (ii) Explain in terms of the forces acting on the parachutist why she reaches terminal velocity. (3)

(c) Explain why the data shown above can be presented as a line graph. (2)

HOW SCIENCE WORKS QUESTIONS

Weighty problems

Weight is something we are all familiar with and take very much for granted. You now understand that it is about the force of gravity acting on a mass. In the past this realisation had a big impact on science. Sir Isaac Newton attempted to explain why the Earth didn't fall apart as it spun on its own axis. Many people thought the Earth can't be spinning because it would fall apart if it was. Newton worked out that the force of gravity was easily strong enough to stop the Earth falling apart. Newton suggested a way the Earth's spinning motion could be tested: dropping an object from the top of a very tall tower.

The commonly accepted theory was that the object would fall to Earth behind the tower. Newton said that as the top of the tower was travelling much faster than the surface of the Earth, it would fall in front of the tower. Unfortunately there was not a tower tall enough to test the prediction!

Newton even worked out that gravity would eventually take the object to the centre of the Earth if it were able to go through the Earth. Robert Hooke pointed out an error in Newton's thinking and suggested it would follow an ellipse around the centre of the Earth.

Newton worked on this idea and many years later Edmund Halley used Newton's calculations to work out when a comet would return to be seen from the Earth. Halley died aged 85, some 16 years before his prediction about the comet was proved to be correct.

Use this passage to help you to answer these questions.

a) The observation that the Earth did not fall apart as it rotated produced which hypothesis from Newton? (1)

b) What was the prediction that was made from this hypothesis? (1)

c) What was the unscientific expectation for the object falling from the tower? (1)

d) What was the technology that was missing to test this prediction? (1)

Theories are there to be tested. Newton's theories about motion needed to be tested.

e) What was Halley's prediction that had been based on Newton's theories? (1)

f) Did Halley's prediction support Newton's theory? How do you know? (1)

P2 3.1 Energy and work

LEARNING OBJECTIVES

1 What do we mean by 'work' in science?
2 What is the relationship between work and energy?
3 What happens to the work done against frictional forces?

Working out

Figure 1 Working out

In a fitness centre or a gym, you have to work hard to keep fit. Raising weights and pedalling on an exercise bike are just two ways to keep fit. Whichever way you choose to keep fit, you have to apply a force to move something. So the work you do causes transfer of energy.

a) When you pedal on an exercise bike, where does the energy transferred go to?

When an object is moved by a force, we say **work** is done on the object by the force. The force transfers energy to the object. So we say the work done on the object is the energy transferred. For example, if you raise an object and increase its gravitational potential energy by 20 J, the work you do on the object is 20 J.

Work done = energy transferred

The work done by a force depends on the force and the distance moved. We use the following equation to calculate the work done by a force when it moves an object:

work done = force × distance moved in the direction of the force
(joules, J)　　(newtons, N)　　　　　　　　(metres, m)

DID YOU KNOW?

You use energy when you hold an object stationary in your outstretched hand. The biceps muscle of your arm is in a state of contraction. Energy must be supplied to keep the muscles contracted. No work is done on the object. All the energy transferred to the muscle is transformed to heat energy.

Note
Change of gravitational potential energy (in J) =

weight × change of height
(in N)　　　(in m)

Worked example
A 20 N weight is raised through a height of 0.4 m. Calculate i) the work done, ii) the gain of gravitational potential energy of the object.

Solution
i) The force needed to lift the weight = 20 N

Work done = force × distance moved in the direction of the
force = 20 N × 0.4 m
= 8.0 J
ii) Gain of gravitational potential energy = work done = 8.0 J

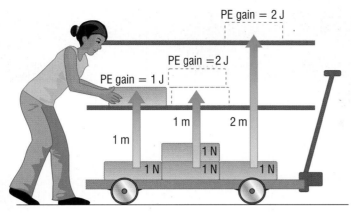

Figure 2 Using joules

b) A weightlifter raises a 200 N metal bar through a height of 1.5 m. Calculate the gain of gravitational potential energy.

PRACTICAL

Doing work

Carry out a series of experiments to calculate the work done in performing some simple tasks.

- Comment on the accuracy of your measurements. How sensitive are your measuring instruments? How accurately can you read them in your experiments?

Friction at work

Work done to overcome friction is mainly transformed into heat energy.

1 If you rub your hands together vigorously, they become warm. Your muscles do work to overcome the friction between your hands. The work you do is transformed into heat energy.

2 Brake pads become hot if the brakes are applied for too long. Friction between the brake pads and the wheel discs opposes the motion of the wheel. The kinetic energy of the vehicle is transformed into heat energy. A small proportion of the energy may be transformed into sound if the brakes 'squeal'.

SUMMARY QUESTIONS

1 Calculate the work done when:

  a) a force of 20 N makes an object move 4.8 m in the direction of the force,
  b) an object of weight 80 N is raised through a height of 1.2 m.

2 a) A student of weight 450 N steps on a box of height 0.20 m.
    i) Calculate the gain of gravitational potential energy of the student.
    ii) Calculate the work done by the student if she steps on and off the box fifty times.
  b) The student steps off the floor onto a platform and gains 270 J of gravitational potential energy. Calculate the height of the platform.

NEXT TIME YOU...

. . . step on a box, calculate your increase of gravitational potential energy. Your muscles push you up with a force equal and opposite to your weight. So your gain of gravitational potential energy is equal to your weight × the height of the step.

Figure 3 Steps

KEY POINTS

1 Work done = energy transferred.
2 Work done (joules) = force (newtons) × distance moved in the direction of the force (metres).

P2 3.2 Kinetic energy

PRACTICAL

Investigating kinetic energy

The kinetic energy of an object is the energy it has due to its motion. It depends on: ● its mass, ● its speed.

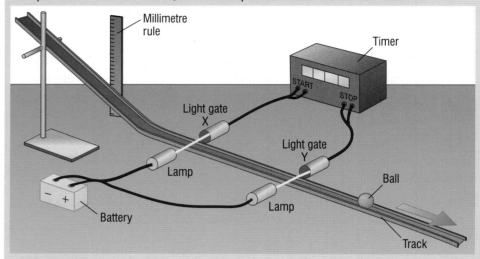

Figure 1 Investigating kinetic energy

Figure 1 shows how we can investigate how the kinetic energy of a ball depends on its speed.

1 The ball is released on a slope from a measured height above the foot of the slope. We can calculate the gravitational potential energy it loses from its weight × its drop of height. The kinetic energy it gains is equal to its loss of gravitational potential energy.

2 The ball is timed, using light gates, over a measured distance between X and Y after the slope.

● Why do light gates improve the quality of the data you can collect in this investigation?

Some sample measurements for a ball of mass 0.5 kg are shown in the table.

Height drop to foot of slope (metres, m)	0.05	0.10	0.16	0.20
Initial kinetic energy of ball (joules, J)	0.25	0.50	0.80	1.00
Time to travel 1.0 m from X to Y (seconds, s)	0.98	0.72	0.57	0.50
Speed (metres/second, m/s)	1.02	?	?	2.00

Work out the speed in each case. The first and last values have been worked out for you. *Can you see a link between speed and height?* If the height drop is increased by four times then the speed doubles. The height drop is proportional to the (speed)^2.

a) Check the other measurements to see if they fit this rule.

The exact link between the kinetic energy of an object and its speed is given by the equation

kinetic energy $= \frac{1}{2} \times$ **mass** $\times$ **speed²**
(joules, J)   (kilograms, kg)   (metre/second)², (m/s)²

Worked example

Calculate the kinetic energy of a vehicle of mass 500 kg moving at a speed of 12 m/s.

Solution

Kinetic energy $= \frac{1}{2} \times$ mass $\times$ speed² $= 0.5 \times 500$ kg $\times (12$ m/s$)^2 = 36\,000$ J.

Elastic potential energy

When you stretch a rubber band or a bowstring, the work you do is stored in it as **elastic potential energy**. Figure 2 shows one way you can transform elastic potential energy into kinetic energy.

An object is **elastic** if it regains its shape after being stretched or squashed. A rubber band is an example of an elastic object.

Elastic potential energy is the energy stored in an elastic object when work is done on it to change its shape.

Figure 2 Using elastic potential energy

SCIENCE @ WORK

Sports scientists design running shoes:
- to reduce the force of each impact when the runner's foot hits the ground,
- to return as much kinetic energy as possible to each foot in each impact.

Figure 3 A sports shoe

b) Some of the kinetic energy of the foot is wasted in each impact. What is this energy transformed into?

SUMMARY QUESTIONS

1. a) A catapult is used to fire an object into the air. Describe the energy transformations when the catapult is i) stretched, ii) released.
   b) An object of weight 2.0 N fired vertically upwards from a catapult reaches a maximum height of 5.0 m. Calculate:
      i) the gain of gravitational potential energy of the object,
      ii) the kinetic energy of the object when it left the catapult.

2. A car moving at a constant speed has 360 000 J of kinetic energy. When the driver applies the brakes, the car stops in a distance of 95 m.

   a) Calculate the force that stops the vehicle.
   b) What happens to the kinetic energy of the car?
   c) The speed of the car was 30 m/s when its kinetic energy was 360 000 J. Calculate its mass. [Higher]

KEY POINTS

1. **Elastic potential energy** is the energy stored in an elastic object when work is done on the object.
2. The **kinetic energy** of a moving object depends on its mass and its speed.
3. Kinetic energy (J) =

   $\frac{1}{2} \times$ **mass** $\times$ **speed²**
   (kg)   (m/s)²

   [Higher]

P2 3.3   Momentum

1 How can we calculate momentum?
2 What is its unit?
3 What happens to the total momentum of two objects when they collide?

Figure 1 A contact sport

Momentum is important to anyone who plays a contact sport. In a game of rugby, a player with a lot of momentum is very difficult to stop.

The momentum of a moving object = its mass × its velocity.

The unit of momentum is the kilogram metre/second (kg m/s).

a) Calculate the momentum of a 40 kg person running at 6 m/s.

PRACTICAL

Investigating collisions

When two objects collide, the momentum of each object changes. Figure 2 shows how to use a computer and a motion sensor to investigate a collision between two trolleys.

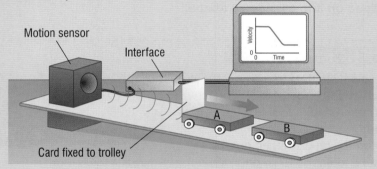

Figure 2 Investigating collisions

Trolley A is given a push so it collides with a stationary trolley B. The two trolleys stick together after the collision. The computer gives the velocity of A before the collision and the velocity of both trolleys afterwards.

● What does each section of the velocity–time graph show?

1 **For two trolleys of the same mass**, the velocity of trolley A is halved by the impact. The combined mass after the collision is twice the moving mass before the collision. So the momentum (= mass × velocity) after the collision is the same as before the collision.

2 **For a single trolley pushed into a double trolley**, the velocity of A is reduced to one-third. The combined mass after the collision is three times the initial mass. So once again, the momentum after the collision is the same as the momentum before the collision.

In both tests, the total momentum is unchanged (i.e. is conserved) by the collision. We can use this rule to predict what happens whenever objects collide or push each other apart in an 'explosion'.

Momentum is conserved in any collision or explosion provided no external forces act on the objects that collide or explode.

If a vehicle crashes into the back of a line of cars, each car in turn is 'shunted' into the one in front. Momentum is transferred along the line of cars to the one at the front.

Figure 3 A 'shunt' collision

Worked example

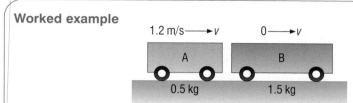

A 0.5 kg trolley A is pushed at a velocity of 1.2 m/s into a stationary trolley B of mass 1.5 kg. The two trolleys stick to each other after the impact.

Calculate:
a) the momentum of the 0.5 kg trolley before the collision,
b) the velocity of the two trolleys straight after the impact.

Solution
a) Momentum = mass × velocity = 0.5 kg × 1.2 m/s = 0.6 kg m/s.
b) The momentum after the impact = the momentum before the impact = 0.6 kg m/s
   (1.5 kg + 0.5 kg) × velocity after the impact = 0.6 kg m/s

the velocity after the impact = $\dfrac{0.6\,\text{kg m/s}}{2\,\text{kg}}$ = 0.3 m/s

b) Calculate the speed after the collision if trolley A had a mass of 1.0 kg.

SUMMARY QUESTIONS

1 Complete a) and b) using the words below:

   force   mass   momentum   velocity

   a) The momentum of a moving object is its ...... × its ....
   b) ...... is conserved when objects collide, provided no external ...... acts.

2 A 1000 kg rail wagon moving at a velocity of 5.0 m/s on a level track collides with a stationary 1500 kg wagon. The two wagons move together after the collision.

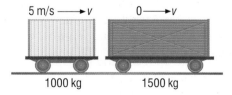

   a) Calculate the momentum of the 1000 kg wagon before the collision.
   b) Show that the two wagons move at a velocity of 2.0 m/s after the collision.

P2 3.4 More on collisions and explosions

LEARNING OBJECTIVES

1 Why does momentum have a direction as well as size?
2 When two objects fly apart, why is their total momentum zero?

PRACTICAL

Investigating a controlled explosion

When a bomb explodes, fragments of metal fly off in all directions. The fragments fly off with enormous momentum in different directions. Figure 1 shows a more controlled explosion using trolleys. When the trigger rod is tapped, a bolt springs out and the trolleys recoil from each other.

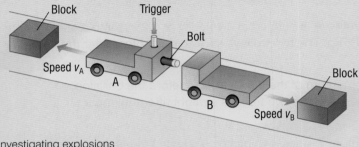

Figure 1 Investigating explosions

Using trial and error, we can place blocks on the runway so the trolleys reach them at the same time. This allows us to compare the speeds of the trolleys. Some results are shown in Figure 2.

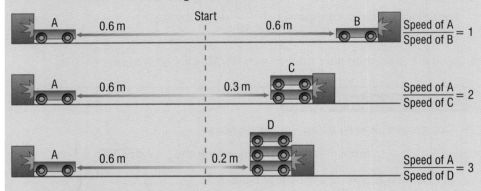

Figure 2 Using different masses

● Did your results agree exactly with the ones above? If not, try to explain why.

● Two single trolleys travel equal distances in the same time. This shows that they recoil at equal speeds.
● A double trolley only travels half the distance that a single trolley does. Its speed is half that of the single trolley.

In each test,

1 the mass of the trolley $\times$ the speed of the trolley is the same, and
2 they recoil in opposite directions.

So momentum has size and direction. The results show that the trolleys recoil with equal and opposite momentum.

a) Why does a stationary rowing boat recoil when someone jumps off it?

Conservation of momentum in an explosion

In the trolley examples:

- momentum of A after the explosion = (mass of A × velocity of A)
- momentum of B after the explosion = (mass of B × velocity of B)
- total momentum before the explosion = 0 (because both trolleys were at rest).

Using conservation of momentum gives:

$$\text{(mass of A} \times \text{velocity of A)} + \text{(mass of B} \times \text{velocity of B)} = 0$$

Therefore

(mass of A × velocity of A) = −(mass of B × velocity of B)

This tells us that A and B move apart with equal and opposite amounts of momentum.

Momentum in action

When a shell is fired from an artillery gun, the gun barrel recoils backwards. The recoil of the gun barrel is slowed down by a spring. This lessens the backwards motion of the gun.

Figure 3 An artillery gun in action

> **Worked example**
>
> An artillery gun of mass 2000 kg fires a shell of mass 20 kg at a velocity of 120 m/s. Calculate the recoil velocity of the gun.
>
> **Solution**
>
> Applying the conservation of momentum gives:
>
> mass of gun × recoil velocity of gun = −(mass of shell × velocity of shell)
>
> If we let V represent the recoil velocity of the gun,
>
> $$2000 \text{ kg} \times V = -(20 \text{ kg} \times 120 \text{ m/s})$$
>
> $$V = \frac{-2400 \text{ kg m/s}}{2000 \text{ kg}} = -1.2 \text{ m/s}$$

b) A 600 kg cannon recoils at a speed of 0.5 m/s when a 12 kg cannon ball is fired from it.
   Calculate the velocity of the cannon ball when it leaves the cannon.

SUMMARY QUESTIONS

1 A 30 kg skater and a 40 kg skater standing in the middle of an ice rink push each other away. Complete the following sentences using words from the list.

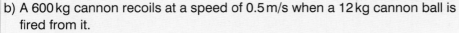

   40 kg   30 kg

   force   momentum   velocity

   a) They move apart with equal and opposite ....
   b) The 30 kg skater moves away with a bigger ...... than the other skater.
   c) They push each other with equal and opposite ....

2 In question 1, the 30 kg skater moves away at 2.0 m/s. Calculate:

   a) her momentum,
   b) the velocity of the other skater.

KEY POINTS

1 Momentum has size and direction.
2 When two objects push each other apart, they move apart with equal and opposite momentum.

P2 3.5   Changing momentum

LEARNING OBJECTIVES

1 What does a force do to the momentum of an object?
2 How can we calculate the change in momentum caused by a force? [Higher]

Figure 1 A crash test

Crumple zones at the front end and rear end of a car are designed to lessen the force of an impact. The force changes the momentum of the car.

- In a front-end impact, the momentum of the car is reduced.
- In a rear-end impact, the momentum of the car is increased.

In both cases the effect of a crumple zone is to increase the impact time and so lessen the impact force.

Car makers test the design of a crumple zone by driving a remote control car into a brick wall.

PRACTICAL

Investigating impacts

We can test an impact using a trolley and a brick, as shown in Figure 2. When the trolley hits the brick, the Plasticine flattens on impact, making the impact time longer. This is the key factor that reduces the impact force.

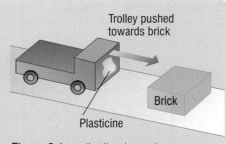

Trolley pushed towards brick

Brick

Plasticine

Figure 2 Investigating impacts

a) Why is rubber matting under a child's swing a good idea?

HIGHER

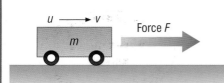

Figure 3 Force and momentum

Force and momentum

Let's see why increasing the impact time reduces the impact force.

Suppose the force acts on the trolley for a time t and causes the velocity to change from u to v.

- The deceleration due to the impact $= \dfrac{\text{change of velocity}}{\text{time taken}} = \dfrac{v - u}{t}$
- Using force $=$ mass $\times$ acceleration:

$$\text{the force on the trolley, } F = \frac{m(v - u)}{t} = \frac{mv - mu}{t}$$

where m is the mass of the trolley

- The initial momentum of the trolley $= mu$, and the final momentum of the trolley $= mv$

So the force,

$$F = \frac{\text{final momentum} - \text{initial momentum}}{\text{time taken}} = \frac{\text{change of momentum}}{\text{time taken}}$$

$$\textbf{force, } F = \frac{\textbf{change of momentum}}{\textbf{time taken}}$$

The equation shows that:

1 Making the time longer (increasing the value of *t*) makes the force smaller. Crumple zones in cars are designed to make impact times longer so impact forces are reduced.

b) What difference does it make if the impact time is made shorter instead of longer?

2 When a resultant force acts on a moving object, a change of momentum takes place.

In general, the force needed to cause a change of momentum is given by:

force = **change of momentum** (kilogram metre/second, kg m/s) / **time taken** (seconds, s)
(newtons, N)

Worked example

A bullet of mass 0.004 kg moving at a speed of 90 m/s is stopped by a bullet-proof vest in 0.0003 s.

Calculate the impact force.

Solution

Initial momentum of bullet = mass × velocity = 0.004 kg × 90 m/s
= 0.36 kg m/s

Final momentum of bullet = 0

$$\text{Impact force} = \frac{\text{change of momentum}}{\text{time taken}} = \frac{0.36\,\text{kg m/s}}{0.0003\,\text{s}} = 1200\,\text{N}$$

c) Calculate the impact force if the impact time had been 0.0002 s.

KEY POINTS

1 The more time an impact takes, the less the force exerted.

2 $\text{Force (newtons)} = \dfrac{\text{change of momentum (kilogram metre/second)}}{\text{time taken (seconds)}}$

[Higher]

SUMMARY QUESTIONS

1 Copy and complete each of the following sentences using a word or words from the list.

decreases   **increases**   **is zero**   **stays the same**

a) The momentum of a moving object …… if no forces act on it.
b) In an impact in which a moving object is speeded up, its momentum …… .
c) When an object is thrown into the air, the force of gravity on it …… its momentum as it goes up.

2 a) Calculate the initial momentum of an 800 kg car travelling at 30 m/s.
b) What force is required to stop the car in i) 12 s, ii) 30 s? [Higher]

Motor News

CLUNK CLICK!

When seat belts were first introduced, some car users claimed that they should not be forced by law to wear them. A very successful campaign was launched to convince car users to 'belt up'. It included the catchy phrase 'Clunk click every trip'. As a result, deaths and injuries in road accidents fell significantly. A seat belt stops its wearer from continuing forwards when the car stops suddenly. Someone without a seat belt would hit the windscreen in a 'short sharp' impact and suffer major injury.

- The time taken to stop someone in a car is longer with a seat belt than without it. So the decelerating force is reduced by wearing a seat belt.
- The seat belt acts across the chest so it spreads the force out. Without the seat belt, the force would act on the head when it hits the windscreen.

NEWS

Air bags

An airbag in action

A crazy motorist was sent to prison for three years yesterday at Newtown County Court. He drove for twenty miles at top speed down the wrong side of a motorway. He was stopped when he drove into a police car blocking his route. One of the police officers said, 'We braced ourselves for the impact when he didn't stop. The airbags in our car inflated and took the force of the impact.' The bravery of the police officers was commended by the judge.

QUESTION

1 Explain why an inflated air bag in front of a car user reduces the force on a user of a 'head-on' crash.

G-FORCES

We sometimes express the effect of an impact on an object or person as a force-to-weight ratio. We call this the 'g-force'. For example, a g-force of 2g means the force on an object is twice its weight. You would experience a g-force of

- about 3–4 g on a fairground ride that whirls you round,
- about 10 g in a low-speed car crash,
- more than 50 g in a high-speed car crash-force. You would be lucky to survive though!

Analysing a road crash

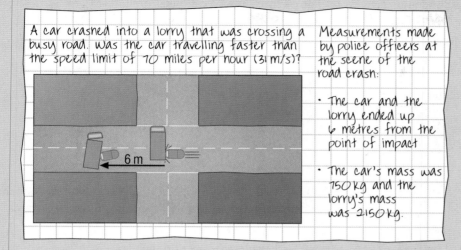

A car crashed into a lorry that was crossing a busy road. Was the car travelling faster than the speed limit of 70 miles per hour (31 m/s)?

6 m

Measurements made by police officers at the scene of the road crash:

- The car and the lorry ended up 6 metres from the point of impact
- The car's mass was 750 kg and the lorry's mass was 2150 kg.

QUESTION

2 The speed of a vehicle for a braking distance of 6 m is 9 m/s.
  a) Use this speed to calculate the momentum of the car and the lorry immediately after the impact.
  b) Use conservation of momentum to calculate the velocity of the car immediately before the collision.
  c) Was the car travelling over the speed limit before the crash?

Safety costs

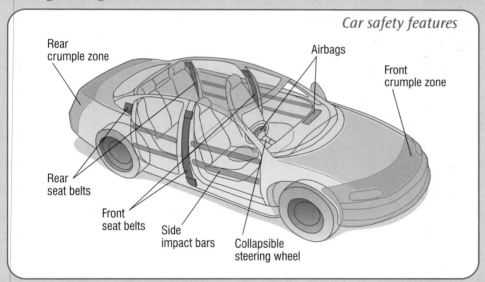

Car safety features

Rear crumple zone, Airbags, Front crumple zone, Rear seat belts, Front seat belts, Side impact bars, Collapsible steering wheel

Car makers need to sell cars. If their cars are too expensive, people won't buy them. Safety features add to the cost of a new car. Some safety features (e.g. seat belts) are required by law and some (e.g. side impact bars) are optional. The table shows the main safety features in a new car.

Car make and price: Nippy, £6500	
Front seat belts	✔
Rear seat belts	✔
Airbags	
Front crumple zone	✔
Rear crumple zone	
Side impact bars	
Collapsible steering wheel	✔

ACTIVITY

a) With the help of your friends, find out what safety features are in some other new cars. Find out if they are compulsory or optional. List the price (including tax) of each car.
b) Use your information to say if cheaper cars have fewer safety features than more expensive cars.
c) What do you think could be done to make more cars safer?

ACTIVITY

Do you think all cars should have the best safety features money can buy? Or should owners choose these as options? What are the points for and against these views?

Which do you support?

SUMMARY QUESTIONS

1 a) Copy and complete the following sentences using words from the list.

> **equal to   greater than   less than**

When a braking force acts on a vehicle and slows it down,
   i) the work done by the force is …… the energy transferred from the object,
   ii) the kinetic energy after the brakes have been applied is …… the kinetic energy before they were applied.

b) A student pushes a trolley of weight 150 N up a slope of length 20 m. The slope is 1.2 m high.

11 N

20 m   1.2 m

   i) Calculate the gravitational potential energy gained by the trolley.
   ii) The student pushed the trolley up the slope with a force of 11 N. Show that the work done by the student was 220 J.
   iii) Give one reason why all the work done by the student was not transferred to the trolley as gravitational potential energy.

2 A 700 kg car moving at 20 m/s is stopped in a distance of 80 m when the brakes are applied.

a) Show that the kinetic energy of the car at 20 m/s is 140 000 J.

b) Calculate the braking force on the car.   [Higher]

3 A student of mass 40 kg standing at rest on a skateboard of mass 2.0 kg jumps off the skateboard at a speed of 0.30 m/s. Calculate:

a) i) the momentum of the student,
   ii) the recoil velocity of the skateboard,

b) the kinetic energy of i) the student, ii) the skateboard, after they move apart.   [b] – Higher]

4 A car bumper is designed not to bend in impacts at less than 4 m/s. It was fitted to a car of mass 900 kg and tested by driving the car into a wall at 4 m/s. The time of impact was measured and found to be 1.8 s. Work out the impact force.   [Higher]

EXAM-STYLE QUESTIONS

1 The picture shows a catapult.

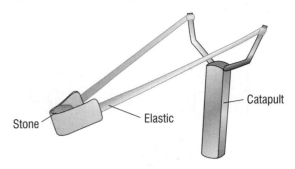

Catapult

Stone   Elastic

(a) When a force is applied to the stone, work is done in stretching the elastic and the stone moves backwards.

   (i) Write down the equation you could use to calculate the work done.   (1)

   (ii) The average force applied to the stone is 20 N. This moves it backwards 0.15 m. Calculate the work done and give its unit.   (3)

(b) The work done is stored as energy.

   (i) What type of energy is stored in the stretched elastic?   (1)

   (ii) What type of energy does the stone have when it is released?   (1)

2 (a) The diagram shows three cars, **A**, **B** and **C**, travelling along a straight, level road at 25 m/s.

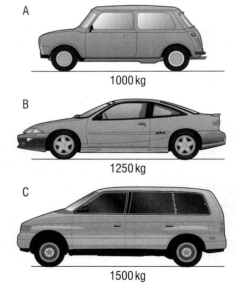

A

1000 kg

B

1250 kg

C

1500 kg

   (i) Explain which vehicle, **A**, **B** or **C** has the greatest momentum.   (2)

   (ii) Would you need a more sensitive weighing device to be more certain of your answer to part (i)? Give your reasoning.   (2)

(b) The diagram shows three identical cars, **D**, **E** and **F**, all of mass 1500 kg, travelling along a straight, level road at different speeds.

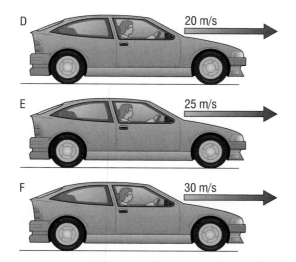

D   20 m/s

E   25 m/s

F   30 m/s

Explain which vehicle, **D**, **E** or **F** has the greatest momentum. (2)

(c) Calculate the momentum of car **E**, include the unit with your answer. (4)

3 A student is doing an investigation of the conservation of momentum with a horizontal air track and two 'gliders'.

(a) Explain what is meant by conservation of momentum. (2)

(b) Apart from collisions, give another type of event in which conservation of momentum applies. (1)

(c) The diagram shows the air track and the two 'gliders', **X** and **Y**.

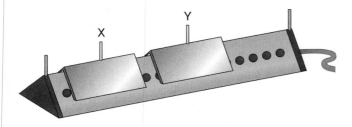

X   Y

The mass of **X** is 0.2 kg and its velocity is 1.5 m/s to the right.

The mass of **Y** is 0.3 kg and it is stationary. When 'glider' **X** collides with trolley **Y** they move off together.

Calculate the velocity of the 'gliders' after the collision and give their direction. (4)

HOW SCIENCE WORKS QUESTIONS

Claire was interested in how ancient catapults were used to fire rocks at the enemy. She designed a catapult that was similar to one she found in a history book. She couldn't work out the angle at which to fire the catapult, so she used 'stoppers' to test three different positions. Her catapult looked like this:

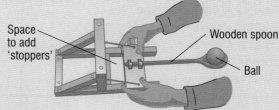

Space to add 'stoppers'

Wooden spoon

Ball

As the ball was fired the spoon was pulled by the force of the elastic bands. The spoon hit the wooden support and the ball was fired into the distance. The three positions in which the wooden spoon was stopped are shown in the diagram opposite.

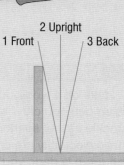

2 Upright

1 Front

3 Back

Here are Claire's results:

	Distance travelled (cm)		
	Front	Upright	Back
1st go	110	114	110
2nd go	117	116	112
3rd go	109	121	108
Mean	112	117	110

a) Claire made a prediction that the backward position would make the ball travel the furthest. Do the results support her prediction? Explain your answer. (1)

b) If you had to have a new prediction, what might it be? (1)

c) Do the results show precision? Explain your answer. (1)

d) What is the independent variable in Claire's investigation? (1)

e) Would you describe this as a discrete, categoric or ordered variable? (1)

f) How could it be changed into a continuous variable? (1)

g) What would be the advantage of using a continuous independent variable? (3)

P2 4.1   Electrical charges

Have you ever stuck a balloon on a ceiling? All you need to do is to rub the balloon on your clothing before you touch it on the ceiling. The rubbing action charges the balloon with **static electricity**. The charge on the balloon attracts it to the ceiling.

a) Why does a TV screen crackle when you switch it on?

DEMONSTRATION

The Van de Graaff generator

A Van de Graaff generator can make your hair stand on end. The dome charges up when the generator is switched on. Massive sparks are produced if the charge on the dome builds up too much.

Figure 1 The Van de Graaff generator

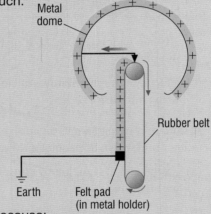

Metal dome

Rubber belt

Earth   Felt pad (in metal holder)

The Van de Graaff generator charges up because:

– the belt rubs against a felt pad and becomes charged,
– the belt carries the charge onto an insulated metal dome,
– sparks are produced when the dome can no longer hold any more charge.

● Why should you keep away from a Van de Graaff generator?

Inside the atom

The protons and neutrons make up the nucleus of the atom. Electrons move about in the space round the nucleus.

● A proton has a positive charge.
● An electron has an equal negative charge.
● A neutron is uncharged.

An uncharged atom has equal numbers of electrons and protons. Only electrons can be transferred to or from an atom.

1 Adding electrons to an uncharged atom makes it negative (because the atom then has more electrons than protons).

2 Removing electrons from an uncharged atom makes it positive (because the atom has fewer electrons than protons).

○ Electron
● Proton
○ Neutron

Figure 2 Inside an atom

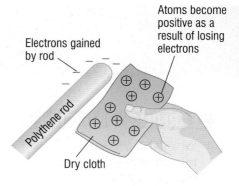

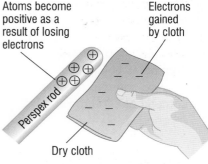

Figure 3 Charging by friction

Charging by friction

Some insulators become charged by rubbing them with a dry cloth.

- Rubbing a polythene rod with a dry cloth transfers electrons to the surface atoms of the rod from the cloth. So the polythene rod becomes negatively charged.
- Rubbing a perspex rod with a dry cloth transfers electrons from the surface atoms of the rod onto the cloth. So the perspex rod becomes positively charged.

b) Glass is charged positively when it is rubbed with a cloth.
Does glass gain or lose electrons when it is charged?

PRACTICAL

The force between two charged objects

Two charged objects exert a force on each other. Figure 4 shows how you can investigate this force.

- What happens?

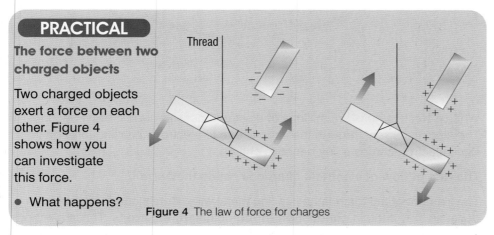

Figure 4 The law of force for charges

Your results in the experiment above should show that:

- two objects with the same type of charge (i.e. like charges) repel each other.
- two objects with opposite types of charge (i.e. unlike charges) attract each other.

Like charges repel. Unlike charges attract.

c) What force keeps the electrons inside an atom?

SUMMARY QUESTIONS

1 Choose words from the list to complete a) and b) below:

to   from   loses   gains

a) When a polythene rod is charged using a dry cloth, it becomes negative because it ...... electrons that transfer ...... it ...... the cloth.

b) When a perspex rod is charged using a dry cloth, it becomes positive because it ...... electrons that transfer ...... it ...... the cloth.

2 When rubbed with a dry cloth, perspex becomes positively charged. Polythene and ebonite become negatively charged. State whether or not attraction or repulsion takes place when:

a) a perspex rod is held near a polythene rod,
b) a perspex rod is held near an ebonite rod,
c) a polythene rod is held near an ebonite rod.

KEY POINTS

1 Like charges repel; unlike charges attract.
2 Insulating materials that lose electrons when rubbed become positively charged.
3 Insulating materials that gain electrons when rubbed become negatively charged.

P2 4.2   Charge on the move

Charge and current

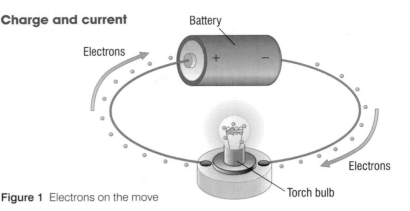

Figure 1 Electrons on the move

When a torch lamp is on, millions of electrons pass through it every second. The electric current through the lamp is due to electrons passing through it. Each electron carries a tiny negative charge.

The rate of flow of electrical charge is called the *current*.

The filament of the torch lamp is a fine metal wire. Metals conduct electricity because they contain **conduction (or delocalised) electrons**. These electrons move about freely inside the metal. They are not confined to a single atom. When the torch is switched on, the battery pushes electrons through the filament.

Insulators can't conduct electricity because all the electrons are held in atoms.

a) When electrons pass through a wire in a circuit, do they move towards the positive or the negative end of the wire?

Charging a conductor

A conductor can only hold charge if it is insulated from the ground. If it isn't insulated, it won't hold any charge because electrons transfer between the conductor and the ground.

To charge an insulated conductor, it needs to be brought into contact with a charged object.

● If the object is positively charged, electrons transfer from the conductor to the object. So the conductor becomes positive because it loses electrons.

● If the object is negatively charged, electrons transfer to the conductor from the object. So the conductor becomes negative because it gains electrons.

b) A negatively charged rod is touched against a metal can on the ground. Why *doesn't* the can become negatively charged?

PRACTICAL

Using an electroscope

Figure 2 shows an electroscope, a device that detects charge, being charged. The charged rod makes direct contact with the cap. The leaf of the electroscope is repelled by the metal plate when the electroscope is charged. This happens because they both gain the same type of charge.

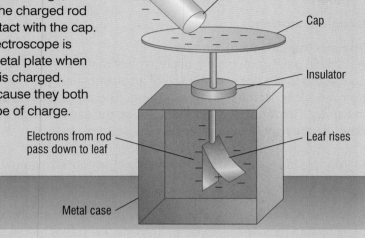

Figure 2 Charging a conductor

- Charged polythene rod
- Cap
- Insulator
- Electrons from rod pass down to leaf
- Leaf rises
- Metal case

- What happens to the leaf if you repeat the test with a positively charged rod?

Discharging

To discharge a charged conductor safely, a conducting path (e.g. a wire) needs to be provided between the object and the ground. The conducting path allows electrons to transfer between the object and the ground. Then we say that the object is **earthed**. (See Figure 3.)

c) A positively charged metal can is discharged by earthing it. Does the can gain or lose electrons?

Sparks and strikes

If we supply a conductor with more and more charge, its **electric potential energy** increases. The **potential difference** (i.e. voltage) between the conductor and the ground increases.

If the potential difference becomes high enough, a *spark* may jump between the conductor and any nearby earthed object. A lightning strike is a dramatic example of what happens when a charged thundercloud can hold no more charge. (See Figure 4.)

HIGHER

SUMMARY QUESTIONS

1 Complete the following sentences:

   a) An electric current is …… .
   b) A metal is a conductor because it contains …… .
   c) A …… metal object loses electrons when it is connected to the ground.

2 a) Why can't we charge a metal object if it is earthed?
   b) A drawing pin is fixed to the dome of a Van de Graaff machine with its point in the air. Explain why this stops the dome charging up when the machine is switched on. [Higher]

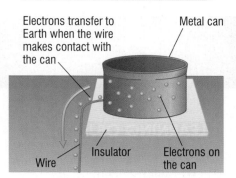

Electrons transfer to Earth when the wire makes contact with the can

Metal can

Wire

Insulator

Electrons on the can

Figure 3 Earthing a negatively charged conductor

DID YOU KNOW?

A lightning strike is a massive flow of charge between a thundercloud and the ground. A lightning conductor on a tall building prevents lightning strikes by allowing the thundercloud to discharge gradually. The conductor is joined to the ground by a thick copper strip. This allows charge to flow safely between the conductor tip and the ground.

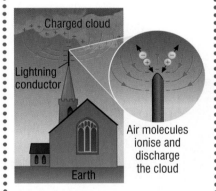

Charged cloud

Lightning conductor

Air molecules ionise and discharge the cloud

Earth

Figure 4 A lightning conductor

KEY POINTS

1 Electrical current is the rate of flow of charge.
2 A metal object can only hold charge if it is isolated from the ground.
3 A metal object is earthed by connecting it to the ground.
4 If a metal object gains too much charge, it will produce sparks. [Higher]

P2 4.3 Uses and dangers of static electricity

LEARNING OBJECTIVES

1 In what ways is static electricity useful?
2 In what ways is static electricity dangerous?
3 How can we get rid of static electricity where it is dangerous?

Using electrostatics

The electrostatic paint sprayer

Automatic paint sprayers are used to paint metal panels. The spray nozzle is connected to the positive terminal of an electrostatic generator. The negative terminal is connected to the metal panel. The panel attracts paint droplets from the spray. The droplets of paint all pick up the same charge and repel each other, so they spread out to form a fine cloud of paint.

a) Why are the spray nozzle and the panel oppositely charged?

The electrostatic precipitator

Coal-fired power stations produce vast quantities of ash and dust. Electrostatic precipitators remove this material from the flue gases before they get into the atmosphere.

The particles of ash and dust pass through a grid of wires in the precipitator. Look at Figure 2. The grid wires are negative so the particles become negatively charged when they touch it. The charged particles are attracted onto the positively charged metal plates. The plates are shaken at intervals so the ash and dust that build up on them drop to the floor of the precipitator. They are then removed.

Figure 1 An electrostatic paint sprayer

b) What difference would it make if the grid was not charged?

The photocopier

The key part of a photocopier is a charged drum or plate. This loses charge from the parts of its surface exposed to light. Figure 3 shows how a photocopier works.

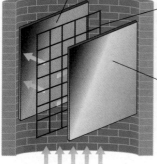

Ash and dust collect on plates

Grid of charged wires

Metal plates charged oppositely to the grid wires

Waste gases carrying ash and dust

Figure 2 An electrostatic precipitator

1 Photocopiers with a photoconducting drum – drum positively charged until light falls on it.

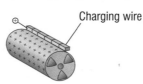

Charging wire

2 Light reflected off the paper onto the drum. The areas of black do not reflect so the drum keeps its charge in these areas.

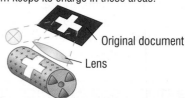

Original document

Lens

3 The black toner sticks to the drum where it is still charged and is pressed onto paper.

Toner

4 The paper is finally heated to stick the toner to it permanently.

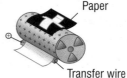

Paper

Transfer wire

Figure 3 Inside a photocopier

c) Why are photocopies sometimes charged when they come out of the photocopier?

Electrostatics hazards

Pipe problems

When a road tanker pumps oil or petrol into a storage tank, the connecting pipe must be earthed. If it isn't, the pipe could become charged. A build-up of charge would cause a spark. This could cause an explosion as the fuel vapour reacts with oxygen in the air.

Static electricity is also generated when grains of powder are pumped through pipes. Friction between the grains and the pipe charges them. An explosion could happen due to a spark igniting the powder.

d) Why is the rubber hose of a petrol pump made of special conducting rubber?

Antistatic floors

In a hospital, doctors use anaesthetic gases during operations. Some of these gases are explosive. If the gas escapes into the air, a tiny spark could make it explode. To eliminate static charge in operating theatres, an **antistatic material** is used for the floor surface. This material is a poor electrical insulator so it conducts charge to Earth.

e) Why do the doctors and nurses wear antistatic clothes in an operating theatre?

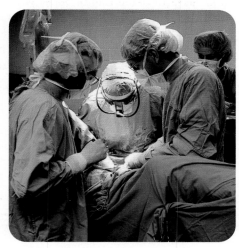

Figure 4 Operating theatres have antistatic floors

PRACTICAL

Getting rid of the charge

Charge up an electroscope.

- How do you discharge it? Explain what happens.

GET IT RIGHT!

Remember that electrostatic charge has its uses as well as its dangers.

SUMMARY QUESTIONS

1 Complete a) and b) using the words below:

attracted   gain   lose   repelled

a) Positively charged paint droplets from a paint spray are …… by the spray nozzle. The droplets …… electrons when they reach the negatively charged metal panel.

b) Dust particles in an electrostatic precipitator touch a positively charged wire. The particles …… electrons to the wire and are then …… by a negatively charged metal plate.

2 a) The delivery pipe between the road tanker and the storage tank must be earthed before any petrol is pumped from the tanker. Why is this an important safety measure?

b) Why does an operating theatre in a hospital have antistatic floor covering?

KEY POINTS

1 A spark from a charged object can make powder grains or certain gases explode.

2 To eliminate static electricity,
a) use antistatic materials, and
b) earth metal pipes and objects.

P2 4.4   Static issues

An electric discovery

What does the word 'charge' mean? Someone who runs at top speed 'charges along' filled with adrenalin. An electrically charged object is filled with static electricity. The term 'electric charge' was first used over 300 years ago when scientists discovered that certain materials such as ebonite, glass and resin attracted bits of paper when they are rubbed. They knew this effect had been discovered by the ancient Greeks using amber, a naturally occurring fossil resin. So they used the word 'electric', from the Greek word for 'amber', to describe the attractive power of these materials. The action of rubbing a suitable material was said to *charge* it with electricity.

Further experiments showed that:

- identical charged materials always repel each other,
- ebonite and glass attract,
- ebonite and resin repel,
- glass and resin attract.

More tests showed that there are two types of charge and they cancel each other out. So the two types of charge were called 'positive' and 'negative'.

QUESTION

1 a) Why did scientists conclude from these results that there are only two types of charge?

b) In terms of electrons, explain why equal and opposite amounts of charge cancel each other out.

Powder tests

The diagram shows how to test the charging of powder grains. The powder is poured through a pipe into a metal can on an electroscope.

If the powder is charged, the metal plate of the electroscope and the gold leaf attached to it both become charged. As a result, the leaf is repelled by the plate.

To find out if the powder charge is positive or negative, a negatively charged rod (e.g. polythene) held near the can will make the leaf rise further if the charge on the electroscope is negative.

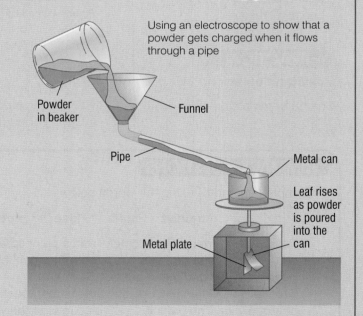

Using an electroscope to show that a powder gets charged when it flows through a pipe

Powder in beaker

Funnel

Pipe

Metal can

Leaf rises as powder is poured into the can

Metal plate

a)
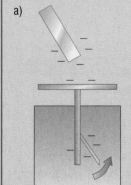

b)
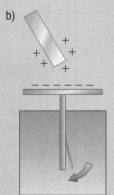

An electroscope test. a) The leaf rises when a negative rod is brought near. b) The leaf falls when a positive rod is brought near.

QUESTION

2 An electroscope is charged negatively by touching the cap with a negatively charged rod. Explain, in terms of electrons, why this makes the leaf go up and stay up.

The ink jet printer

An ink jet printer has an 'ink gun' inside that directs a jet of charged ink droplets at the paper. The ink droplets pass between two metal 'deflecting' plates before reaching the paper.

- By making one plate positive and the other negative, the droplets can be deflected as they pass between the plates. This happens because the droplets are attracted to the oppositely charged plate.
- The plates are made positive and negative by applying a potential difference to them. The potential difference is controlled by signals from the computer. The computer is programmed to make the inkjet print characters and graphics on the paper at high speed.

An ink jet printer

QUESTION

3 What do you think would happen if the ink droplets are too big?

A chip problem

Computer chips can be damaged by static electricity. Most microcomputers contain *CMOS* chips. Tiny amounts of charge on the pins of a CMOS chip can destroy its electrical properties. To prevent chips being damaged by static electricity, manufacturers insert them into antistatic foam sheets before packaging them.

Special tools are available to transfer chips to and from circuits to prevent them becoming charged in the transfer. Touching the chip briefly when a charged object is nearby would cause it to become charged. The figure shows how this can happen.

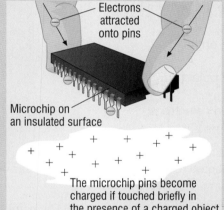

Electrons attracted onto pins

Microchip on an insulated surface

The microchip pins become charged if touched briefly in the presence of a charged object

Microchip damage

ACTIVITY

A company that makes computers has found that some of its chips don't work. The supplier says the company must be more careful when the chips are used. Imagine you work in the company. You think the problem is at the supplier. Send an e-mail to the supplier to find out.

Global junk

Computers sooner or later become out of date. But what happens to them then? At the present time, thousands of old or damaged computers are shipped out every year to junkyards in poor countries. People survive there by taking valuable material out of these computers and selling it. However, this is often dangerous work and chemicals from the junk get into local water supplies. Most of the junk is not biodegradable. It's mounting up all the time.

Computer junk

ACTIVITY

What can we do to stop this problem?

a) Discuss ways to tackle the problem.
b) Present a five-minute radio slot to raise awareness of the issue and to suggest some solutions.

SUMMARY QUESTIONS

1 a) Helen has just had a shock. She got up from a plastic chair to open the door and got an electric shock when she touched the door handle.
  i) How did she become charged?
  ii) Why did she feel a shock when she touched the door handle?

  b) An object was charged by rubbing it with a dry cloth. When it was held near a negatively charged rod, it repelled the rod.
  i) State if the object was charged positively or negatively.
  ii) Would the object attract or repel a positively charged rod?

2 Complete the sentences below using words from the list.

from   on   to

  a) A polythene rod is charged negatively by rubbing it with a cloth.
  i) Electrons transfer …… the cloth …… the rod.
  ii) The electrons …… the rod cannot move about freely.

  b) A positively charged rod is touched on an insulated metal object.
  i) Electrons transfer …… the metal object …… the rod.
  ii) If the metal object is then 'earthed', electrons transfer …… it …… the ground.

3 A paint sprayer in a car factory is used to paint a metal panel. The spray nozzle is connected to the negative terminal of a voltage supply unit. The metal panel is connected to the positive terminal of the voltage supply unit.

  a) What type of charge is gained by the paint droplets when they leave the spray nozzle?

  b) Why is the metal panel made positive?

  c) Why is there an electric current along the wires joining the metal panel and the paint spray nozzle to the voltage supply unit?

4 a) i) In an ink jet printer, what difference would it make if the droplets were not charged?
  ii) In an electrostatic precipitator, how are the dust particles charged?

  b) When an airplane is being refuelled, explain why a wire is connected between the aircraft and the fuel tanker?

EXAM-STYLE QUESTIONS

1 A plastic rod is rubbed with a dry cloth.

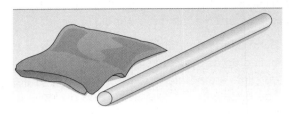

  (a) The rod becomes negatively charged. Explain how this happens. (3)

  (b) What charge is left on the cloth? (1)

  (c) What happens if the negatively charged rod is brought close to another negatively charged rod. (1)

2 The picture shows an electrostatic paint spray being used to apply paint to a sheet of metal.

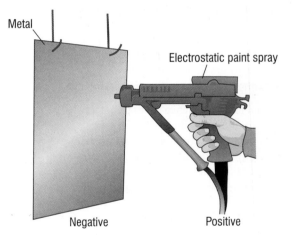

  (a) The paint droplets are given a positive charge as they leave the nozzle. Explain why. (2)

  (b) The sheet of metal is given a negative charge. Explain why. (3)

  (c) (i) A painter wanted to find out the best distance between the nozzle of the paint spray and the sheet of metal to be painted. What could the painter use to measure the independent variable in this investigation? (1)

  (ii) Why would it be a good idea for the painter to carry out some trials before deciding upon the range of the independent variable? (2)

3 The picture shows an electrostatic smoke precipitator. This is used to separate smoke particles from waste gases in a chimney.

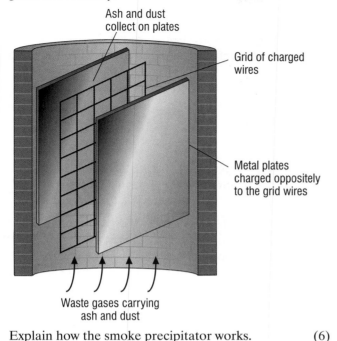

Ash and dust collect on plates

Grid of charged wires

Metal plates charged oppositely to the grid wires

Waste gases carrying ash and dust

Explain how the smoke precipitator works. (6)

4 A photocopier uses static electricity to make photocopies.

The following sentences describe how the photocopier works.
The sentences are in the wrong order.

A Black ink powder is attracted to the charged parts of the plate.

B The paper is heated so the powder melts and sticks to the paper.

C The copying plate is given a charge.

D This is now a photocopy of the original page.

E Where light hits the plate the charge leaks away, leaving a pattern of the page.

F Black ink powder is transferred onto a piece of paper.

G An image of the page to be copied is projected onto the charged copying plate.

Arrange the sentences in the right order. Start with sentence **C** and finish with sentence **D**.

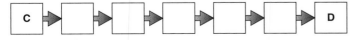

C → ☐ → ☐ → ☐ → ☐ → ☐ → D

(4)

HOW SCIENCE WORKS QUESTIONS

Lightning conductors are very important in protecting buildings from lightning strikes. New designs must be thoroughly tested. They must work first time and every time. They have to be tested in a standard way. This method is described in the diagram below.

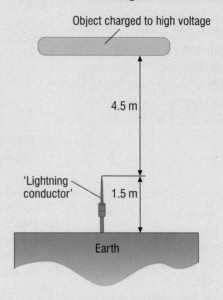

Object charged to high voltage

4.5 m

'Lightning conductor'   1.5 m

Earth

The conditions must be followed strictly. This includes the temperature of the room and the humidity. The charge is built up on the object above the lightning conductor and photographs are taken of the 'lightning' as it forms. This allows accurate measurements to be made of the time taken for the lightning conductor to respond. The measurements are made in microseconds.

a) Explain why it is important that the testing is carried out in exactly the same way each time. (1)

b) To find the correct temperature for these tests, the scientists carried out surveys.
Suggest when they carried out the surveys. (1)

c) What do you think they were measuring? (1)

d) How many sets of data do you think they collected? (1)

e) What is the sensitivity of the equipment used to time the response of the lightning conductor? (1)

f) Explain why repeat tests on the same lightning conductor might give different results. (1)

g) Should this testing be carried out by the company manufacturing the lightning conductors or by an independent company? Explain your answer. (1)

P2 5.1 · Electric circuits

LEARNING OBJECTIVES

1 Why are electric circuits represented by circuit diagrams?
2 What are the circuit symbols for a cell, a switch and other common components?

An electric torch can be very useful in a power cut at night. But it needs to be checked to make sure it works. Figure 1 shows what is inside a torch. The circuit in Figure 1 shows us how the torch is connected to the switch and the two cells.

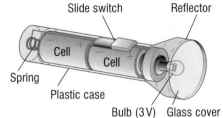

Figure 1 An electric torch

a) Why does the switch have to be closed to turn the lamp on?

A circuit diagram is a very helpful way of showing how the components in a circuit are connected together. Each component has its own symbol. Figure 2 shows the symbols for some of the components you will meet in this course. The function of each component is also described in Figure 2. You need to recognise these symbols and remember what each component is used for – otherwise you'll get mixed up in your exams. More importantly, you could get a big shock if you mix them up!

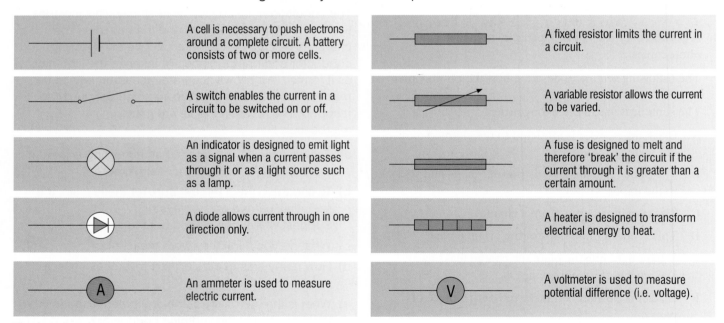

A cell is necessary to push electrons around a complete circuit. A battery consists of two or more cells.	A fixed resistor limits the current in a circuit.
A switch enables the current in a circuit to be switched on or off.	A variable resistor allows the current to be varied.
An indicator is designed to emit light as a signal when a current passes through it or as a light source such as a lamp.	A fuse is designed to melt and therefore 'break' the circuit if the current through it is greater than a certain amount.
A diode allows current through in one direction only.	A heater is designed to transform electrical energy to heat.
An ammeter is used to measure electric current.	A voltmeter is used to measure potential difference (i.e. voltage).

Figure 2 Components and symbols

NEXT TIME YOU...

... switch a light bulb on, remember it's part of a very long circuit that goes all the way back to a transformer at a local sub-station.

b) What components are in the circuit diagram in Figure 3?

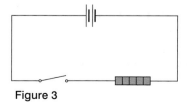

Figure 3

PRACTICAL

Circuit tests

Connect a variable resistor in series with the torch lamp and a battery, as shown in Figure 4. Adjusting the slider of the variable resistor alters the amount of current flowing through the bulb and therefore affects its brightness.

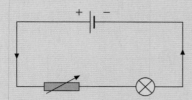

Figure 4 Using a variable resistor

- In Figure 4, the torch lamp goes dim when the slider is moved one way. What happens if the slider is moved back again?
- What happens if you include a diode in the circuit?

SCIENCE @ WORK

Drivers need to know what road signs mean, otherwise there would be chaos on our roads. Electricians and circuit designers need to know what circuit signs and symbols mean for the same reason. We mark the direction of the current in a 'direct current' circuit from + to − round the circuit. This convention was agreed long before electrons were discovered.

DID YOU KNOW...

You would damage a portable radio if you put the batteries in the wrong way round unless a diode is in series with the battery. The diode only allows current through when it is connected as shown in Figure 5. If the battery is reversed in the circuit, the diode stops electrons passing round the circuit.

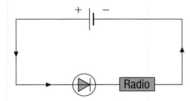

Figure 5 Using a diode

c) Would the radio in Figure 5 work if the diode was 'turned round' in the circuit?

SUMMARY QUESTIONS

1 Name the numbered components in the circuit diagram.

2 a) Redraw the circuit diagram in question 1 with a diode in place of the switch so it allows current through.
  b) What further component would you need in this circuit to alter the current in it?

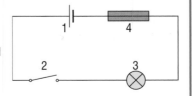

KEY POINTS

1 Every component has its own agreed symbol.
2 A circuit diagram shows how components are connected together.
3 A battery consists of two or more cells connected together.

P2 5.2

Resistance

LEARNING OBJECTIVES

1 Where should you put an ammeter and a voltmeter in a circuit?
2 What is resistance and what is its unit?
3 What is Ohm's law?
4 What happens if you reverse the current in a resistor?

Ammeters and voltmeters

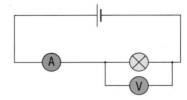

Figure 1 Using an ammeter and a voltmeter

Look at the ammeter and the voltmeter in the circuit in Figure 1.

● The ammeter measures the current through the torch lamp. It is connected in **series** with the lamp so the current through them is the same. The ammeter reading gives the current in amperes (A) (or milliamperes, (mA) for small currents, where 1 mA = 0.001 A).
● The voltmeter measures the potential difference (p.d.) across the torch lamp. It is connected in **parallel** with the torch lamp so it measures the pd across it. The voltmeter reading gives the p.d. in volts (V).

Electrons passing through a torch lamp have to push their way through lots of vibrating atoms. The atoms resist the passage of electrons through the torch lamp.

We define the **resistance** of an electrical component as:

$$\textbf{Resistance} \text{ (ohms)} = \frac{\textbf{potential difference (volts)}}{\textbf{current (amperes)}}$$

The unit of resistance is the *ohm*. The symbol for the ohm is the Greek letter Ω.

We can write the definition above as:

$$R = \frac{V}{I}$$

where V = potential difference (volts)
I = current (amperes)
R = resistance (ohms).

Worked example

The current through a wire is 2.0 A when the potential difference across it is 12 V.

Calculate the resistance of the wire.

Solution

$$R = \frac{12\,V}{2.0\,A} = 6.0\,\Omega$$

GET IT RIGHT!

Ammeters are always connected in series and voltmeters are always connected in parallel.

a) The current through a wire is 0.5 A when the current through it is 4.0 V. Calculate the resistance of the wire.

PRACTICAL

Investigating the resistance of a wire

Does the resistance of a wire change when the current through it is changed? Figure 2 shows how we can use a variable resistor to change the current through a wire. Make your own measurements and use them to plot a current–potential difference graph like the one in Figure 2.

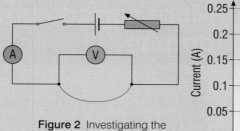

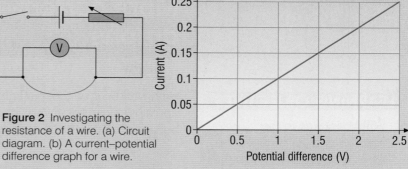

Figure 2 Investigating the resistance of a wire. (a) Circuit diagram. (b) A current–potential difference graph for a wire.

- Discuss how your measurements compare with the ones from the table used to plot the graph in Figure 2.
- Calculate the resistance of the wire you tested.

Current (A)	0.05	0.10	0.15	0.20	0.25
Potential difference (V)	0.50	1.00	1.50	2.00	2.50

b) Calculate the resistance of the wire that gave the results in the table.

Current–potential difference graphs

The graph in Figure 2 and your own graph should show:

- a straight line through the origin,
- that the current is directly proportional to the potential difference.

Reversing the potential difference makes no difference to the shape of the line. The resistance is the same whichever direction the current is in.

The graph shows that the resistance (= potential difference/current) is constant. This was first discovered for a wire at constant temperature by Georg Ohm and is known as **Ohm's law**:

The current through a resistor at constant temperature is directly proportional to the potential difference across the resistor.

We say a wire is an **ohmic conductor** because its resistance is constant.

SUMMARY QUESTIONS

1 a) Draw a circuit diagram to show how you would use an ammeter and a voltmeter to measure the current and potential difference across a wire.
   b) The potential difference across a resistor was 3.0 V when the current through it was 0.5 A. Calculate the resistance of the resistor.

2 Rearranging the equation $R = \dfrac{V}{I}$ gives $V = IR$ or $I = \dfrac{V}{R}$

Use these equations to calculate the missing values in each line of the table.

Resistor	Current (A)	Potential difference (V)	Resistance (Ω)
W	2.0	12.0	?
X	4.0	?	20
Y	?	6.0	3.0
Z	0.5	12.0	?

KEY POINTS

1 Resistance (ohms)=

$$\dfrac{\text{potential difference (volts)}}{\text{current (amperes)}}$$

2 The current through a resistor at constant temperature is directly proportional to the potential difference across the resistor.

P2 5.3

More current–potential difference graphs

1 What happens to the resistance of a filament lamp as its temperature increases?
2 How does the current through a diode depend on the potential difference across it?
3 What happens to the resistance of a thermistor as its temperature increases and of an LDR as the light level increases?

Have you ever switched a light bulb on only to hear it 'pop' and fail? Electrical appliances can fail at very inconvenient times. Most electrical failures are because too much current passes through a component in the appliance.

PRACTICAL

Investigating different components

The current through a component in a circuit depends on its resistance. We can use the circuit in Figure 2 on the previous page to find out what affects the resistance of a component. We can also see if reversing the component in the circuit has any effect.

Make your own measurements using a filament lamp and a diode.

Plot your measurements on a current–potential difference graph.

● Why can you use a line graph to display your data? (See page 280.)

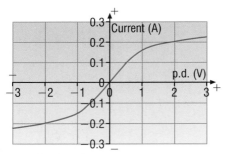

Figure 1 A current–potential difference graph for a filament lamp

Using current–potential difference graphs

A filament lamp

Figure 1 shows the current–potential difference graph for a torch lamp (i.e. a low-voltage filament lamp). The 'reverse' measurements are plotted on the negative sections of each axis.

● The line **curves** away from the current axis. So the current is **not** directly proportional to the potential difference. The filament lamp is a non-ohmic conductor.
● The resistance (= potential difference/current) increases as the current increases. So the resistance of a filament lamp increases as the filament temperature increases.
● Reversing the potential difference makes no difference to the shape of the curve. The resistance is the same for the same current, regardless of its direction.

a) Calculate the resistance of the lamp at i) 0.1 A, ii) 0.2 A.

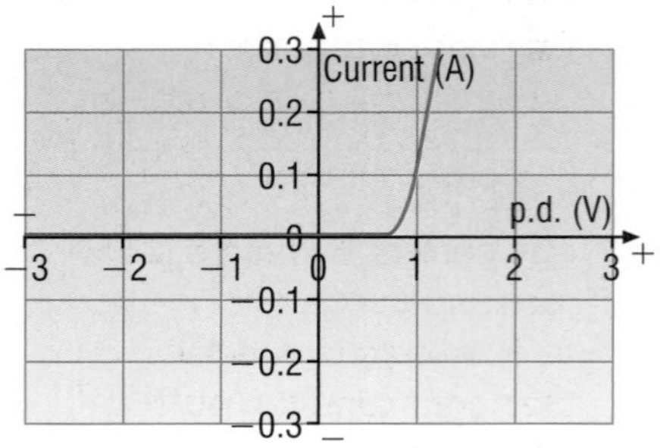

The diode

Look at Figure 2 for a diode:
● In the 'forward' direction, the line curves towards the current axis. So the current is not directly proportional to the potential difference. A diode is not an ohmic conductor.
● In the reverse direction, the current is negligible. So its resistance in the reverse direction is much higher than in the forward direction.

Figure 2 A current–potential difference graph for a diode

b) What can we say about the forward resistance as the current increases?

PRACTICAL

Thermistors and light-dependent resistors (LDRs)

We use thermistors and LDRs in sensor circuits. A thermistor is a temperature-dependent resistor. The resistance of an LDR depends on how much light is on it.

Test a thermistor and then an LDR in series with a battery and an ammeter.

- What did you find out about each component tested?

a)   b)

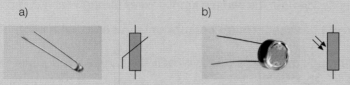

Figure 3 a) A thermistor and its circuit symbol, b) an LDR and its circuit symbol

Current–potential difference graphs for a thermistor and an LDR

For a thermistor, Figure 4 shows the current–potential difference graph at two different temperatures.

- At constant temperature, the line is straight so its resistance is constant.
- If the temperature is increased, its resistance decreases.

For a light dependent resistor, Figure 5 shows the current–potential difference graph in bright light and in dim light.

c) What does the graph tell us about an LDR's resistance if the light intensity is constant?
d) If the light intensity is increased, what happens to the resistance of the LDR?

SUMMARY QUESTIONS

1 Complete a) to d) using the words below:

diode   filament lamp   resistor   thermistor

a) The resistance of a ...... decreases as its temperature increases.
b) The resistance of a ...... depends on which way round it is connected in a circuit.
c) The resistance of a ...... increases as the current through it increases.
d) The resistance of a ...... does not depend on the current through it.

2 A thermistor is connected in series with an ammeter and a 3.0 V battery, as shown.

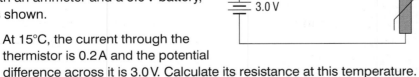

a) At 15°C, the current through the thermistor is 0.2 A and the potential difference across it is 3.0 V. Calculate its resistance at this temperature.
b) State and explain what happens to the ammeter reading if the thermistor's temperature is increased.

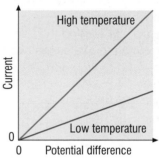

Figure 4 Thermistor graphs

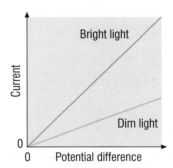

Figure 5 LDR graphs

KEY POINTS

1 *Filament lamp:* resistance increases with increase of the filament temperature.
2 *Diode:* 'forward' resistance low; 'reverse' resistance high.
3 *Thermistor:* resistance decreases if its temperature increases.
4 *LDR:* resistance decreases if the light intensity on it increases.

P2 5.4   Series circuits

1 What can we say about the current and potential difference for components in a series circuit?
2 Why do we often connect cells in series?
3 How can we find the total resistance of a series circuit?

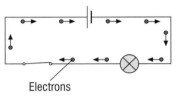

Electrons

Figure 1 A torch lamp circuit

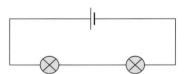

Figure 2 Lamps in series

Circuit rules

In the torch circuit in Figure 1, the lamp, the cell and the switch are connected in series with each other. The same number of electrons pass through each component every second. So the same current passes through each component.

The same current passes through components in series with each other.

a) If the current through the lamp is 0.12A, what is the current through the cell?

In Figure 2, each electron from the cell passes through two lamps. Each electron is pushed through each lamp by the cell. The potential difference (or *voltage*) of the cell is a measure of the energy transferred from the cell by each electron that passes through it. Since each electron in the circuit in Figure 2 goes through both lamps, the potential difference of the cell is shared between the lamps. This rule applies to any series circuit.

The total potential difference of the voltage supply in a series circuit is shared between the components.

b) In Figure 2, if the potential difference of the cell is 1.2V and the potential difference across one lamp is 0.8V, what is the potential difference across the other lamp?

Cells in series

What happens if we use two or more cells in series in a circuit. Provided we connect the cells so they act in the 'same direction', each electron gets a push from each cell. So an electron would get the same push from a battery of three 1.5V cells in series as it would from a single 4.5V cell.

In other words:

The total potential difference of cells in series is the sum of the potential difference of each cell.

PRACTICAL

Investigating potential differences in a series circuit

Figure 3 shows how to test the potential difference rule for a series circuit. The circuit consists of a filament lamp in series with a variable resistor and a cell. We can use the variable resistor to see how the voltmeter readings change when we alter the current. Make your own measurements.

● How do they compare with the data in the table on the next page?

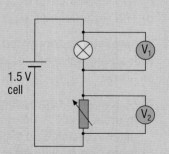

1.5 V cell

Figure 3 Voltage tests

Filament lamp	Voltmeter V_1 (volts)	Voltmeter V_2 (volts)
normal	1.5	0.0
dim	0.9	0.6
very dim	0.5	1.0

GET IT RIGHT!

Remember that in a series circuit the same current passes through all the components.

The measurements in the table show that the voltmeter readings for each setting add up to 1.5 V. This is the potential difference of the cell. The share of the cell's potential difference across each component depends on the setting of the variable resistor.

c) What would voltmeter V_2 read if voltmeter V_1 showed 0.4 V?

The resistance rule for components in series

In Figure 3, suppose the current through the lamp is 0.1 A when the lamp is dim.

Using data from the table above:

- The resistance of the lamp would then be $9\,\Omega$ ($= 0.9$ V/0.1 A).
- The resistance of the variable resistor at this setting would be $6\,\Omega$ ($= 0.6$ V/0.1 A).

If we replaced these two components by a single resistor, what should its resistance be for the same current of 0.1 A? We can calculate this because we know the potential difference across it would be 1.5 V (from the cell). So the resistance would need to be $15\,\Omega$ ($= 1.5$ V/0.1 A). This is the sum of the resistance of the two components. The rule applies to any series circuit.

The total resistance of components in series is equal to the sum of their separate resistances.

d) What is the total resistance of a $2\,\Omega$ resistor in series with a $3\,\Omega$ resistor?

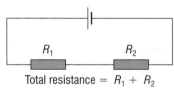

Total resistance $= R_1 + R_2$

Figure 4 Resistors in series

SUMMARY QUESTIONS

1 Complete a) and b) using the list below:

**greater than   less than
the same as**

For the circuit in the diagram,

Two 1.5 V cells

P $2\,\Omega$ Q $10\,\Omega$

a) the current through the battery is …… the current through resistor P.
b) the potential difference across resistor Q is …… the potential difference across the battery.

2 For the circuit in question 1, each cell has a potential difference of 1.5 V.

a) Calculate: i) the total resistance of the two resistors,
ii) the total potential difference of the two cells.
b) Show that the current through the battery is 0.25 A.
c) Calculate the potential difference across each resistor.

KEY POINTS

1 For components in series:
a) the current is the same in each component,
b) the potential differences add to give the total potential difference,
c) the resistances add to give the total resistance.

P2 5.5 Parallel circuits

LEARNING OBJECTIVES

1 What can we say about the current and potential difference for components in a parallel circuit ?

2 How can we calculate currents and potential differences in parallel circuits?

DID YOU KNOW?

A bypass is a parallel route. A heart bypass is another route for the flow of blood. A road bypass is a road that passes a town centre instead of going through it. For components in parallel, charge flows separately through each component. The total flow of charge is the sum of the flow through each component.

PRACTICAL

Investigating parallel circuits

Figure 1 shows how you can investigate the current through two lamps in parallel with each other. You can use ammeters in series with the lamps and the cell to measure the current through the lamp.

Set up your own circuit and collect your data.

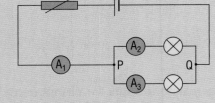

Figure 1 At a junction

- How do your measurements compare with the ones in the table for different settings of the variable resistor shown below?
- Discuss if your own measurements show the same pattern.

Look at the sample data below:

Ammeter A_1 (A)	Ammeter A_2 (A)	Ammeter A_3 (A)
0.50	0.30	0.20
0.30	0.20	0.10
0.18	0.12	0.06

In each case, the reading of ammeter A_1 is equal to the sum of the readings of ammeters A_2 and A_3.

This shows that the current from the cell is equal to sum of the currents through the two lamps. This rule applies wherever components are in parallel.

a) If ammeter A_1 reads 0.40 A and A_2 reads 0.1 A, what would A_3 read?

The total current through the whole circuit is the sum of the currents through the separate components.

Potential difference in a parallel circuit

Figure 2 shows two resistors X and Y in parallel with each other. A voltmeter is connected across each resistor. The voltmeter across resistor X shows the same reading as the voltmeter across resistor Y. This is because each electron from the cell either passes through X or through Y. So it delivers the same amount of energy from the cell, whichever resistor it goes through. In other words:

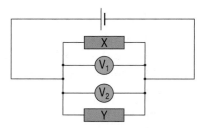

Figure 2 Components in parallel

For components in parallel, the potential difference across each component is the same.

Calculations on parallel circuits

Components in parallel have the same potential difference across them. The current through each component depends on the resistance of the component.

- The bigger the resistance of the component, the smaller the current through it. The resistor which has the largest resistance passes the smallest current.
- We can calculate the current using the equation:

$$\text{current (amperes)} = \frac{\text{potential difference (volts)}}{\text{resistance (ohms)}}$$

b) A $3\,\Omega$ resistor and a $6\,\Omega$ resistor are connected in parallel in a circuit. Which resistor passes the most current?

Worked example

The circuit diagram shows three resistors $R_1 = 1\,\Omega$, $R_2 = 2\,\Omega$ and $R_3 = 6\,\Omega$ connected in parallel to a 6V battery.

Calculate:

i) the current through each resistor,
ii) the current through the battery.

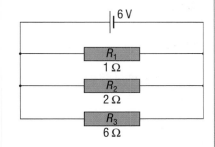

Solution

i) $I_1 = \dfrac{V_1}{R_1} = \dfrac{6}{1} = 6\,\text{A}$

$I_2 = \dfrac{V_2}{R_2} = \dfrac{6}{2} = 3\,\text{A}$

$I_3 = \dfrac{V_3}{R_3} = \dfrac{6}{6} = 1\,\text{A}$

ii) The total current from the battery $= I_1 + I_2 + I_3 = 6\,\text{A} + 3\,\text{A} + 1\,\text{A} = 10\,\text{A}$

SUMMARY QUESTIONS

1 Choose words from the list to complete a) and b):

current   potential difference

a) Components in parallel with each other have the same ....
b) For components in parallel, each component has a different ....

2 The circuit diagram shows three resistors $R_1 = 2\,\Omega$, $R_2 = 3\,\Omega$ and $R_3 = 6\,\Omega$ connected to each other in parallel and to a 6V battery.

Calculate:

a) the current through each resistor,
b) the current through the battery.

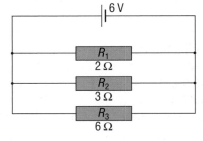

KEY POINTS

1 For components in parallel,
   a) the potential difference is the same across each component,
   b) the total current is the sum of the currents through each component,
   c) the bigger the resistance of a component, the smaller its current is.

P2 5.6   Circuits in control

A magic eye

When you go shopping, doors often open automatically in front of you. An automatic door has a sensor that detects anyone who approaches it. Children think there's a magic eye. But Figure 1 shows you it's no more than an electric circuit.

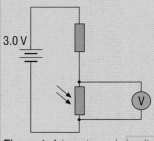

Figure 1 A 'magic eye' circuit

3.0 V

The 'light beam' sensor in Figure 1 is a light-dependent resistor (LDR) in series with a resistor and a battery. A voltmeter is connected across the LDR to show what happens when the LDR is covered. If you make and test this circuit, you should find the voltmeter reading goes up when the LDR is covered. This can be used to switch an electric motor or an alarm circuit on.

ACTIVITIES

a) Use your knowledge of electric circuits to discuss why the voltmeter reading in Figure 1 goes up when you cover the LDR?

b) Design a circuit using a thermistor instead of an LDR to switch an electric fan on if the room gets too hot.

The development of microelectronics

- The first amplifier, the electronic valve, was invented in the 1920s.
- The first electronic switch, the transistor, was invented in the 1940s.
- The microchip was invented in the 1970s.
- The World Wide Web was invented in the 1990s.

The latest computers contain microchips which each contain millions of tiny electronic switches. We measure the capacity of a chip in *bytes*, where a byte is a sequence of bits of data (0's and 1's).

ACTIVITY

Imagine a microchip that could be inserted into the human brain to control your actions and thoughts. Would this be good or bad? Discuss with your friends why it could be good and why it might be bad.

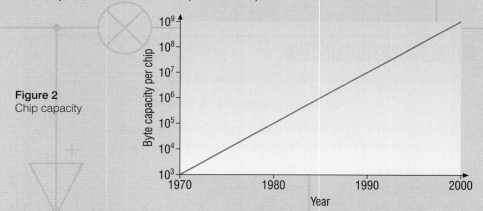

Figure 2
Chip capacity

Figure 2 shows the growth in the capacity of chips since the first one was invented. As chip capacity has increased, electronic devices have become smaller and smaller, as well as more and more sophisticated. They have also become cheaper and cheaper. If cars had changed in the same way, everyone in the world could have a car for less than £1 that would travel 10 000 kilometres on a litre of petrol.

ACTIVITY

Do you think this government policy is a good or a bad idea?

Either: Write a poem about it

or hold a discussion about the issue.

News Flash

No more school!

The Government today announced that children will not have to go to school for lessons any more. Instead, each child will sit in front of a home computer every day. Children who do not go on-line for their lessons will be sent to 'boot camps' to learn. The schools will reopen as amusement arcades with entertainers instead of teachers.

ACTIVITY

Do you think this government policy is a good or a bad idea?

Either: Write a poem about it

or hold a discussion about the issue.

Robots in charge

ACTIVITY

Science fiction writers often write far-fetched stories about robots.

a) Robots are only automated machines programmed to do certain tasks. So why does the word 'robot' catch everyone's attention?

b) Use a science-fiction story to discuss the boundary between science fiction and science.

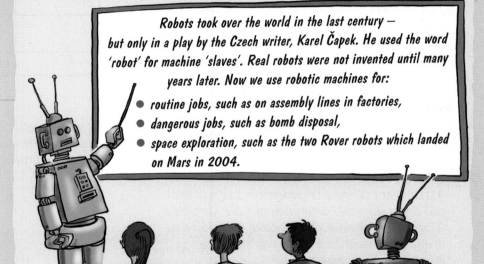

Robots took over the world in the last century —
but only in a play by the Czech writer, Karel Čapek. He used the word 'robot' for machine 'slaves'. Real robots were not invented until many years later. Now we use robotic machines for:

● routine jobs, such as on assembly lines in factories,

● dangerous jobs, such as bomb disposal,

● space exploration, such as the two Rover robots which landed on Mars in 2004.

Electronic logic

We use logic circuits in lots of electronic devices, including computers. A logic circuit has an output that depends on the inputs. Figure 3 shows the symbols for two simple logic circuits, an AND gate and an OR gate. Figure 3 shows an AND gate with a temperature sensor and a light sensor connected to its inputs. If the temperature AND the light intensity are too high, the output of the AND gate is high and it switches an alarm circuit on.

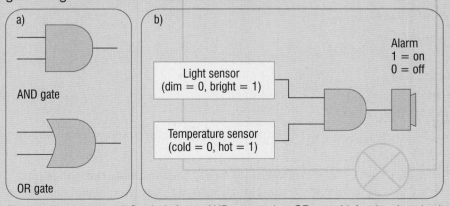

QUESTIONS

1 What could you use the circuit for in Figure 3b)?

2 If the AND gate was replaced by an OR gate, the alarm would switch on if the temperature OR the light intensity is too high. What could you use this circuit for?

Figure 3 Logic gates. a) Symbols for an AND gate and an OR gate. b) An alarming circuit.

SUMMARY QUESTIONS

1 Sketch a circuit diagram to show:

a) a torch bulb, a cell and a diode connected in series so that the torch bulb is on,

b) a variable resistor, two cells in series and a torch bulb whose brightness can be varied by adjusting the variable resistor.

2 Match each component in the list to each statement a) to d) that describes it.

diode   filament lamp   resistor   thermistor

a) Its resistance increases if the current through it increases.

b) The current through it is proportional to the potential difference across it.

c) Its resistance decreases if its temperature is increased.

d) Its resistance depends on which way round it is connected in a circuit.

3 a) Sketch a circuit diagram to show two resistors P and Q connected in series to a battery of two cells in series with each other.

b) In the circuit in a), resistor P has a resistance of $4\,\Omega$, resistor Q has a resistance of $2\,\Omega$ and each cell has a potential difference of 1.5 V. Calculate
   i) the total potential difference of the two cells,
   ii) the total resistance of the two resistors,
   iii) the current in the circuit,
   iv) the potential difference across each resistor.

4 a) Sketch a circuit diagram to show two resistors R and S in parallel with each other connected to a single cell.

b) In the circuit in a), resistor R has a resistance of $2\,\Omega$, resistor S has a resistance of $4\,\Omega$ and the cell has a potential difference of 2 V. Calculate
   i) the current through resistor R,
   ii) the current through resistor S,
   iii) the current through the cell, in the circuit.

5 Complete the following sentences using words from the list below:

different from   equal to   the same as

a) For two components X and Y in series, the potential difference across X is ...... the potential difference across Y.

b) For two components X and Y in parallel, the potential difference across X is ...... the potential difference across Y.

EXAM-STYLE QUESTIONS

1 In a circuit diagram, symbols are used to represent different components.

Complete the table below. The first line has been done for you.

Symbol	Component	What the component does
—(A)—	ammeter	Measures the current in a circuit
—(V)—	voltmeter	a)
—⊣⊢—	b)	Supplies energy to a circuit
c)	diode	d)
e)	f)	Varies resistance as the temperature varies
—⊘—	g)	h)

(8)

2 A student sets up a circuit to investigate how the potential difference across a filament lamp varies with the current through it.

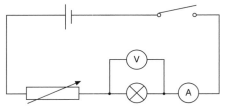

(a) How can the student vary the current through the lamp? (1)

(b) (i) Copy the axes below and sketch the shape of the graph the student would expect to obtain. (2)

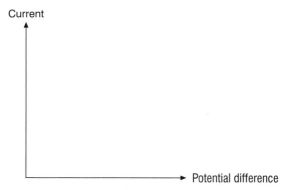

(ii) Explain the shape of the graph you have drawn. (2)

(iii) What do we call the line drawn through points on a graph plotted from experimental data which smooths out variations in measurements? (1)

3 The diagram shows an electric circuit.

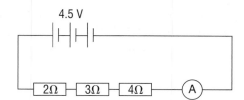

(a) Calculate the total resistance in the circuit. (1)

(b) What is the current through the 4 Ω resistor? (3)

(c) What is the potential difference across the 4 Ω resistor? (2)

4 The diagram shows an electric circuit.

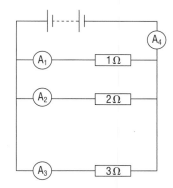

The reading on ammeter A_1 is 6 A and on A_3 is 2 A.

(a) (i) What is the reading on ammeter A_2? (4)

　　(ii) What is the reading on ammeter A_4? (1)

(b) The graphs **A**, **B**, **C** and **D** show how the current through a component varies with the potential difference across it.

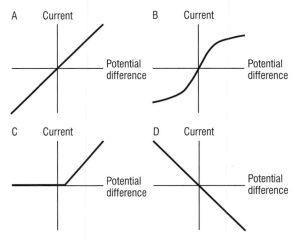

Which graph represents

(i) a resistor at constant temperature?

(ii) a diode? (2)

(c) Why can't the data in part (b) be presented as bar charts? (2)

The laboratory has just bought a new digital thermometer. It uses a thermistor to measure the temperature. It costs £35 because it is accurate and sensitive. The chief technician is very anxious to know if the thermometer works properly. She read all of the data that came with it. It claims that the thermometer will be accurate to ±0.3°C over a range of −50°C to 150°C and it will read to 0.1°C.

a) What is the range over which this instrument should work accurately? (1)

b) What might happen if you used the instrument to read temperatures below −50°C? (1)

c) What is the sensitivity of the thermometer? (1)

d) What is meant by 'the thermometer will be accurate to ±0.3°C'? (1)

The chief technician wanted to check the claims made by the company selling the thermometer. She decided to test its accuracy for herself. She set up some water baths at different temperatures. She used a £400 thermometer that measured to 0.01°C. A company specialising in testing thermometers had independently calibrated this instrument. She compared the readings given by the two thermometers. These are her results.

Thermistor	Temperature of water bath (°C)		
£400	20.15	26.78	65.43
£35	19.9	26.6	65.6

e) Why did the technician doubt the claims made by the company selling the thermometer? (1)

f) Why was the technician more confident in the expensive thermometer? (1)

g) Find the mean for each of the two sets of data? (2)

h) Suggest how the technician might have ensured that her results were valid. (1)

i) Did she choose a range of temperatures that fully tested the new thermometer? Explain your answer. (1)

j) Were her doubts about the £35 thermometer correct? Explain your answer. (1)

P2 6.1   Alternating current

LEARNING OBJECTIVES

1 What is meant by direct current and alternating current?
2 What is the frequency of the UK mains supply?
3 How do we use an oscilloscope to measure the frequency of an alternating current. [Higher]

DID YOU KNOW?

Breakdown vans usually carry a 'fast charger' to recharge a flat car battery as quickly as possible. A 'flat' battery needs a 12 V battery charger to charge it. An ordinary 'battery charger' converts a.c. from the mains to 12 V d.c. but it can take hours to recharge a flat battery.

Figure 1 A battery charger

The battery in a torch makes the current to go round the circuit in one direction only. We say the current in the circuit is a direct current (d.c.) because it is in one direction only.

When you switch a light on at home, you use alternating current (a.c.) because mains electricity is an a.c. supply.

An alternating current repeatedly reverses its direction. It flows one way then the opposite way in successive cycles. Its **frequency** is the number of cycles it passes through each second.

In the UK, the mains frequency is 50 cycles per second (or 50 Hz). A light bulb works just as well at this frequency as it would with a direct current.

a) Why would a much lower frequency than 50 Hz be unsuitable for a light bulb?

Mains circuits

Every mains circuit has a **live** wire and a **neutral** wire. The current through a mains appliance alternates because the mains supply provides an alternating potential difference between the two wires.

The neutral wire is earthed at the local sub-station. The live wire is dangerous because its potential (i.e. voltage) repeatedly changes from + to − and back every cycle. It reaches over 300 V in each direction, as shown in Figure 2.

PRACTICAL

The oscilloscope

Figure 3 Using an oscilloscope

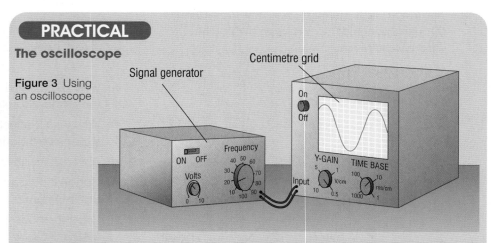

We use an oscilloscope to show how an alternating potential difference (p.d.) changes with time.

1 Connect a low voltage a.c. supply unit to an oscilloscope, as shown in Figure 3.

- The trace on the oscilloscope screen shows that the p.d. increases and decreases continuously.
- The highest (or 'peak') p.d is reached at each peak. Increasing the p.d. of the a.c. supply makes the waves on the screen taller.

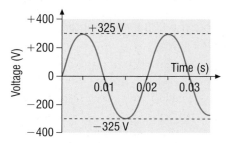

Figure 2 Mains voltage v time

PRACTICAL – continued

- Increasing the frequency of the a.c. supply increases the number of cycles you see on the screen. So the waves on the screen get squashed together.
- How would the trace change if the p.d. of the a.c. supply were reduced?

2 Connect a battery to the oscilloscope. You should see a flat line at constant potential.
- What difference is made by reversing the battery?

HIGHER

Measuring an alternating potential difference

We can use an oscilloscope to measure the peak p.d. and the frequency of a low voltage a.c. supply. For example, in Figure 3,

- the peak voltage is 2.1 V if the peaks are 8.4 cm above the troughs. So each peak is 4.2 cm above the middle which is at zero p.d. The **Y-gain control** at 0.5 V/cm tells us each centimetre of height is due to a p.d. of 0.5 V. So the peak p.d. is 2.1 V (= 0.5 V/cm × 4.2 cm).
- the frequency is 12.5 Hz if each cycle on the screen is 8 cm across. The **time base control** at 10 milliseconds per centimetre (ms/cm) tells us each centimetre across the screen is a time interval of 10 ms. So one cycle takes 80 ms (= 10 ms/cm × 8 cm). The frequency is therefore 12.5 Hz (= 1/80 ms or 1/0.08 s).

More about mains circuits

Look at Figure 2 again. It shows how the potential of the live wire varies with time.

- The live wire alternates between +325 volts and −325 volts. In terms of electrical power, this is equivalent to a direct voltage of 230 volts. So we say the 'voltage' of the mains is 230 V.
- Each cycle takes 0.02 second. So the mains supply alternates at 50 cycles every second. The frequency of the mains supply (the number of cycles per second) is therefore 50 Hz.

b) What is the maximum potential difference between the live wire and the neutral wire?

SUMMARY QUESTIONS

1 Choose the correct potential difference from the list for each appliance a) to d).

    1.5 V   12 V   230 V   325 V

    a) a car battery
    b) the mains voltage
    c) a torch cell
    d) the maximum potential of the live wire.

2 a) In Figure 3, how would the trace on the screen change if the frequency of the a.c. supply was i) increased, ii) reduced?
  b) In Figure 3, what would the frequency be if one cycle had measured 4 cm across the screen for the same time base setting? [Higher]

KEY POINTS

1 Alternating current repeatedly reverses its direction.
2 Mains electricity is an alternating current supply.
3 A mains circuit has a **live wire** which is alternately positive and negative every cycle and a **neutral wire** at zero volts. [Higher]

P2 6.2

Cables and plugs

LEARNING OBJECTIVES

1 What is the casing of a mains plug made from and why?
2 What colour are the live, neutral and earth wires?
3 Which wire is connected to the longest pin in a three-pin plug?

FOUL FACTS

Mains electricity is dangerous. Mains wiring must by law be done by properly qualified electricians.

When you plug in a heater with a metal case into a wall socket, you 'earth' the metal case automatically. This stops the metal case becoming 'live' if the live wire breaks and touches it. If the case did become 'live' and you touched it, you would be electrocuted.

Plugs, sockets and cables

The outer casings of plugs, sockets and cables of all mains circuits and appliances are made of hard-wearing electrical insulators. That's because plugs, sockets and cables contain 'live' wires.

Sockets are made of stiff plastic materials with the wires inside. Figure 1 shows part of a wall socket circuit. It has an 'earth' wire as well as a live wire and a neutral wire.

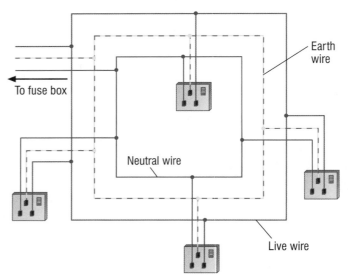

Figure 1 A 'wall socket' circuit

- The 'earth wire' of this circuit is connected to the ground at your home.
- The longest pin of a three-pin plug is designed to make contact with the 'earth wire' of a wall socket circuit. So when you plug an appliance with a metal case to a wall socket, the case is automatically earthed.

a) Why are sockets wired in parallel with each other?

Plugs have cases made of stiff plastic materials. The live pin, the neutral pin and the earth pin, stick out through the plug case. Figure 2 shows inside a three-pin plug.

- The pins are made of brass because brass is a good conductor and does not rust or oxidise. Copper isn't as hard as brass even though it conducts better.
- The case material is an electrical insulator. The inside of the case is shaped so the wires and the pins cannot touch each other when the plug is sealed.

● The plug contains a fuse between the live pin and the live wire. The fuse melts and cuts the live wire off if too much current passes through it.

b) Why is brass, an alloy of copper and zinc, better than copper or zinc for the pins of a three-pin plug?

Cables used for mains appliances (and for mains circuits) consist of two or three insulated copper wires surrounded by an outer layer of rubber or flexible plastic material.

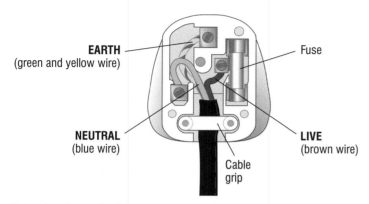

Figure 2 Inside a three-pin plug.

● The brown wire is connected to the live pin.
● The blue wire is connected to the neutral pin.
● The green-yellow wire (of a three-core cable) is connected to the earth pin. A two-core cable does not have an earth wire.

● Copper is used for the wires because it is a good electrical conductor.
● Plastic is a good electrical insulator and therefore prevents anyone touching the cable from receiving an electric shock.
● Two-core cables are used for appliances which have plastic cases (e.g. hairdryers, radios).

Figure 3 Mains cable

c) Why are cables that are worn away or damaged dangerous?

SUMMARY QUESTIONS

1 Choose words from the list to complete the sentences a) to e):

earth   live   neutral   series   parallel

a) The …… wire in a mains plug is blue.
b) If too much current passes through the fuse, it blows and cuts the …… wire off.
c) Appliances plugged into the same mains circuit are in …… with each other.
d) The metal frame of an appliance is connected to the …… wire of a mains circuit when it is plugged in.
e) The fuse in a plug is in …… with the live wire.

2 a) Match the list of parts 1–4 in a three-pin plug with the list of materials A–D.

1 cable insulation   2 case   3 pin   4 wire
A brass   B copper   C rubber   D stiff plastic

b) Explain your choice of material for each part in a).

KEY POINTS

1 **Cables** consist of two or three insulated copper wires surrounded by an outer layer of flexible plastic material.

2 **Sockets** and **plugs** are made of stiff plastic materials which enclose the electrical connections.

3 In a **three-pin plug** or a three-core cable, the live wire is brown, the neutral wire is blue, the earth wire is yellow/green. The earth wire is used to earth the metal case of a mains appliance.

P2 6.3   Fuses

If you need to buy a fuse for a mains appliance, make sure you know the fuse rating. Otherwise, the new fuse might 'blow' as soon as it is used or, even worse, it might let too much current through and cause a fire.

● A fuse contains a thin wire that heats up and melts if too much current passes through it. If this happens, we say the fuse 'blows'.
● The rating of a fuse is the maximum current that can pass through it without melting the fuse wire.

A fuse in a mains plug must always have the correct rating for the appliance.

If the rating is too large, the fuse will not blow when it should. The heating effect of the current could set the appliance on fire.

a) What would happen if the rating of the fuse was too small?

Figure 1 a) Cartridge fuses, b) a rewireable fuse

The importance of earthing

Figure 2 shows why an electric heater is made safer by earthing its frame.

In Figure 2a), the heater works normally and its frame is earthed. The frame is safe to touch.

In Figure 2b), the earth wire is broken. The frame would become live if the live wire touched it.

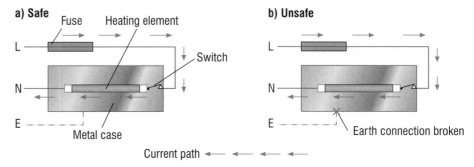

Figure 2 Earthing an electric heater

In Figure 2c), the heater element has touched the unearthed frame so the frame is live. Anyone touching it would be electrocuted. The fuse provides no protection to the user because a current of no more than 20 mA can be lethal.

In Figure 2d), the earth wire has been repaired but the heater element still touches the frame. The current is greater than normal and passes through part of the heater element via the live and the earth wires. Because the frame is earthed, anyone touching it would not be electrocuted. But Figure 2d) is still dangerous because the current might not be enough to blow the fuse and the appliance might overheat.

b) Why is the current in Figure 2d) greater than normal?

Circuit breakers

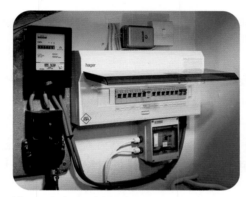

Figure 3 A circuit breaker

A circuit breaker is an electromagnetic switch that opens (i.e. 'trips') and cuts the current off if the current is greater than a certain value. It can then be reset once the fault that made it trip has been put right.

Circuit breakers are sometimes fitted in 'fuse boxes' in place of fuses. They work faster than fuses and can be reset quicker.

c) What should you do if a circuit breaker trips again after being reset?

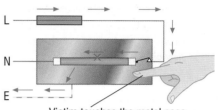

c) Deadly   Heating element touches the metal case, making it live

L

N

E — — — —   Earth connection broken

d) Still dangerous

L

N

E — — — —

Victim touches the metal case, and if the Earth wire is broken, will conduct the current to Earth

Figure 2 (cont) Earthing an electric heater

SUMMARY QUESTIONS

1 a) What is the purpose of a fuse in a mains circuit?
   b) Why is the fuse of an appliance always on the live side?
   c) What advantages does a circuit breaker have compared with a fuse?

2 The diagram shows the circuit of an electric heater that has been wired incorrectly.

   a) Does the heater work when the switch is closed?
   b) When the switch is open, why is it dangerous to touch the element?
   c) Redraw the circuit correctly wired.

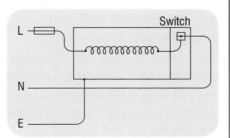

KEY POINTS

1 A **fuse** contains a thin wire that heats up and melts, cutting the current off, if too much current passes through it.

2 A **circuit breaker** is an electromagnetic switch that opens (i.e. 'trips') and cuts the current off if too much current passes through it.

P2 6.4

Electrical power and potential difference

When you use an electrical appliance, it transforms electrical energy into other forms of energy. The **power** of the appliance, in watts, is the energy it transforms, in joules, per second. We can show this as the following equation:

$$\text{Power (watts, W)} = \frac{\text{energy transformed (joules, J)}}{\text{time (seconds, s)}}$$

Worked example

A lamp bulb transforms 30 000 J of electrical energy when it is on for 300 s. Calculate its power.

Solution

$$\text{Power} = \frac{\text{energy transformed}}{\text{time}} = \frac{30\,000\,J}{300\,s} = 100\,W$$

a) The human heart transforms about 30 000 J of energy in a school day of about 8 hours. Calculate an estimate of the power of the human heart.

Figure 1 An artificial heart

Calculating power

Millions of millions of electrons pass through the circuit of an artificial heart every second. Each electron transfers a small amount of energy to it from the battery. So the total energy transferred to it each second is large enough to enable the device to work.

For any electrical appliance:

● the current through it is a measure of the number of electrons passing through it each second (i.e. the charge flow per second),

● the potential difference across it is a measure of how much energy each electron passing through it transfers to it (i.e. the electrical energy transferred per unit charge),

● the power supplied to it is the energy transferred to it each second. This is the electrical energy it transforms every second.

Therefore:

the energy transfer to = the charge flow × the energy transfer
the device each second   per second   per unit charge

In other words:

power supplied =   current   × potential difference
(watts, W)   (amperes, A)   (volts, V)

For example, the power supplied to

● a 4 A, 12 V electric motor is 48 W ($= 4\,A \times 12\,V$),
● a 0.1 A, 3 V torch lamp is 0.3 W($= 0.1\,A \times 3.0\,V$).

b) Calculate the power supplied to a 5 A, 230 V electric heater.

Maths note

The equation can written as:

electrical power, $P = I V$ where I = current, and
V = potential difference

Rearranging this equation gives:

$$\text{potential difference, } V = \frac{P}{I} \quad \text{or}$$

$$\text{current, } I = \frac{P}{V}$$

Choosing a fuse

Domestic appliances are often fitted with a 3 A, or a 5 A or a 13 A fuse. If you don't know which one to use for an appliance, you can work it out from the power rating of the appliance and its potential difference (voltage).

Worked example

i) Calculate the normal current through a 500 W, 230 V heater.
ii) Which fuse, a 3 A, or a 5 A or a 13 A, would you use for the appliance?

Solution

i) Current $= \dfrac{500\,W}{230\,V} = 2.2\,A$

ii) A 3 A fuse would be needed.

c) Why would a 13 A fuse be unsuitable for a 230 V, 100 W table lamp?

SUMMARY QUESTIONS

1 Choose words from the list to complete sentences a) and b):

current   potential difference   power

a) When an electrical appliance is on, …… is supplied to it as a result of …… passing through it.
b) When an electrical appliance is on, a …… is applied to it which causes …… to pass through it.

2 a) Calculate the power supplied to each of the following devices in normal use.
   i) a 12 V, 3 A light bulb,   ii) a 230 V, 2 A heater,
   b) Which type of fuse, 3 A or 5 A or 13 A, would you select for:
   i) a 24 W, 12 V heater?   ii) a 230 V, 800 W microwave oven?

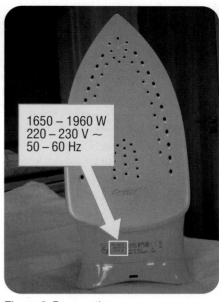

Figure 2 Power rating

1650 – 1960 W
220 – 230 V ~
50 – 60 Hz

NEXT TIME YOU…

. . . change a fuse, do a quick calculation to make sure its rating is correct for the appliance.

Figure 3 Changing a fuse

KEY POINTS

1 The **power** supplied to a device is the energy transfer to it each second.
2 **Electrical power** supplied (watts) = current (amperes) × potential difference (volts)

P2 6.5 — Electrical energy and charge

LEARNING OBJECTIVES

1 What is electric current?
2 What is the unit of electric charge?
3 What energy transformations take place when charge flows through a resistor?

Electrons

Charge flow = current × time

Figure 1 Charge and current

Calculating charge

When an electrical appliance is on, electrons are forced through the appliance by the potential difference of the voltage supply unit. The potential difference causes a flow of charge through the appliance carried by electrons. The rate of flow of charge is the electric current through the appliance.

The unit of charge, the **coulomb (C)**, is the amount of charge flowing through a wire or a component in 1 second when the current is 1 A.

The charge passing along a wire or through a component in a certain time depends on:

● the current, and
● the time.

We can calculate the charge using the equation:

$$\textbf{charge flow} = \textbf{current} \times \textbf{time}$$
$$\text{(coulombs)} \quad \text{(amperes)} \quad \text{(seconds)}$$

For example:

● when the current is 2 A for 5 s, the charge flow is 10 C (= 2 A × 5 s)
● when the current is 4 A for 20 s, the charge flow is 80 C (= 4 A × 20 s)

> **Worked example**
> Calculate the charge flow when the current is 8 A for 80 s.
>
> **Solution**
> Charge flow = current × time = 8 A × 80 s = 640 C.

a) Calculate the charge flowing in 50 s when the current is 3 A.

Energy and potential difference

When a resistor is connected to a battery, electrons are made to pass through the resistor by the battery. Each electron repeatedly collides with the vibrating atoms of the resistor, transferring energy to them. The atoms of the resistor therefore gain kinetic energy and vibrate even more. The resistor becomes hotter.

When charge flows through a resistor, electrical energy is transformed into heat energy.

The energy transformed in a certain time in a resistor depends on:

● the amount of charge that passes through it, and
● the potential difference across the resistor.

Because energy = power × time = potential difference × current × time, we can calculate the energy transformed using the equation

$$\textbf{energy transformed} = \textbf{potential difference} \times \textbf{charge flow}$$
$$\text{(joules, J)} \qquad \text{(volts, V)} \qquad \text{(coulombs, C)}$$

For example:

- when the charge flow is 10 C and the potential difference is 10 V, the energy transformed = 100 J (= 10 V × 10 C),
- when the charge flow is 20 C and the potential difference is 10 V, the energy transformed = 200 J (= 10 V × 20 C)

> **Worked example**
> Calculate the energy transformed in a component when the charge flow is 30 C and the potential difference is 20 V.
>
> **Solution**
> Energy transformed = 20 V × 30 C = 600 J.

b) Calculate the energy transformed when the charge flow is 30 C and the p.d. is 4 V.

Energy transformations in a circuit

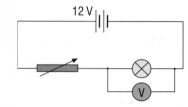

Figure 2 Energy transformations in a circuit

The circuit in Figure 2 shows a 12 V battery in series with a torch lamp and a variable resistor. When the voltmeter reads 10 V, the potential difference across the variable resistor is 2 V.

Each coulomb of charge:

- leaves the battery with 12 J of energy (because energy from the battery = charge × battery potential difference)
- delivers 10 J of energy to the torch lamp (because energy transfer to torch lamp = charge × potential difference across torch lamp). This is transformed into light and heat energy in the torch lamp.
- delivers 2 J of energy supplied to the variable resistor. This is transformed into heat energy in the variable resistor.

> **SUMMARY QUESTIONS**
>
> 1 Choose words from the list to complete sentences a) to d):
>
> > **charge   current   energy   potential difference**
>
> a) The coulomb is the unit of ....
> b) Charge flowing through a resistor transfers ...... to the resistor.
> c) A ...... is the rate of flow of charge.
> d) Energy transformed = ... × charge.
>
> 2 a) Calculate the charge flow for:
>   i) a current of 4 A for 20 s,
>   ii) a current of 0.2 A for 60 minutes,
>   b) Calculate the energy transfer:
>   i) for a charge flow of 20 C when the potential difference is 6.0 V,
>   ii) in 20 s, for a current of 3 A that passes through a resistor when the potential difference is 5 V.

GET IT RIGHT!

Make sure you know and understand the relationship between charge, current and time.

KEY POINTS

1 An electric current is the rate of flow of charge.
2 When charge flows through a resistor, electrical energy is transferred as heat.
3 Charge (coulombs) = current (amperes) × time (seconds).
4 Energy transferred (joules) = potential difference (volts) × charge flow (coulombs).

P2 6.6 Safety matters

Spot the hazards!

Imagine you are a safety inspector who has been asked to check the electrics in Shockem Hall. How many electrical faults and hazards can you find just by looking around the main hall?

Circuit breakers for safety

A special 'RCCB' socket should be used for outdoor appliances such as lawnmowers. These sockets each contain a residual current circuit breaker instead of a fuse. This type of circuit breaker switches the current off if the live current and the neutral current differ by more than 30 mA. This can happen, for example, if the insulation of the live wire becomes worn and current 'leaks' from the live wire to 'earth'.

A residual current circuit breaker

1 What other appliances would you use an RCCB for besides a lawn mower?

List them in the table like the one below.

Appliance	Hazard	Rating
Lawnmower	The blades might cut the cable	
Electric drill		

2 Design a hazard rating icon like a star rating but use something different to stars. A '4-star hazard' doesn't sound right.

The Evening Post

Family rescued in house fire!

The Fire Service rescued two children and their parents from the upper floor of a burning house in Lower Town last night. Fortunately, all family members were safe and well. The fire spread to two neighbouring properties before being brought under control. A fire service spokesperson said the fire was caused by an electrical fault.

Cutting out the cowboys

The UK government has passed a law to stop unqualified people doing electrical work. This is because many accidents have happened due to shoddy electrical work, not just by unqualified 'cowboy' electricians but also by householders in their own homes. If you want to be an electrician, you have to train for several years as an apprentice and study for exams. When you qualify, you can register as an approved electrician.

ACTIVITY

The new law is intended to reduce accidents due to unsafe electrical work. But what other effects will it have? It might make rewiring jobs by qualified electricians too expensive and create more work for the cowboys.
Discuss whether this new law is a good law and if there are other ways of regulating electrical work.

ACTIVITY

a) What do these expressions mean? See if you and your friends can add more electrical examples.
b) Use the jargon in a discussion with your friends about something that happened in your favourite TV soap. Award one point each time jargon is used and see who wins.
c) Is jargon unsafe? Can it be misunderstood? Think of a situation where jargon is dangerous.

Electrical jargon

People often complain about jargon – the words that experts use. But sometimes, we use jargon without realising it, especially electrical jargon because we all use electricity. Sometimes, we even use it in our everyday conversations.

Here are some examples:

'Don't blow a fuse.'

'She's a sparky character.'

'Can't you short-circuit the usual procedure?'

Holiday time!

ACTIVITY

Find out what type of adaptor you would need if you go on holiday to Spain.

Holiday Essentials

shavers only

| 115V | 230V |

When you go abroad... be careful if you intend to take mains appliances with you.

* If the voltage is not 230 V (as in the UK and Europe), the appliance must have a 'dual voltage' switch that can be changed from 230 V to the new voltage. You **must** change the switch back when you return.

* If the voltage is 230 V, you may need to take a suitable plug adaptor with you for each appliance. This is because sockets abroad may be different to those at home.

* Only use one appliance per socket or you might blow a fuse!

SUMMARY QUESTIONS

1 a) In a mains circuit, which wire:
   i) is earthed at the local sub-station,
   ii) alternates in potential?

   b) An oscilloscope is used to display the potential difference of an alternating voltage supply unit. How would the trace change if:
   i) the p.d. is increased,
   ii) the frequency is increased?

2 Complete a) and b) using words below:

   earth   live   neutral

   a) When a mains appliance is switched on, current passes through it via the ...... wire and the ...... wire.

   b) In a mains circuit:
   i)   the ...... wire is blue,
   ii) the ...... wire is brown,
   iii) the ...... wire is green yellow.

3 a) Complete the sentences:
   i) Wall sockets are connected in ...... with each other.
   ii) A fuse in a mains plug is in ...... with the appliance and cuts off the ...... wire if too much current passes through the appliance.

   b) i) What is the main difference between a fuse and a circuit breaker?
   ii) Give two reasons why a circuit breaker is safer than a fuse.

4 a) i) Calculate the current in a 230 V, 2.5 kW electric kettle.
   ii) Which fuse, 3 A or 5 A or 13 A, would you fit in the kettle plug?

   b) Calculate the power supplied to a 230 V electric toaster when the current through it is 4.0 A.

5 Calculate the charge flow through a resistor when the current is 6 A for 200 s.   [Higher]

6 A 5 Ω resistor is in series with a lamp, a switch and a 12 V battery.

   a) Draw the circuit diagram.

   b) When the switch is closed for 60 seconds, a direct current of 0.6 A passes through the resistor. Calculate:
   i)   the energy supplied by the battery,
   ii) the energy transformed in the resistor,
   iii) the energy transformed in the lamp.   [Higher]

EXAM-STYLE QUESTIONS

1 An electric heater is connected to a 230 V mains supply. The current flowing through the heater is 12 A.

   (a) What is the power of the heater?   (2)

   (b) The heater is switched on for 30 minutes. Calculate how much charge flows through the heater during this time and give the unit.   (4)

2 The diagram shows a three-pin plug.

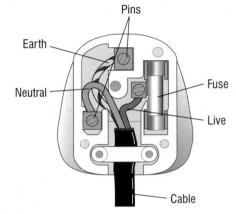

   (a) State the colour of each wire.

   Live .... Neutral .... Earth ....   (3)

   (b) State and explain which parts of the plug are made out of . . .

   (i) plastic   (ii) brass   (4)

3 Explain:

   (a) why appliances with metal cases need to be earthed, but appliances with plastic cases do not.   (4)

   (b) which wire in a circuit should contain the fuse.   (2)

   (c) why the rating of the fuse in an appliance should be slightly higher than the normal working current through the appliance.   (2)

4 Cells and the electrical mains are both sources of electrical energy.
   Describe the currents and potential differences from each of these types of supply.   (7)

5 Most domestic appliances are connected to the 230 V mains supply with a 3-pin plug containing a fuse. 3A, 5A and 13A fuses are available.

   (a) A food mixer has a normal current of 2A. What is the power of the mixer?   (2)

   (b) What fuse should be used in the plug for a 2.8 kW kettle?   (4)

(c) (i) A 9kW shower is wired directly to the mains. It has a separate fuse in the household fuse box. Explain why? (3)

(ii) The fuse for the shower keeps melting. The householder replaces it with a nail. Why is this dangerous? (2)

6 The pictures show situations in which electricity is not being used safely.

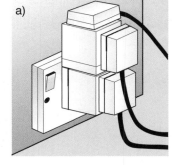

a)

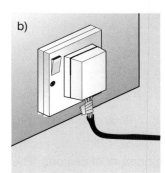

b)

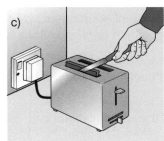

c)

For each picture (a), (b) and (c), explain how electricity is not being used safely. (6)

7 An oscilloscope can be used to measure the potential difference of different electrical supplies.

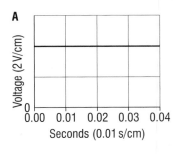

A

Voltage (2 V/cm)

0.00 0.01 0.02 0.03 0.04
Seconds (0.01 s/cm)

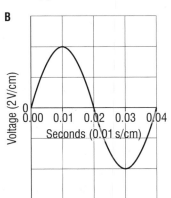

B

Voltage (2 V/cm)

0.00 0.01 0.02 0.03 0.04
Seconds (0.01 s/cm)

The diagrams show the traces produced on a centimetre grid by two different supplies.

(a) What is the potential difference of supply A? (3)

(b) (i) What type of supply is supply B? (1)

(ii) What is the peak potential difference of supply B? (1)

(iii) What is the frequency of supply B? (3)

[Higher]

HOW SCIENCE WORKS QUESTIONS

'There I was watching Rovers beat United, when it blew a fuse. No, it wasn't the United manager, it was the box. I reckon it was down to the United fans switching off their tellies when we scored that second goal. It must have been some sort of surge. Anyway, I fixed it before the end of the game. I put a bit of wire into where the fuse had burned and the telly worked perfectly. Unfortunately the house burned down! Anyway Rovers won and that's the important thing . . .'

a) Would you say that putting a piece of wire to replace a fuse was based on good science? Explain your answer. (1)

b) Do you think there was a link between Rovers scoring a second goal and the television fuse blowing? Was it causal, due to association or due to chance? Explain your answer. (1)

The fire brigade did a thorough investigation into the cause of the fire. They recovered a reel of the wire used in place of the 3A fuse that should have been used. Their scientists at the Fire Service laboratory found that six equal lengths of this wire fused at currents of 6.5A, 6.1A, 6.2A, 5.8A, 6.0A and 6.1A. They also discovered a fault in the television had caused it to overheat. This had caused the curtains to catch fire and burn the house down.

c) i) Calculate the mean value of the measurements above. (1)

ii) Comment of the precision of the results. (1)

iii) Why did they test equal lengths? (1)

d) Is it likely that there was a causal link between the 'repair' of the fuse and the house burning down? Explain your answer. (1)

e) Why can you trust this investigation? (1)

P2 7.1

Nuclear reactions

LEARNING OBJECTIVES

1 How does the nucleus of an atom change when it emits an alpha particle or a beta particle?
2 How can we represent a nuclear reaction?
3 Where does background radiation come from?

The atom has a nucleus composed of protons and neutrons surrounded by electrons. In a nuclear reaction, neutrons and protons crash into each other and get rearranged. At speeds approaching the cosmic speed limit, the speed of light, they can even annihilate each other or create new particles.

The table gives the relative masses and the relative electric charges of a proton, a neutron and an electron.

	Relative mass	Relative charge
proton	1	+1
neutron	1	0
electron	0.0005	−1

An uncharged atom has equal numbers of protons and electrons. A charged atom, an **ion**, has unequal numbers of protons and electrons.

The atoms of the same element each have the same number of protons. The number of protons in a nucleus is denoted by **Z**. It is called the **atomic number** (or proton number).

Isotopes are atoms of the same element with different numbers of neutrons.

The number of protons and neutrons in a nucleus is called its **mass number**, denoted by **A**.

An isotope of an element X, which has Z protons and A protons and neutrons, is represented by the symbol ^A_ZX. For example, the uranium isotope $^{238}_{92}$U contains 92 protons and 146 neutrons (= 238 − 92) in each nucleus. So its relative mass is 238 and its relative charge is 92.

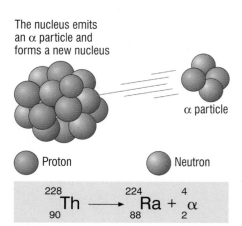

Number of protons and neutrons

^A_ZX

Chemical symbol

Number of protons

Example: the symbol for the uranium isotope with 92 protons and 146 neutrons is

$^{238}_{92}$U (or sometimes U-238)

Figure 1 Representing an isotope

a) How many protons and how many neutrons are in the nucleus of the uranium isotope $^{235}_{92}$U?

Radioactive decay

An unstable nucleus becomes more stable by emitting an α (alpha) or a β (beta) particle or by emitting γ (gamma) radiation.

α emission

- An α particle consists of two protons and two neutrons. Its relative mass is 4 and its relative charge is 2. So we can represent it by the symbol $^4_2$α.
- When an unstable nucleus emits an α particle, its atomic number goes down by 2 and its mass number goes down by 4.

For example, the thorium isotope $^{228}_{90}$Th decays by emitting an α particle. So it forms the radium isotope $^{224}_{88}$Ra.

The nucleus emits an α particle and forms a new nucleus

α particle

Proton   Neutron

$^{228}_{90}$Th $\longrightarrow$ $^{224}_{88}$Ra + $^4_2$α

Figure 2 α emission

b) How many protons and how many neutrons are in $^{228}_{90}$Th and $^{224}_{88}$Ra?

β emission

- A β particle is an electron created and emitted by a nucleus which has too many neutrons compared with protons. A neutron in its nucleus changes into a proton and a β particle. This is instantly emitted at high speed by the nucleus.
- The relative mass of a β particle is effectively zero and its relative charge is -1. So we can represent a β particle by the symbol $_{-1}^{0}\beta$.
- When an unstable nucleus emits a β particle, its atomic number goes up by 1 but its mass number stays the same (because the neutron changes into a proton).

For example, the potassium isotope $_{19}^{40}K$ decays by emitting a β particle. So it forms a nucleus of the calcium isotope $_{20}^{40}Ca$.

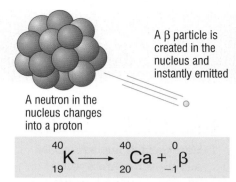

A neutron in the nucleus changes into a proton

A β particle is created in the nucleus and instantly emitted

$$_{19}^{40}K \longrightarrow {}_{20}^{40}Ca + {}_{-1}^{0}\beta$$

Figure 3 β emission

c) How many protons and how many neutrons are in $_{19}^{40}K$ and $_{20}^{40}Ca$?

γ emission

γ radiation is emitted by some unstable nuclei after an α particle or a β particle has been emitted. γ radiation is uncharged and has no mass. So it does not change the number of protons or the number of neutrons in a nucleus.

The origins of background radiation

Background radiation is ionising radiation from space (cosmic rays), from devices such as X-ray tubes and from radioactive isotopes in the environment. Some of these isotopes are present because of nuclear weapons testing and nuclear power stations. But most of it is from substances in the Earth. For example, radon gas is radioactive and is a product of the decay of uranium in rocks found in certain areas.

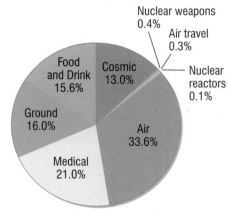

Figure 4 The origins of background radioactivity

KEY POINTS

		Change in the nucleus	Particle emitted
1	α decay	Nucleus loses 2 protons and 2 neutrons	2 protons and 2 neutrons emitted as an α particle
2	β decay	A neutron in the nucleus changes into a proton	An electron is created in the nucleus and instantly emitted

---

SUMMARY QUESTIONS

1 How many protons and how many neutrons are there in the nucleus of each of the following isotopes?

  a) $_{6}^{12}C$

  b) $_{27}^{60}Co$

  c) $_{92}^{235}U$

2 A substance contains the radioactive isotope $_{92}^{238}U$, which emits alpha radiation. The product nucleus X emits beta radiation and forms a nucleus Y. How many protons and how many neutrons are present in:

  a) a nucleus of $_{92}^{238}U$,

  b) a nucleus of X,

  c) a nucleus of Y?

P2 7.2 The discovery of the nucleus

LEARNING OBJECTIVES

1 How was the nuclear model of the atom established?
2 What other models of the atom were there?

Ernest Rutherford had already made important discoveries about radioactivity when he decided to use alpha (α) particles to probe the atom. He asked two of his research workers, Hans Geiger and Ernest Marsden, to investigate the scattering of α particles by a thin metal foil.

Figure 1 shows the arrangement they used.

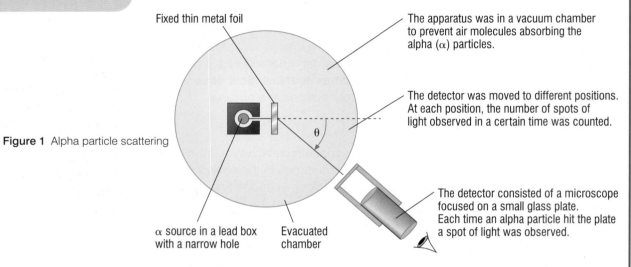

Fixed thin metal foil

The apparatus was in a vacuum chamber to prevent air molecules absorbing the alpha (α) particles.

The detector was moved to different positions. At each position, the number of spots of light observed in a certain time was counted.

Figure 1 Alpha particle scattering

The detector consisted of a microscope focused on a small glass plate. Each time an alpha particle hit the plate a spot of light was observed.

α source in a lead box with a narrow hole

Evacuated chamber

PRACTICAL

Lucky strike!

Fix a small metal disc about 2 cm thick at the centre of a table. Hide the disc under a cardboard disc about 20 cm in diameter. See if you can hit the metal disc with a rolling marble.

The radioactive isotope they used had a long half life so its activity stayed the same during the experiment. They measured the number of α particles deflected per second through different angles. The results showed that:

● most of the alpha particles passed straight through the metal foil,
● the number of alpha particles deflected per minute decreased as the angle of deflection increased,
● about 1 in 10 000 alpha particles were deflected by more than 90°.

a) If you kicked a football at an empty goal and the ball bounced back at you, what would you conclude?

Rutherford was astonished by the results. He said it was like firing 'naval shells' at cardboard and discovering the occasional shell rebounds. He knew that α particles are positively charged. He deduced from the results that there is a nucleus at the centre of every atom which is:

● positively charged because it repels α particles (remember that like charges repel),
● much smaller than the atom because most α particles pass through without deflection,
● where most of the mass of the atom is located.

Using this model, Rutherford worked out the proportion of α particles that would be deflected for a given angle. He found an exact agreement with Geiger and Marsden's measurements. He used his theory to estimate the diameter of the nucleus and found it was about 100 000 times smaller than the atom.

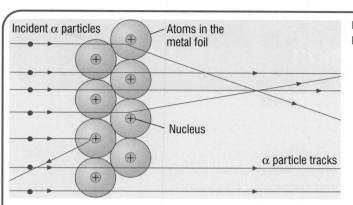

Figure 2 Alpha (α) particle paths

Rutherford's nuclear model of the atom was quickly accepted because:

- it agreed exactly with the measurements Geiger and Marsden made,
- it explains radioactivity in terms of changes that happen to an unstable nucleus when it emits radiation,
- it predicted the existence of the neutron, which was later discovered.

b) What difference would it have made if Geiger and Marsden's measurements had not fitted Rutherford's nuclear model?

Goodbye to the plum pudding atom!

Before the nucleus was discovered in 1914, scientists didn't know what the structure of the atom was. They did know atoms contained electrons and they knew these are tiny negatively charged particles. But they didn't know how the positive charge was arranged in an atom, although there were different models in circulation. Some scientists thought the atom was like a 'plum pudding' model with:

- the positively charged matter in the atom evenly spread about (like in a pudding), and
- electrons buried inside (like plums in the pudding).

Rutherford's discovery meant farewell to the 'plum pudding' atom.

DID YOU KNOW?

Imagine a marble at the centre of a football stadium. That's the scale of the nucleus inside the atom. Almost all the mass of the atom is in its nucleus. The density of the nucleus is about a thousand million million times the density of water. A match box of nuclear matter would weigh about a million million tonnes!

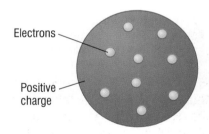

Figure 3 The plum pudding atom

SUMMARY QUESTIONS

1 Complete a) to c) using the words below:

charge   diameter   mass

a) A nucleus has the same type of …… as an alpha particle.
b) A nucleus has a much smaller …… than the atom.
c) Most of the …… of the atom is in the nucleus.

2 a) The diagram shows 4 possible paths, labelled A, B, C and D, of an alpha particle deflected by a nucleus. Which path would the alpha particle travel along?

b) Explain why each of the other paths in a) is not possible.

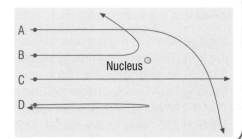

KEY POINTS

1 Alpha particles in a beam are sometimes scattered through large angles when they are directed at a thin metal foil.

2 Rutherford used the measurements from alpha-scattering experiments to prove that an atom has a small positively charged central nucleus where most of the mass of the atom is located.

P2 7.3   Nuclear fission

Chain reactions

Energy is released in a nuclear reactor as a result of a process called **nuclear fission**. In this process, the nucleus of an atom of a fissionable substance splits into two smaller 'fragment' nuclei. This event can cause other fissionable nuclei to split, so producing a **chain reaction** of fission events.

Fission neutrons

When a nucleus undergoes fission, it releases

- two or three neutrons (referred to as 'fission' neutrons) at high speeds,
- energy in the form of radiation and kinetic energy of the fission neutrons and the fragment nuclei.

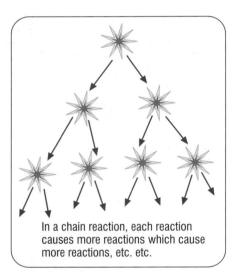

In a chain reaction, each reaction causes more reactions which cause more reactions, etc. etc.

Figure 1 A chain reaction

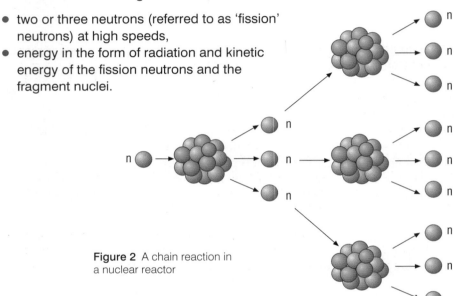

Figure 2 A chain reaction in a nuclear reactor

The fission neutrons may cause further fission resulting in a chain reaction. In a nuclear reactor, exactly one fission neutron from each fission event on average goes on to produce further fission.

a) What would happen if more than one fission neutron per event on average went on to produce further fission?

Fissionable isotopes

The fuel in a nuclear reactor must contain fissionable isotopes.

- Most reactors at the present time are designed to use 'enriched uranium' as the fuel. This consists mostly of the non-fissionable uranium isotope $^{238}_{92}U$ (U-238) and about 2–3% of the uranium isotope $^{235}_{92}U$ (U-235) which is fissionable. In comparison, natural uranium is more than 99% U-238.
- The U-238 nuclei in a nuclear reactor do not undergo fission but they change into other heavy nuclei, including plutonium-239 (the isotope $^{239}_{94}Pu$). This isotope is fissionable but not in a uranium reactor.

GET IT RIGHT!

During nuclear fission a large nucleus breaks up into two smaller nuclei. Make sure you know how to spell 'fission' – two 's's.

FOUL FACTS

A nuclear bomb is two lumps of pure U-235 or Pu-239. Each lump can't produce a chain reaction because it loses too many fission neutrons. But if you bring them together . . . !

Inside a nuclear reactor

A nuclear reactor consists of uranium fuel rods spaced evenly in the reactor core. Figure 3 shows a cross-section of a Pressurised Water Reactor (PWR).

- The reactor core is a thick steel vessel containing the fuel rods, control rods and water at high pressure. The fission neutrons are slowed down by collisions with the atoms in the water molecules. This is necessary as fast neutrons do not cause further fission of U-235. We say the water acts as a **moderator** because it slows the fission neutrons down.

- **Control rods** in the core absorb surplus neutrons. This keeps the chain reaction under control. The depth of the rods in the core is adjusted to maintain a steady chain reaction.

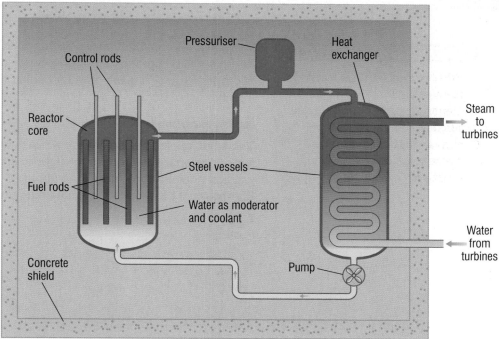

Figure 3 A nuclear reactor

- The water acts as a **coolant**. Its molecules gain kinetic energy from the neutrons and the fuel rods. The water is pumped through the core and through sealed pipes to and from a heat exchanger outside the core. The water transfers thermal energy to the heat exchanger from the core.

- The reactor core is a thick steel vessel, designed to withstand the very high temperature and pressure in the core. The core is enclosed by thick concrete walls which absorb radiation that escapes through the walls of the steel vessel.

b) What would happen if the control rods were removed from the core?

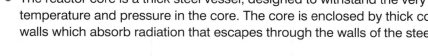

SUMMARY QUESTIONS

1 Complete a) and b) using the list below:

nucleus   uranium-235   uranium-238   plutonium-239

a) Nuclear fission happens when a ...... of ...... or ...... splits.
b) A nucleus of ...... in a nuclear reactor changes without fission into a nucleus of ....

2 Put the statements A, B and C in the list below into the correct sequence of boxes 1–4 to describe a steady chain reaction in a nuclear reactor.

A a U-235 nucleus splits
B a neutron hits a U-235 nucleus
C neutrons are released

Steady chain reaction
1
energy is released
2
3
4

KEY POINTS

1 **Nuclear fission** occurs when a uranium-235 nucleus or a plutonium-239 nucleus splits.
2 A **chain reaction** occurs in a nuclear reactor when each fission event causes further fission events.
3 In a *nuclear reactor*, one neutron per fission on average goes on to produce further fission.

P2 7.4 Nuclear fusion

Imagine if we could get energy from water. Stars release energy as a result of fusing small nuclei like hydrogen to form larger nuclei. Water contains lots of hydrogen atoms. A glass of water could provide the same amount of energy as a tanker full of petrol – if we could make a fusion reactor here on the Earth.

Fusion reactions

Two small nuclei release energy when they are fused together to form a single larger nucleus. The process releases energy only if the relative mass of the product nucleus is no more than about 55 (about the same as an iron nucleus). Energy must be supplied to create bigger nuclei.

Figure 1 A fusion reaction

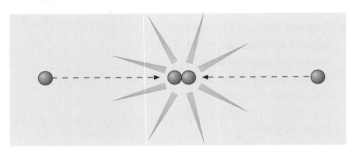

The Sun is mostly 75% hydrogen and about 25% helium. The core is so hot that it consists of a 'plasma' of bare nuclei with no electrons. These nuclei move about and fuse together when they collide. When they fuse, they release energy. Figure 2 shows how protons fuse together to form a $^4_2$He nucleus. Energy is released at each stage.

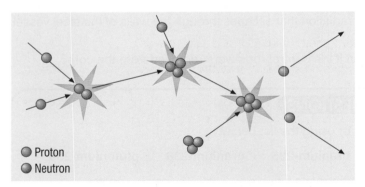

○ Proton
○ Neutron

Figure 2 Fusion reactions in the Sun

- When two protons (i.e. hydrogen nuclei) fuse, they form a 'heavy hydrogen' nucleus, $^2_1$H. A positron, the antimatter counterpart of the electron, is created and emitted at the same time.
- Two more protons collide separately with two $^2_1$H nuclei and turn them into heavier nuclei.
- The two heavier nuclei collide to form the helium nucleus $^4_2$He.
- The energy released at each stage is carried away as kinetic energy of the product nucleus and other particles emitted.

a) Look at Figure 2 and work out what is formed when a proton collides with a $^2_1$H nucleus.

Fusion reactors

There are enormous technical difficulties with fusion. The 'plasma' of light nuclei must be heated to very high temperatures before the nuclei will fuse. This is because two nuclei approaching each other will repel each other due to their positive charge. If the nuclei are moving fast enough, they can overcome the force of repulsion and fuse together.

In a fusion reactor:

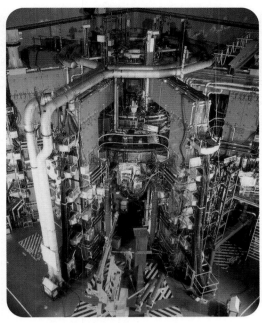

Figure 3 An experimental fusion reactor

- the plasma is heated by passing a very large electric current through it,
- the plasma is contained by a magnetic field so it doesn't touch the reactor walls. If it did, it would go cold and fusion would stop.

Scientists have been working on these problems since the 1950s. A successful fusion reactor would release more energy than it uses to heat the plasma. At the present time, scientists working on experimental fusion reactors are able to do this by fusing 'heavy hydrogen' nuclei to form helium nuclei – but only for a few minutes!

b) Why is a fusion reactor unlikely to explode?

A promising future

Practical fusion reactors could meet all our energy needs.

- The fuel for fusion reactors is readily available as 'heavy hydrogen' and is present in sea water.
- The reaction product, helium, is a non-radioactive inert gas so is harmless.
- The energy released could be used to generate electricity.

SUMMARY QUESTIONS

1 Complete a) and b) using the words below:

larger   small   stable

a) When two …… nuclei moving at high speed collide, they form a …… nucleus.

b) Energy is released in nuclear fusion if the product nucleus is not as …… as an iron nucleus.

2 a) Why does the plasma of light nuclei in a fusion reactor need to be very hot?

b) Why would a fusion reactor that needs more energy than it produces not be much use?

KEY POINTS

1 Nuclear fusion occurs when two nuclei are forced close enough together so they form a single larger nucleus.

2 Energy is released when two light nuclei are fused together.

3 A fusion reactor needs to be at a very high temperature before nuclear fusion can take place.

P2 7.5   Nuclear energy issues

The Manhattan project

In the Second World War, scientists in Britain and America were recruited to work in Arizona on the Manhattan project, the project to build the first atomic bomb. They knew they would be in deadly competition with scientists in Nazi Germany. They also knew that if they lost the race, the war would be lost.

By 1945, the first atomic bomb was ready to be used. Nazi Germany had already surrendered. The allied forces were still involved in bitter fighting against Japan in the Far East. Their leaders knew the planned invasion of Japan would claim the lives of many allied troops. An atomic bomb was dropped on the Japanese city of Hiroshima to force Japan to surrender. The explosion killed 140 000 people. The Japanese government did not give in until after a second atomic bomb was dropped on the Japanese city of Nagasaki a week later.

> ### ACTIVITY
>
> Discuss these questions as a small group:
>
> a) Most people think the British and American governments were right to build an atomic bomb. But do you think scientists should continue to work on deadly weapons?
>
> b) Many people think the power of the atomic bomb should have been demonstrated to Japan by dropping it on an uninhabited island. What do you think?

Cold fusion

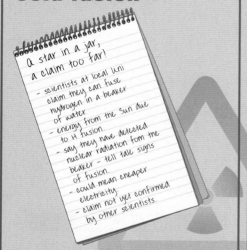

A star in a jar, a claim too far!

- scientists at local uni claim they can fuse hydrogen in a beaker of water.
- energy from the sun due to H fusion.
- say they have detected nuclear radiation from the beaker – tell tale signs of fusion.
- could mean cheaper electricity.
- claim not yet confirmed by other scientists.

> ### ACTIVITY
>
> Imagine you're a journalist and you've got a 'scoop' on cold fusion. Your editor wants you to write it up for the front page – nothing too complicated. Prepare a front-page feature on your scoop. Remember the claims have not been confirmed yet.

The fast-breeder reactor

This fast-breeder reactor uses plutonium-239 as its fuel. It can 'breed' its own plutonium by fusion from uranium-238. Present and planned uranium reactors will use up the world's supply of uranium within about 200 years. Fast-breeder reactors would extend that to thousands of years. As in the uranium reactor, control rods in the reactor core are used to keep the rate of fission events constant. This ensures energy is released at a constant rate. **But** if somehow, plutonium got stuck in a pipe . . . !

> ### ACTIVITY
>
> a) Finish the sentence at the end of the paragraph.
>
> b) The UK government built and tested an experimental fast-breeder reactor on the coast of Northern Scotland at Dounreay. It has now been closed. So why are many people still worried about it? Imagine you are one of them. Write a letter to your local newspaper about your concerns.

Nuclear reprocessing – a hot problem!

Used fuel rods contain uranium-238 and plutonium-239. After removal from a reactor, a used fuel rod is left to cool in a large tank of water for up to a year. Then the fuel in it is removed and the uranium and plutonium content is taken out chemically. This process is called reprocessing. The rest of the fuel is stored in sealed containers at secure sites. Reprocessed uranium and plutonium can be used in fast-breeder reactors to generate electricity. Plutonium can also be used to make nuclear bombs.

The UKs THORP reprocessing plant in Cumbria reprocesses waste from other countries as well as from the UK. Lots of scientists are employed there. It generates income but it also generates lots of controversy. Many people think it should be closed.

ACTIVITY

Should we reprocess nuclear waste for other countries? Should we reprocess our own nuclear waste or just store it? Discuss the issue as a group. Send an e-mail to your MP to tell him/her what you think.

Atom smashers

Here's something you don't need to know for your GCSE exam – yet! We now know that neutrons and protons are made of smaller particles called **quarks**. Physicists use big machines (like the one in the picture) called accelerators to make charged particles travel extremely fast. They discovered that a beam of fast-moving electrons is scattered by three small particles inside each neutron and proton. They worked out that

- a proton is made of two 'up' quarks and a 'down' quark,
- a neutron is made of two 'down' quarks and an 'up' quark.

You'll learn more about the quark family at AS level!

ACTIVITY

What conclusions can you make about the charge of an 'up' quark and the charge of a 'down' quark?

New improved nuclear reactors

Most of the world's nuclear reactors presently in use will need to be replaced in the next 20 years. They were built to last for no more than about 30 to 40 years. We all want electricity and we want it without burning fossil fuel. Reactor companies have been developing new improved 'third-generation' nuclear reactors to replace existing nuclear reactors when they are taken out of use.

These new types of reactors have:

- a standard design to cut down capital costs and construction time,
- a longer operating life – typically 60 years,
- improved safety features,
- much less effect on the environment.

Some of the new reactors are designed with 'passive' safety features, where natural processes (for example, convection of outside air through cooling panels along the reactor walls) are used to prevent accidents. Such features are additional to 'active' safety controls, such as the use of control rods and safety valves. Some scientists claim these 'new' features are about giving nuclear power a more 'positive image'.

ACTIVITY

New reactors are being built in many countries. Should new reactors be built in the UK? Discuss the benefits and the drawbacks of such a programme.

SUMMARY QUESTIONS

1 a) How many protons and how many neutrons are in a nucleus of each of the following isotopes?
  i) $^{14}_{6}C$,   ii) $^{228}_{90}Th$

b) $^{14}_{6}C$ emits a β particle and becomes an isotope of nitrogen (N).
  i) How many protons and how many neutrons are in this nitrogen isotope?
  ii) Write down the symbol for this isotope.

c) $^{228}_{90}Th$ emits an α particle and becomes an isotope of radium (Ra).
  i) How many protons and how many neutrons are in this isotope of radium?
  ii) Write down the symbol for this isotope.

2 a) Complete the sentences using words from the list.

decreases   increases   stays the same

When energy is released at a steady rate in a nuclear reactor,
  i) the number of fission events each second in the core ....
  ii) the amount of uranium-235 in the core ....
  iii) the number of radioactive isotopes in the fuel rods ....

b) Explain what would happen in a nuclear reactor if:
  i) the coolant fluid leaked out of the core,
  ii) the control rods were pushed further into the reactor core.

3 a) i) What do we mean by nuclear fusion?
  ii) Why do two nuclei repel each other when they get close?
  iii) Why do they need to collide at high speed in order to fuse together?

b) Give two reasons why nuclear fusion is difficult to achieve in a reactor.

4 a) Complete the sentences using words from the list.

fission   fusion

  i) In a ...... reactor, two small nuclei join together and release energy.
  ii) In a ...... reactor, a large nucleus splits and releases energy.
  iii) The fuel in a ...... reactor contains uranium-235.

b) State two advantages that nuclear fusion reactors would have in comparison with nuclear fission reactors.

EXAM-STYLE QUESTIONS

1 The diagram shows two isotopes of the element carbon.

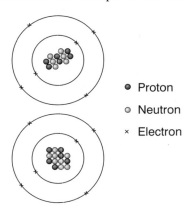

- ● Proton
- ○ Neutron
- × Electron

(a) What are isotopes of an element? (2)

(b) (i) What is the atomic number of carbon?

  (ii) What are the mass numbers of the two isotopes of carbon shown in the diagram? (3)

(c) Which of the particles ●, ○ and ×, shown in the diagram:

  (i) has a negative charge?

  (ii) has no charge?

  (iii) has the smallest mass? (3)

2 In a nuclear reactor, energy is produced by the process of nuclear fission.

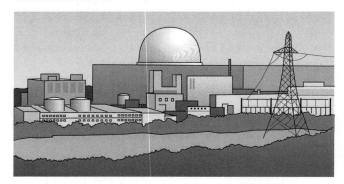

Describe as fully as you can the process of nuclear fission.

The answer has been started for you. Copy and complete:

Atoms of uranium—235 are bombarded by neutrons. .... (6)

3 Nuclear fusion is the process by which energy is released in stars.
Describe as fully as you can the process of nuclear fusion. (4)

4 (a) Radon is formed when radium-226 decays by the emission of an alpha particle.

   Copy and complete the nuclear equation below.

   $$^{226}_{88}\text{Ra} \longrightarrow \text{Rn} + \alpha$$ (4)

   (b) Nitrogen is formed when carbon-14 decays by the emission of a beta particle.

   Copy and complete the nuclear equation below.

   $$^{14}_{6}\text{C} \longrightarrow \text{N} + \beta$$ (4)

   (c) What changes take place in the carbon-14 nucleus when it decays by emitting a beta particle? (3)

5 Background radiation is with us all the time and comes from many different sources, such as radon gas.

   (a) Name two other sources of background radiation. (2)

   (b) Some scientists are measuring the amount of radon gas inside a house. The gas is released into the air from rocks in the ground. Suggest what the scientists could do to make their measurements as reliable as possible. (4)

   (c) The table gives some values for the dose of background radiation from the ground in different parts of the UK.

Area of UK	Dose in millisieverts per year
South west	0.35
South east	0.20
Midlands	0.25
North west	0.30
North east	0.23

   (i) What type of variable is the 'Area of UK'? (1)

   (ii) What would be the best way to represent this data on a bar chart or line graph? (1)

HOW SCIENCE WORKS QUESTIONS

Iodine-125 is a radioactive isotope used by doctors as a gamma emitter for measuring bone density in humans. It can also be used in the treatment of prostate cancer.

It is important to know how the activity of iodine-125 changes with time. The following measurements were taken in two identical tests of iodine-125.

Time (days)	0	50	100	150	200	250
Sample A (counts/min)	100	56	31	17	10	6
Sample B (counts/min)	100	55	31	18	9	5

a) Are the differences in activity between the two samples due to random or systematic variations? Explain your answer. (1)

b) The tests were carried on for several years and the results stayed more or less constant after a couple of years. This was said to be due to the ever-present background radiation.
   Explain why the background radiation introduces a systematic error into the measurements. (1)

c) What are the environmental issues involved in using this isotope? (1)

PRESS RELEASE

Fifteen-year studies of prostate cancer patients using iodine-125 have been completed. The Medical Director from a US company confirmed that results show only 4% of patients had died from the prostate cancer. A British consultant urologist said that after 5 years, 93% of patients were disease-free.

d) Suggest two questions you might want to ask the scientists who gave this press release. (2)

EXAMINATION-STYLE QUESTIONS

1 When an air-rifle is fired a small explosion takes place which pushes the pellet forwards and the air-rifle backwards.

See pages 216–17

(a) The mass of an air-rifle is 2 kg. The mass of the pellet is 0.0005 kg and its speed as it leaves the rifle is 100 m/s.

Calculate the speed with which the air-rifle moves backwards *(3 marks)*

GET IT RIGHT!
The total momentum before the explosion is zero.

(b) The picture shows a batsman hitting a cricket ball.

The batsman 'follows through' when hitting the ball, so the force is applied to the ball for a longer time. Why does he do this?

(3 marks)
[Higher]

2 A student is investigating terminal velocity. She drops a metal ball into a tall beaker containing glycerine.

See pages 204–5

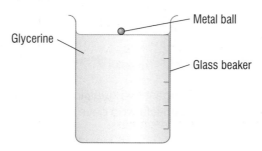

Glycerine —
Metal ball
Glass beaker

Initially the metal ball accelerates because of the force of gravity. Eventually the resultant force on the ball bearing becomes zero.

(a) Why does the resultant force become zero? *(3 marks)*

The student watches the ball slowly moving through the glycerine. As it does, she times how long it takes to get to each mark on the beaker.

(b) Describe what precautions she should take to make her results as accurate as possible. *(2 marks)*

(c) Copy the axes below and sketch the line you would expect on the graph of speed of ball against time. *(3 marks)*

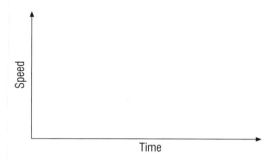

3   At one time scientists believed in a 'plum pudding' model of the atom.

See pages 264–5

(a) What is meant by the 'plum pudding' model of the atom? *(2 marks)*

(b) Rutherford and Marsden carried out an experiment that led to this model being replaced by the nuclear model.

They fired alpha particles at thin gold foil. Some of the observations from their experiment are given below.
For each observation write down the matching explanation.
One has been done for you.

Observation	Explanation
Most of the particles go straight through the gold foil without being deflected.	
Some particles are deflected through small angles.	The nucleus is charged.
A few alpha particles are deflected back through angles greater than 90°.	

(3 marks)
[Higher]

See pages 210–13

4   In a fitness centre people use machines containing pulleys to move 'weights'.

(a) Some of the 'weights' are marked '5 kg'.

This is incorrect physics. Explain why. *(2 marks)*

(b) Calculate the work done on a 30 N weight when one of the machines raises it 2 m. Give a unit with your answer. *(4 marks)*

(c) A running machine displays the speed a person would be travelling if they were running on the road.

Calculate the kinetic energy of a person of mass 70 kg running at a speed of 5 m/s. Give a unit with your answer. *(4 marks)*
[Higher]

GET IT RIGHT!
There are three marks here, so try to make three points.

GET IT RIGHT!
Remember to square the speed when calculating kinetic energy.

How science works

How science works for us

Science works for us all day, every day.

Working as a scientist you will have knowledge of the world around you and particularly about the subject you are working with. You will observe the world around you. An enquiring mind will then lead you to start asking questions about what you have observed.

Science usually moves forward by slow steady steps.

Each small step is important in its own way. It builds on the body of knowledge that we already have.

Thinking scientifically

Deciding on what to measure

Variables can be one of four different types:

- A **categoric variable** is one that is best described by a label (usually a word). The colour of eyes is a categoric variable, e.g. blue or brown eyes.
- A **discrete variable** is one that you describe in whole numbers. The number of leaves on different plants is a discrete variable.
- An **ordered variable** is one where you can put the data into order, but not give it an actual number. The height of plants compared to each other is an ordered variable, e.g. the plants growing in the woodland are taller than those on the open field.
- A **continuous variable** is one that we measure, so its value could be any number. Temperature (as measured by a thermometer or temperature sensor) is a continuous variable, e.g. 37.6°C, 45.2°C.

When designing your investigation you should always try to measure continuous data whenever you can. This is not always possible, so you should then try to use ordered data. If there is no other way to measure your variable then you have to use a label (categoric variable).

Making your investigation reliable and valid

When you are designing an investigation you must make sure that others can repeat any results you get – this makes it **reliable**.

You must also make sure you are measuring the actual thing you want to measure. If you don't, your data can't be used to answer your original question. This seems very obvious but it is not always quite so easy. You need to make sure that you have **controlled** as many other variables as you can, so that no-one can say that your investigation is not **valid**.

How might an independent variable be linked to a dependent variable?

The **independent variable** is the one you choose to vary in your investigation.

The **dependent variable** is used to judge the effect of varying the independent variable.

These variables can be linked together for one of three reasons:

- It could be because one variable has caused a change in the other, e.g. the more plants there are in a pond, the more oxygen there is in the water. This is a **causal link**.
- It could be because a third variable has caused changes in the two variables you have investigated, e.g. fields that have more grass also have more dandelions in them. There is an **association** between the two variables. This is caused by a third variable – how many sheep there are in the field!
- It could be due simply to **chance**, e.g. the type of weeds growing in different parts of your garden!

KEY POINTS

1 Be on the lookout for non-scientific opinions.
2 Continuous data can give you more information than other types of data.
3 Check that evidence is reliable and valid.
4 Be aware that just because two variables are related, does not mean that there is a causal link.

Starting an investigation

Observation

As scientists we use observations to ask questions. We can only ask useful questions if we know something about the observed event. We will not have all of the answers, but we know enough to start asking the correct questions.

When you are designing an investigation you have to observe carefully which variables are likely to have an effect.

Observations, backed up by really creative thinking and good scientific knowledge can lead into a **hypothesis**.

What is a hypothesis?

A hypothesis is a 'great idea'. Why is it so great – well because it is a great observation that has some really good science to try to explain it.

When making hypotheses you can be very imaginative with your ideas. However, you should have some scientific reasoning behind those ideas so that they are not totally bizarre.

Remember, your explanation might not be correct, but you think it is. The only way you can check out your hypothesis is to make it into a prediction and then test it by carrying out an investigation.

Observation ✛ knowledge ➡ hypothesis ➡ prediction ➡ investigation

Starting to design a valid investigation

An investigation starts with a prediction. You, as the scientist, predict that there is a relationship between two variables.

- An independent variable is one that is changed or selected by you, the investigator.
- A dependent variable is measured for each change in your independent variable.
- All other variables become *control variables*, kept constant, if possible, so that your investigation is a fair test.

If your measurements are going to be accepted by other people then they must be valid. Part of this is making sure that you are only measuring the variable that you want to measure.

> ### KEY POINTS
> 1 Observation is often the starting point for an investigation.
> 2 Hypotheses can lead to predictions and investigations.
> 3 You must design investigations that produce valid results if you are to be believed.

Building an investigation

Fair testing

A fair test is one in which only the independent variable affects the dependent variable. All other variables are controlled.

This is easy to set up in the laboratory, but almost impossible in fieldwork. Plants and animals do not live in environments that are simple and easy to control. They live complex lives with variables changing constantly.

So how can we set up the fieldwork investigations? The best you can do is to make sure that all of the many variables change in much the same way, except for the one you are investigating. Then at least the plants get the same weather, even if it is constantly changing.

If you are investigating two variables in a large population then you will need to do a survey. Again it is impossible to control all of the variables. Imagine you were investigating the effect of diet on diabetes. You would have to choose people of the same age and same family history to test. The larger the sample size you test, the more reliable your results will be.

Control groups are used in investigations to try to make sure that you are measuring the variable that you intend to measure. When investigating the effects of a new drug, the control group will be given a placebo. The control group think they are taking a drug but the placebo does not contain the drug. This way you can control the variable of 'thinking that the drug is working' and separate out the effect of the actual drug.

Choosing values of a variable

Trial runs will tell you a lot about how your early thoughts are going to work out.

- Do you have the correct conditions?
- Have you chosen a sensible range?
- Have you got enough readings that are close together?
- Will you need to repeat your readings?

Accuracy

Your investigation must provide accurate data. Accurate data is essential if your results are going to have any meaning.

How do you know if you have accurate data?

It is very difficult to be certain. Accurate results are very close to the *true value*. It is not always possible to know what that true value is.

- Sometimes you can calculate a theoretical value and check it against the experimental evidence. Close agreement between these two values could indicate accurate data.
- You can draw a graph of your results and see how close each result is to the line of best fit.
- Try repeating your measurements with a different instrument and see if you get the same readings.

How do you get accurate data?

- Using instruments that measure accurately will help.
- The more carefully you use the measuring instruments, the more accuracy you will get.

Precision

Your investigation must provide data with sufficient precision. If it doesn't then you will not be able to make a valid conclusion.

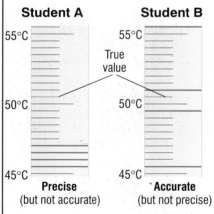

The difference between accurate and precise results

Imagine measuring the temperature after a set time when a fuel is used to heat a fixed volume of water. Two students repeated this experiment, four times each. Their results are marked on the thermometer scales below:

Student A	Student B
55°C	55°C
	True value
50°C	50°C
45°C	45°C
Precise (but not accurate)	**Accurate** (but not precise)

- A precise set of results is grouped closely together.
- An accurate set of results will have a mean (average) close to the true value.

How do you get precise and reliable data?

- You have to repeat your tests as often as necessary to improve reliability.
- You have to repeat your tests in exactly the same way each time.
- Use measuring instruments that have the appropriate scale divisions needed for a particular investigation. Smaller scale divisions can improve precision.

A word of caution!

Be careful though – just because your results show precision does not mean your results are accurate. (See the diagram on page 278.)

Imagine you carry out an investigation into the energy value of a type of crisp. You get readings of the amount of energy released that are all about the same. This means that your data will have precision, but it doesn't mean that they are necessarily accurate.

Making measurements

Using instruments

You cannot expect perfect results.

When you choose an instrument you need to know that it will give you the accuracy that you want, i.e. it will give you a true reading.

When you choose an instrument you need to decide how precise you need to be. Some instruments have smaller scale divisions than others. Instruments that measure the same thing can have different sensitivities. The *sensitivity* of an instrument refers to the smallest change in a value that can be detected. Choosing the wrong scale can cause you to miss important data or make silly conclusions.

You also need to be able to use an instrument properly.

Errors

Even when an instrument is used correctly, the results can still show differences.

Results may differ because of a **random error**. This is most likely to be due to a poor measurement being made. It could be due to not carrying out the method consistently.

The error may be a **systematic error**. This means that the method was carried out consistently but an error was being repeated.

Anomalies (see also section on 'Identifying patterns and relationships')

Anomalies are results that are clearly out of line. They are not those that are due to the natural variation that you get from any measurement. These should be looked at carefully. There might be a very interesting reason why they are so different. If they are simply due to a random error then they should be ignored.

If anomalies can be identified while you are doing an investigation, then it is best to repeat that part of the investigation.

If you find anomalies after you have finished collecting the data for an investigation, then they must be discarded.

KEY POINTS

1 Care must be taken to ensure fair testing – as far as is possible.
2 You can use a trial run to make sure that you choose the best values for your variables.
3 Careful use of the correct equipment can improve accuracy.
4 If you repeat your results carefully you can improve their reliability.

KEY POINTS

1 Results will nearly always vary.
2 Better instruments give more accurate results.
3 Sensitivity in an instrument is the smallest change that it can detect.
4 Human error can produce random and systematic errors.
5 We examine anomalies – they might give us some interesting ideas. If they are due to a random error, we repeat them. If there is no time to repeat them, we discard them.

Presenting data

Tables

Tables are really good for getting your results down quickly and clearly. You should design your table *before* you start your investigation.

The range of the data

Pick out the maximum and the minimum values and you have the range. You should always quote these two numbers when asked for a range. For example, the range is between . . . (the lowest value) and . . . (the highest value) – and don't forget to include the units!

The mean of the data

Add up all of the measurements and divide by how many there are.

Bar charts

If you have a categoric or an ordered independent variable and a continuous dependent variable then you should use a bar chart.

Line graphs

If you have a continuous independent and a continuous dependent variable then use a line graph.

Scatter graphs (or scattergrams)

These are used in much the same way as a line graph, but you might not expect to be able to draw such a clear line of best fit. For example, if you want to see if lung capacity is related to how long people can hold their breath, you will draw a scatter graph of your results.

Using data to draw conclusions

Identifying patterns and relationships

Now you have a bar chart or a graph of your results you can begin looking for patterns in your results. You must have an open mind at this point.

Firstly, there could still be some anomalous results. You might not have picked these out earlier. How do you spot an anomaly? It must be a significant distance away from the pattern, not just within normal variation.

A line of best fit will help to identify any anomalies at this stage. Ask yourself – do the anomalies represent something important or were they just a mistake?

Secondly, remember a line of best fit can be a straight line or it can be a curve – you have to decide from your results.

The line of best fit will also lead you into thinking what the relationship is between your two variables. You need to consider whether your graph shows a *linear* relationship. This simply means can you be confident about drawing a straight line of best fit on your graph? If the answer is yes, then is this line positive or negative?

A directly proportional relationship is shown by a positive straight line that goes through the origin (0,0).

Your results might also show a curved line of best fit. These can be predictable, complex or very complex!

Drawing conclusions

Your graphs are designed to show the relationship between your two chosen variables. You need to consider what that relationship means for your conclusion. You must also take into account the reliability and the validity of the data you are considering.

You will continue to have an open mind about your conclusion.

You will have made a prediction. This could be supported by your results, it might not be supported, or it could be partly supported. It might suggest some other hypothesis to you.

You must be willing to think carefully about your results. Remember it is quite rare for a set of results to completely support a prediction and be completely reliable.

There are three possible links between variables. They can be:

- causal,
- due to association, or
- due to chance.

You must decide which is the most likely. Remember a positive relationship does not always mean a causal link between the two variables.

Your conclusion must go no further than the evidence that you have. Any patterns you spot are only strictly valid in the range of values you tested. Further tests are needed to check whether the pattern continues beyond this range.

The purpose of the prediction was to test a hypothesis. The hypothesis can:

- be supported,
- be refuted, or
- lead to another hypothesis.

You have to decide which it is on the evidence available.

Poor science can often happen if a wrong decision is made here. Newspapers have said that living near electricity sub-stations can cause cancer. All that scientists would say is that there is possibly an association. Getting the correct conclusion is very important.

Evaluation

If you are still uncertain about a conclusion, it might be down to the reliability and the validity of the results. You could check these by:

- looking for other similar work on the Internet or from others in your class,
- getting somebody else to re-do your investigation,
- trying an alternative method to see if you get the same results.

KEY POINTS

1 Drawing lines of best fit help us to study the relationship between variables.
2 The possible relationships are linear, positive and negative; directly proportional; predictable and complex curves.
3 Conclusions must go no further than the data available.
4 The reliability and validity of data can be checked by looking at other similar work done by others, perhaps on the Internet. It can also be checked by using a different method or by others checking your method.

Scientific evidence and society

Now you have reached a conclusion about a piece of scientific research, what comes next? If it is pure research then your fellow scientists will want to look at it very carefully. If it affects the lives of ordinary people then society will also want to examine it closely.

You can help your cause by giving a balanced account of what you have found out. It is much the same as any argument you might have. If you make ridiculous claims then nobody will believe anything you have to say.

Be open and honest. If you only tell part of the story then someone will want to know why! Equally, if somebody is only telling you part of the truth you cannot be confident with anything they say.

You must be on the lookout for people who might be biased when representing scientific evidence. Some scientists are paid by companies to do research. When you are told that a certain product is harmless, check out who is telling you this.

We also have to be very careful in reaching judgements according to who is presenting scientific evidence to us. An example could be when the evidence comes with some political significance. If the evidence might provoke public or political problems then it might be played down. Equally others might want to exaggerate the findings. They might make more of the results than the evidence suggests.

The status of the experimenter may place more, or less, weight on evidence.

KEY POINTS

1 Scientific evidence must be presented in a balanced way that points out clearly how reliable and valid the evidence is.
2 The evidence must not contain any bias from the experimenter.
3 The evidence must be checked to appreciate if there has been any political influence.
4 The status of the experimenter can influence the weight placed on the evidence.
5 Scientific knowledge can be used to develop technologies.
6 People can exploit scientific and technological developments to suit their own purposes.
7 The uses of science and technology can raise ethical, social, economic and environmental issues.
8 These issues are decided upon by individuals and by society.
9 There are many questions left for science to answer.
10 Science cannot answer questions that start with 'Should we . . .?'

Glossary

A

Acceleration Change of velocity per second (in metres per second per second, m/s^2).

Acid A substance that produces hydrogen ions when it dissolves in water.

Activation energy The minimum amount of energy needed for a given chemical reaction to take place.

Active site The site on an enzyme where the reactants bind.

Active transport The movement of substances against a concentration gradient across a cell membrane, using energy.

Aerobic Using oxygen.

Aerobic respiration The process by which food molecules are broken down using oxygen to release energy for the cells.

Alkali A soluble base.

Alleles Different forms of the same gene.

Alpha emission A process in which a large unstable nucleus becomes stable by emitting an alpha particle.

Alpha particle scattering Scattering of alpha particles (usually in a narrow beam) by nuclei of the atoms of a thin metal foil.

Amino acids The building blocks of protein.

Anhydrous An anhydrous substance does not contain water.

Anode Positive electrode.

Antistatic material Material that is a poor insulator and which is used to conduct charge to earth.

Aqueous solution A solution with water as the solvent.

Association When two variables change together, but they are both linked by a third variable. E.g. lack of carbon dioxide in soil and poor growth of plants: both could be linked to too much water in the soil.

Atom economy The efficiency of a chemical reaction in terms of all of the atoms involved.

Atomic number The number of protons in a nucleus, symbol Z (also called the proton number).

B

Bases Compounds which react with acids to neutralise them.

Beta emission A process in which a neutron-rich nucleus becomes stable as a result of a neutron changing into a proton, creating and emitting a beta particle (i.e. an electron) at the instant of change.

Biological detergents Washing detergents that contain enzymes.

Biomass The amount of biological material in an organism.

Biomass fuel Fuel from animal waste or cut-down plants.

Bladder The organ where urine is stored until it is released from the body.

Braking distance The distance travelled by a vehicle during the time its brakes act.

C

Cable Two or three insulated wires surrounded by an outer layer of rubber or flexible plastic.

Carbohydrases Enzymes which speed up the breakdown of carbohydrates.

Carbon cycle The cycling of carbon through the living and non-living world.

Carriers People who have a single recessive allele for a genetic disease.

Catalyst A substance that speeds up the rate of another reaction but is not used up or changed itself.

Categoric variable These tell us the name of the variable, e.g. copper, iron, magnesium.

Cathode Negative electrode.

Causal link One change in a variable has caused a change in another variable. You can only be reasonably certain of this when you have valid and reliable evidence. E.g. increasing the length of the wire causes an increase in resistance.

Cell membrane The membrane around the contents of a cell which controls what moves in and out of the cell.

Chain reaction Reactions in which one reaction causes further reactions, which in turn cause further reactions, etc. A nuclear chain reaction occurs when fission neutrons cause further fission, so more fission neutrons are released. These go on to produce further fission.

Chance When there is no scientific link between the two variables. E.g. increased sea temperatures and increased diabetes.

Charging by friction The process of charging certain insulating materials by rubbing with a dry cloth, causing electrons to transfer between the material and the cloth.

Charging without direct contact The process in which an insulated conductor is charged without being in direct contact with a charged object.

Chip An electronic component which contains an integrated circuit.

Chloride ion A chlorine atom that has gained one electron, which gives it a negative charge.

Chlorophyll The green pigment contained in the chloroplasts.

Chloroplasts The organelles in which photosynthesis takes place.

Circuit Components connected together so that current passes through them.

Circuit breaker An electromagnetic switch that opens and cuts the current off if too much current passes through it.

Collision theory An explanation of chemical reactions in terms of reacting particles colliding with sufficient energy for a reaction to take place.

Combustion The process of burning.

Component A part or device in an electric circuit.

Compost heap A site where garden rubbish and kitchen waste are decomposed by microorganisms.

Concentration gradient The gradient between an area where a substance is at a high concentration and an area where it is at a low concentration.

Conduction electrons Electrons that move about freely inside a metal because they are not attached to individual atoms.

Conservation of momentum Momentum is conserved in any collision or explosion provided no external forces act on the objects that collide or explode.

Constrict To narrow.

Continuous variable A continuous variable can be any numerical value, e.g. your own weight.

Control rods Metal rods (made of boron or cadmium) used to absorb excess fission neutrons in a nuclear reactor so that only one fission neutron per fission on average goes on to produce further fission.

Controlled An experiment is controlled when all variables that might affect your result (apart from the independent variable) have been kept constant.

Coolant Fluid in a sealed circuit pumped through the core of a nuclear reactor to remove thermal energy to a heat exchanger.

Coulomb (C) The unit of electrical charge, equal to the charge passing a point in a (direct current) circuit in 1 second when the current is 1 A.

Covalent bonds The bonds formed when atoms join together by sharing electrons.

Cystic fibrosis A genetic disease that affects the lungs, digestive and reproductive systems. It is inherited through a recessive allele.

Cytoplasm The water-based gel in which the organelles of all living cells are suspended.

D

Daughter cells The cells produced by cell division.

Deceleration Change of velocity per second when an object slows down.

Decompose To split up.

Decomposers Microorganisms that break down waste products and dead bodies.

Delocalised electrons Electrons in a molecule which do not belong to a single atom or a single bond.

Denatured Enzymes that are denatured have their protein structure broken down and can no longer catalyse a reaction.

Dependent variable The variable that you are measuring as a result of changing the independent variable, e.g. the volume of CO_2 produced.

Detritus feeders See **decomposers**.

Differentiated Specialised for a particular function.

Diffusion The net movement of particles of a gas or a solute from an area of high concentration to an area of low concentration (along a concentration gradient).

Dilate To widen.

Discrete variable These are numerical, but can only be whole numbers, e.g. numbers of layers of insulation.

Dominant The characteristic that will show up in the offspring even if only one of the alleles is inherited.

Drag force A force opposing the motion of an object due to fluid (e.g. air) flowing past the object as it moves.

E

Earth wire A wire used to connect the metal case of an appliance to earth so that the case cannot become live.

Earthed Connected to the ground by means of a conducting lead or wire.

Elastic A material is elastic if it is able to regain its shape after it has been squashed or stretched.

Elastic potential energy Energy stored in an elastic object when work is done to change its shape.

Electric current The rate of flow of electric charge (in amperes, A).

Electric potential energy Energy of a charged object due to its charge (in joules, J).

Electrical energy Energy transferred by the movement of charge.

Electrical power The rate of transfer of electrical energy (in watts, W).

Electrolyte A substance that conducts electricity when molten or when dissolved in water.

Electron microscope An instrument used to magnify specimens using a beam of electrons.

Electronic structure The arrangement of electrons around the nucleus of an atom.

Electrons Negative particles found outside the nucleus of an atom.

Empirical formula A chemical formula that shows the ratio of the number of atoms in a compound.

Emulsify To physically break down large droplets into smaller droplets.

Endothermic Involving a net absorption of energy.

Energy level See **shells**.

Enzymes Biological catalysts.

Enzyme substrate complex The combination of the enzyme and the substrate at the active site.

Equilibrium The point at which a reversible reaction takes place at exactly the same rate in both directions.

Exothermic Involving a net release of energy.

F

Fatty acids Building blocks of lipids.

Force A force can change the motion of an object (in newtons, N).

Friction force A force opposing the relative motion of two surfaces where they are in contact with each other.

Fructose syrup A sugar syrup.

Fullerene A type of giant structure made up of carbon atoms.

Fuse A fuse contains a thin wire that melts and cuts the current off if too much current passes through it.

G

Galvanising Covering iron with a protective layer of zinc.

Genetic diseases Diseases which are inherited.

Genetic disorders See **genetic diseases**.

Giant covalent structures Giant structures held together by many covalent bonds which give them high melting points and hardness, e.g. diamond.

Giant structure Large numbers of atoms or ions arranged in a regular way.

Glucagon Hormone involved in the control of blood sugar levels.

Glucose A simple sugar.

Glycerol Building block of lipids.

Glycogen Carbohydrate store in animals.

Grain A metal crystal.

Grain boundaries Where two metal crystals meet.

Gravitational field strength The force of gravity on an object of mass 1 kg (in newtons per kilogram, N/kg).

Gravitational potential energy Energy of an object due to its position in a gravitational field.
Near the Earth's surface, change of g.p.e. (in joules, J) = weight (in newtons, N) × vertical distance moved (in metres, m).

Groups Vertical columns of elements in the periodic table.

H

Haber process The industrial process used to make ammonia.

Homeostasis The maintenance of constant internal body conditions.

Hydrated A hydrated substance contains water.

Hydroponics Growing plants in water enriched by mineral ions rather than soil.

Hypothesis Using theory to suggest explanations for observations, e.g. 'I think that the plants are smaller because they do not have enough water.'

I

Impact force The force acting on an object when it collides with another object; the two objects experience equal and opposite forces.

Independent variable The variable that you have decided to change in an investigation, e.g. temperature of the acid.

Indicator A chemical compound that changes colour according to the pH of the solution it is in.

Inert Unreactive.

Insoluble Unable to dissolve in a given solvent.

Insulin Hormone involved in the control of blood sugar levels.

Ionic bond A chemical bond formed when one atom gives up one or more electrons to another atom.

Isomerase An enzyme which converts one form of a molecule into another.

Isotopes Atoms of the same element which have different numbers of neutrons.

K

Kidneys Organs which filter the blood and remove urea, excess salts and water.

Kinetic energy Energy of a moving object due to its motion; kinetic energy (in joules, J) $= \frac{1}{2} \times$ mass (in kilograms, kg) $\times$ (speed)^2 (in m^2/s^2).

L

Law of force between charged objects Like charges repel; unlike charges attract.

Light microscope An instrument used to magnify specimens using lenses and light.

Limiting factors Factors which limit the rate of a reaction, e.g. photosynthesis.

Lipids Fats and oils.

Live wire The wire of a mains circuit that has a potential that alternates from positive to negative and back each cycle.

Liver A large organ in the abdomen which carries out a wide range of functions in the body.

M

Magnesium A metallic element. Magnesium ions are needed by plants to make chlorophyll.

Mass A measure of the difficulty of changing the motion of an object (in kilograms, kg).

Mass number The total number of protons and neutrons in the nucleus of an atom (symbol A).

Meiosis The two-stage process of cell division which reduces the chromosome number of the daughter cells. It is involved in making the gametes for sexual reproduction

Mitochondria The site of aerobic cellular respiration in a cell.

Mitosis Asexual cell division where two identical daughter cells are formed.

Mixing occurs when two or more substances are physically mixed but not chemically combined.

Moderator A solid or liquid used in a nuclear reactor to slow fission neutrons down so they can cause further fission.

Mole The relative formula mass of a substance in grams.

Molecular formula A formula that shows the total number of the different kinds of atoms in a molecule.

Momentum Mass (in kilograms, kg) $\times$ velocity (in m/s).

Motive force A force on a powered object (e.g. a vehicle) that makes it move.

N

Net Overall.

Neutral Neither acid nor alkaline.

Neutral wire The wire of a mains circuit that is earthed at the local sub-station so its potential is close to zero.

Neutrons Neutral particles found in the nucleus of an atom.

Nitrates Mineral ions needed by plants to form proteins.

Nitrogen Inert gas making up around 80% of the Earth's atmosphere.

Noble gases The unreactive gases which have a complete outer shell of electrons, e.g. neon, argon, helium.

Nuclear fission reactor A reactor that releases energy as a result of nuclear fission inside it.

Nuclear fission The process in which certain nuclei (uranium 235 and plutonium 239) split into two fragments when struck by a neutron, releasing energy and two or three neutrons as a result.

Nuclear fusion The process in which small nuclei are forced together so they fuse with each other to form a larger nucleus, releasing energy in the process.

Nuclear model of the atom Every atom contains a positively charged nucleus consisting of neutrons and protons. This is where most of its mass is concentrated, and it is much smaller than the atom. Electrons move about in the space surrounding the nucleus.

Nucleus (of a cell) An organelle found in many living cells containing the genetic information.

O

Ohm's law The current through a resistor at constant temperature is directly proportional to the potential difference across the resistor.

Ohmic conductor A conductor that has a constant resistance and therefore obeys Ohm's law.

OILRIG Oxidation Is Loss, Reduction Is Gain (of electrons).

Ordered variable Variables that can be put into an order, e.g. small, large, huge lumps of rock. These tell us more than categoric variables.

Organ A group of different tissues working together to carry out a particular function.

Organ systems A group of organs working together to carry out a particular function.

Organelles Membrane-bound structures in the cytoplasm of a cell which carry out particular functions.

Oscilloscope A device used to display the shape of an electrical wave.

Osmosis The net movement of water from an area of high concentration (of water) to an area of low concentration (of water) along a concentration gradient.

Ova The female sex cells, eggs.

Ovaries Female sex organs which produce eggs and sex hormones.

Oxidation Losing electrons.

Oxidised See **oxidation**.

P

Pancreas An organ which produces the hormone insulin and many digestive enzymes.

Parallel circuit rules 1. The potential difference across components in parallel is the same. 2. The total current passing through components in parallel is shared between the components.

Parallel Components connected in a circuit so that the potential difference is the same across each one.

Partially permeable Allowing only certain substances to pass through.

Percentage yield The percentage of product formed in a chemical reaction compared with the maximum possible amount of product that could be formed.

Periods Rows of elements in the periodic table.

pH scale A scale running from 0 to 14 that describes the degree of acidity of a solution.

Phloem The living transport tissue in plants which carries sugars around the plant.

Photosynthesis The process by which plants make food using carbon dioxide, water and light energy.

Plasma A gas consisting of bare nuclei (i.e. atoms stripped of their electrons).

Plug A plug has an insulating case and is used to connect the cable from an appliance to a socket.

Plum pudding model of the atom A model of the atom which supposed that the positive charge was evenly spread throughout its matter and the negative charge was held in tiny particles (electrons) inside the atom.

Potential difference A measure of the difference in electric potential energy per unit charge between two charged objects (in volts, V).

Power The energy transformed per second. The unit of power is the watt (W).

Precipitate A solid material produced from a solution.

Precipitation See **precipitate**.

Protease An enzyme which breaks down proteins.

Protein synthesis The process of building up protein molecules from amino acids on the surface of a ribosome.

Proton number See **atomic number**.

Protons Positive particles found in the nucleus of an atom.

Pyramid of numbers A model of feeding relationships based on the numbers of organism at each level of a food chain.

R

Random error Measurements when repeated are rarely exactly the same. If they differ randomly then it is probably due to human error when carrying out the investigation.

Recessive The characteristic that will show up in the offspring only if both of the alleles are inherited.

Redox A REDuction OXidation reaction in which electrons are lost by one substance and gained by another.

Reduced See **reduction**.

Reduction Gaining electrons.

Relative atomic mass The mass of an atom compared with an atom of $^{12}_{6}C$. This is usually the same as or very similar to the mass number of the element.

Relative formula mass The mass of a chemical compound based on the relative atomic masses of the elements involved.

Reliable Describes data we can trust. E.g. others can get the same results, even using different methods.

Resistance Resistance (in ohms, Ω) = potential difference (in volts, V) ÷ current (in amperes, A).

Resistors in parallel Resistors in a circuit with the same potential difference across each one. The bigger the resistance of a resistor, the smaller the current that passes through it

Resistors in series Resistors in a circuit with the same current passing through them. Their combined resistance = sum of the individual resistances.

Respiration The process by which food molecules are broken down to release energy for the cells.

Resultant force The combined effect of the forces acting on an object.

Reversible reaction A reaction in which the products immediately react together to produce the original reactants.

Ribosomes The site of protein synthesis in a cell.

S

Series circuit rules 1. The current through components in series is the same. 2. The total potential difference across components in series is shared between the components.

Series Components connected in a circuit so that the same current passes through them are in series with each other.

Sewage treatment plant A site where human waste is broken down using microorganisms.

Sex chromosomes The chromosomes which carry the information about the sex of an individual.

Shells The region in which electrons are concentrated as they travel around the nucleus of an atom.

Short-circuit A circuit fault in which two wires at different potentials touch and a large current passes between them at the point of contact.

Socket A mains socket is used to connect the mains plug of a mains appliance to the mains circuit.

Sodium ion A sodium atom that has lost an electron to give it a positive charge.

Soluble Able to dissolve in a given solvent.

Solute The solid which dissolves in a solvent to form a solution.

Solvent A liquid in which some solids will dissolve.

Specialised Adapted for a particular function.

Speed Distance travelled per second (in metres/second, m/s).

Sperm The male sex cells.

Static electricity Charge 'held' by an insulator or an insulated conductor.

Stem cells Undifferentiated cells with the potential to form a wide variety of different cell types.

Stopping distance Braking distance + thinking distance.

Sugars Simple carbohydrates.

Systematic error If the data is inaccurate in a constant way, e.g. all results are 10 mm more than they should be. This is often due to the method being routinely wrong.

T

Terminal velocity The velocity reached by an object when the drag force on it is equal and opposite to the force making it move.

Testes Male sex organs which produce sperm and sex hormones.

Thermal decomposition Splitting up a substance by means of heat.

Thermoregulatory centre The area of the brain which is sensitive to the temperature of the blood.

Thinking distance The distance travelled by the vehicle in the time it takes the driver to react.

Three-pin plug A three-pin plug has a live pin, a neutral pin and an earth pin. The earth pin is used to earth the metal case of an appliance so the case cannot become live.

Time base control An oscilloscope control used to space the waveform out horizontally.

Tissue A group of specialised cells all carrying out the same function.

U

Universal indicator A substance containing a range of indicators to provide a measurement of pH.

Urea A substance produced by the liver as a waste product from breaking down excess amino acids.

Urine The liquid formed by the kidneys.

V

Valid Describes an investigation that successfully gathers the data needed to answer the original question.

Van de Graaff generator A large insulated metal dome charged by the motion of a rubber belt brushing against a friction pad.

Velocity Speed in a given direction (in metres/second, m/s).

Volt (V) The unit of potential difference, equal to energy transfer per unit charge in joules per coulomb.

W

Weight The force of gravity on an object (in newtons).

Work Energy transferred by a force, given by:
Work done (in joules, J) = force (in newtons, N) × distance moved in the direction of the force (in metres, m).

X

Xylem The non-living transport tissue in plants, which transports water around the plant.

Y

Y-gain control An oscilloscope control used to adjust the height of the waveform.

Yield The amount of product formed in a chemical reaction.

Index

urea 59
urine 30, 31, 59, 63

V

vacuoles 4, 5, 7
validity 276, 277, 281
Van de Graaff generators 224
variable resistors 234, 235
variables 276, 277–8, 280–1
variation 73
velocity 186–7, 188–9, 190–1, 200
   and momentum 214–17
   and resultant force 198, 199, 201
   terminal velocity 205
   see also speed
velocity–time graphs 187, 188–9, 190–1,
   200
voltage *see* potential difference
voltmeters 234, 236

W

warm-blooded animals 31, 47, 148
waste products 34–5, 58
   of animals and plants 30, 31, 34–5
     in the carbon cycle 36, 37
   computers as 231
   farm waste 179
   of humans 35, 50, 58–9
   of nuclear reactors 271
water 106, 144
   in the body, controlling 59
   bonding in 96, 97
   cleaning up 113, 174, 175, 177
   and decomposition 35
   diffusion, in cells 9
   in electrolysis 161
   from neutralisation reactions 172, 174
   and osmosis 10–11, 13

   in photosynthesis 2, 16
   in respiration 2, 46
   test for 151
weight 182, 204, 209
work 210–11, 212

X

X chromosomes 76
X-rays 182
xylem 7, 20

Y

Y chromosomes 76
yield 124–5, 130, 151
   in reversible reactions 129, 152–3, 154

Acknowledgements

Action Plus/Glyn Kirk 207tr; Alamy/Education Photos 138.1, /Holt Studios International Ltd 174.2, /Network Photographers 220bl, /Perihelion 36.1, /Photofusion Picture Library 78.1, /Popperfoto 214.1, /Ritterbach/f1online 25bl; ALCAN 110.2b; Ann Fullick 30.2, 39bm, 39br ; Axon Images 22.1; B Drake/Photodisc 19 (NT) 179r; Ben Keiser 125.1; Biocor/NHF 254.1; Blueflag 177m; Corbis/Andrew Wong/Reuters 186.3; Corel 11 (NT) 60.1b; Corel 27 (NT) 47.2; Corel 73 (NT) 13bl; Corel 92 (NT) 31.3; Corel 103 (NT) 13tr; Corel 149 (NT) 148.2; Corel 245 (NT) 99.3; Corel 284 (NT) 136.1; Corel 340 (NT) 97.6; Corel 344 (NT) 39tr; Corel 357 (NT) 60.1a; Corel 414 (NT) 217.3; Corel 459 (NT) 32.1; Corel 467 (NT) 21.3, 142.1; Corel 501 (NT) 86tl; Corel 603 (NT) 25ml; Corel 625 (NT) 123.2; Corel 637 (NT) 224.1; Corel 640 (NT) 186.1; Corel 671 (NT) 24bl; Corel 710 (NT) 148.1; Corel 713 (NT) 20ml; Corel 759 (NT) 229.4; Corel 780 (NT) 64br; Data Harvest 188.2a; DETR 206tl, 220tl; Digital Vision 1 (NT) 152.1; Digital Vision 6 (NT) 192br; Digital Vision 15 (NT) 134.1, 177mr, 231b; Digital Vision 17 (NT) 94bl, 176tl; Don Farrall/Photodisc 29 (NT) 106bl; Frink/Digital Vision LU (NT) 8.1; Groupal Ltd 120.1; Hewlett Packard 231tr; Holt Studios International Ltd/Nigel Cattlin 23.2a, 23.2b; ICI 128.1; Illustrated London News V1 (NT) 87mr, 158.1; Image 100 22 (NT) 3br; ImageState/Alamy 203.3; Imgram ILS V2 CD 5 (NT) 108.3; Jim Breithaupt 255.2; Karl Ammann/Digital Vision AA (NT) 96.1; Keith Brofsky/Photodisc 59 (NT) 15r; Martyn F. Chillmaid 43.1, 50.2a, 50.2b, 50.2c, 185m, 188.2b, 207l, 239.3b, 259mr; National Portrait Gallery 87b; Nike 213.3; Patrick Fullick 111m, 111ml, 111tm; Photodisc 6 (NT) 3tl; Photodisc 10 (NT) 58.1c; Photodisc 19 (NT) 28.1; Photodisc 29 (NT) 163.2; Photodisc 38A (NT) 176tr; Photodisc 44 (NT) 30.1, 142.2, 270t; Photodisc 45 (NT) 52.2, 58.1b; Photodisc 51 (NT) 210.1; Photodisc 67 (NT) 3m; Photodisc 71 (NT) 58.1a, 58.1d, 177tl; Pictoral Press/Alamy 131t; Pilkington Ltd 112tl; Randy Allbritton/Photodisc 72 (NT) 75.3; Rex Features/SIPA 35.2; Rover Group 228.1; Ryan McVay/Photodisc 79 (NT) 2tl; Science Photo Library 12tl, 87tl, 119.2, /Alex Bartel 270b, /Andrew Lambert Photography 170.1a, 170.1b, 170.2, 251.3, 252.1a, /Astrid and Hanns-Frieder Michler 3mr, /Bryan Peterson/AGSTOCKUSA 38tr, /Carlos Dominguez 24mr, /CERN 101br, /Charles D. Winters 248.1, /Chris Knapton 174.3, /Chris Sattlberger 112mr, /Claude Nuridsany and Marie Perennou 112ml, /CNRI 76.1, /Cordelia Molloy 16.1, 21.2, 38tl, 52.1, 54m, 149.3, 255.3, 259b, /Curt Maas/Agstock 33.2, /Darwin Dale 45.4, /David Munns 55bl, /David Nunuk 23.3, /David Parker 101tr, 193t, /Dr Gopal Murti 12ml, /Dr P. Marazzi 51.3, /Dr R. Dourmashkin 9.4, /Erika Craddock 34.1, /Eye Of Science 35.4, 73.3, 112br, /Geoff Kidd 176b, /J.C. Revy 5.3a, 43.2, /James King-Holmes 74.1, 100br, /Jason Kelvin 201.3, /Jerry Mason 193mr, /John Cole 64tr, /John Howard 33.3b, /Keith Kent 184.1, /Lawrence Lawry 110.2a, /M.I. Walker 69.3, /Maria E. Bruno Petriglia 83tr, /Mark Clarke 63.2, /Martyn F. Chillmaid 239.3a, /Maximilian Stock LTD 136.2, 164.1, /Michael Donne 121.2, /NASA 183ml, 183tr, /Nick Wall 271r, /Omikron 12mr, /Peter Menzel 112bl, /Scott Sinklier/Agstock 33.3a, 39tl, /Sheila Terry 100tl, 252.1b, 253.3, 258m, /Simon Fraser/University of Newcastle Upon Tyne 70.1, /Steve Allen 110.1, /Steve Gschmeissner 5.3b, 12b, /Sue Baker 140.1, /Will and Deni McIntyre 81br; Stephen Frink/Digital Vision LU (NT) 13br, 13tl; Topfoto.co.uk/UPPA Ltd 53.3, 219tr; Transport & Road Research Laboratory 218.1, 220mr; UKAEA 269.3

Picture research by Stuart Silvermore, Science Photo Library and johnbailey@ntlworld.com.